P9-DFL-122

the Prisoner

DAVE ROGERS

First published in Great Britain in 1989
by Boxtree Limited
Published in association with ITC Entertainment Ltd

Reprinted in 1990, 1992,1993

This edition published by
Barnes & Noble, Inc., by
arrangement with Boxtree Limited

1993 Barnes & Noble Books

ISBN 1-56619-163-7

Edited by Charlotte Mortensson
Designed by Julia Lilauwalå
Cover design by Dave Goodman
Typeset by Action Typesetters, Gloucester
Printed in Great Britain by
Redwood Press Ltd, Wiltshire

For Boxtree Limited
Broadwall House
21 Broadwall
London SE1 9PL

CONTENTS

ACKNOWLEDGEMENTS

THE AUTHOR wishes to thank the following individuals and organisations for their invaluable help and support during the preparation of this work.

In no particular order of merit: Karen and Roger Langley; Dave Jones and Julie ('Snouty') Benson; Simon Coward and Jane Rawson; Howard Foy; Larry Hall; Roger Caton; Colin Bayley (who was forced to upset his regular viewing pattern – but 'gained' as a result); Andrew Pixley and Neil Alsop for their helpful advice.

The co-ordination team of the *Six Of One* Prisoner Appreciation Society, for their unselfish support in dotting the i's and crossing the t's. In particular Roger Langley for allowing me to use his masterful work *The Making of The Prisoner* as a building block in order to define the true story. The boys and girls of Brit TV Entertainment (Chicago, USA).

Don Mead, Peter Harrington and Sheila Morgan of ITC (Filmbond). The management and staff of Channel 5 Video.

And last but not least, my wife Celia and daughter Leah, who sweated it out and wined and dined the 'caged tiger'.

PREFACE

WHEN I first approached my publisher with the idea of doing a book based upon actor Patrick McGoohan's tour de force portrayal of the enigmatic Number 6 (*The Prisoner*). I had no concept of the task I would be setting myself. No comprehension of the ordeal that lay in store. Nor any notion of the fact that I, too, would soon become a prisoner of sorts – one chained to the television screen and the typewriter keyboard until the task was overcome. A book is a book is a book, I thought – whatever the subject matter. Perhaps that is true of most subjects, but when one is dealing with a series that has taxed the minds of greater scholars than myself, a series which has confused, confounded and resisted all attempts to categorise its unique (some would say bizarre) qualities, a series that has a fan following second to none (whose membership is so eagerly protective of the subject matter), one is not dealing with any old subject matter, but with the sacrosanct progeny of a television product held dear by millions.

My initial task then, was to ward off any criticism that I had not done my homework, by getting to grips with the *facts* surrounding the chronological history of the programmes. But what were they? How does one begin to approach a subject which, during the last 12 years or so, has been treated to acute investigation in an abundance of 'fan' magazines produced by the official *The Prisoner* society, *Six of One* – magazines which tell the whole story in far greater detail than any one volume on the subject can hope to achieve. The answer. Go directly to the horse's mouth, the co-ordinators and production staff of the society itself – the inner domain of *Six of One.*

Their assistance assured, I was off and running – but in which direction? Wherever I turned for research matter, I found myself returning to the society's substantial outpourings. The facts were all there. All I now needed to do was to collate and shape the material into something resembling what I was aiming for – the *true* story behind the making of the programmes. Page after page of typed material was mailed to the society co-ordination team. Page after page was returned with their comments. Many weeks later, I finally had what I was looking for – as complete a comprehensive picture of the background history as I could hope to find. Armed with this, I picked up my pen and settled down to record the storyline of each and every episode of *The Prisoner* ethos in their entirity. The results of my labour you hold in your hand.

The chains are broken *I* am a free man.
Have a nice day. Be seeing you.

Dave Rogers, 31 March 1989

THE PRISONER

'I Am Not A Number, I Am A Free Man'

BY THE TIME the third series of *Danger Man* went into production in 1965, Patrick McGoohan, in his persona of John Drake, was Britain's most highly paid television star, reputedly earning in excess of £2,000 a week. But the actor was beginning to become tired of the show, and the limitations of the character.

Believing that the series had reached its zenith and was fast running out of steam, McGoohan decided to throw in the towel and hang up the mantle of Drake for good, while the programme was still ahead of its nearest competition. 'It was a wonderful series to do,' he would recount later. 'I had a very enjoyable time. We had some excellent directors and some very good scripts, but then it started, as all series do of that nature, to get stale.' Despite the fact that a further series of *Danger Man* – to be filmed in colour for the first time – had been commissioned, approximately 12 weeks before the current series ended, to everyone's surprise, the star gave notice that he would not be continuing as John Drake. Aware that his contract with ATV still had a number of months to run, and that the company still had an option on his services *after* the agreement expired, McGoohan took stock of his position. Having never lost sight of his idea of the man in isolation standing up against authority and bureaucracy intent on trying to bend his mind into the shape they wanted, he decided to approach Lew Grade, then head of ATV, with his idea for a new series – a concept so special to McGoohan's personal beliefs that, if necessary, the actor was prepared to put both himself and his entire *Danger Man* production unit out of work.

History has it that the actor arrived at Lew Grade's office at 6.30 one Saturday morning. 'I always saw Mr Grade on a Saturday morning between six and six-thirty,' McGoohan has stated. 'He used to get to the office at 6 am and I have always been an early riser, so it was a good time to meet. Any business we had to discuss didn't take long because (that was the wonderful thing about him) you got a decision very quickly.' Told by Grade that he wanted him to do another series, something perhaps of a similar nature, the actor replied that he would rather not do any more. 'I've got this thing with me,' said McGoohan, producing some notes, designs and short plot synopses he had prepared, together with some photographs of Portmeirion, the North Wales *Italiante* village which had so impressed him when he had worked there previously during some 1959 location work for his *Danger Man* series. 'You know I don't like to read such things – tell me about it,' said Grade. The actor chatted away for 15 minutes or so, until Grade replied 'You know, it's so crazy, it might just work. When can you start? How much will it cost? When can you deliver?'

McGoohan, it seems, had the answers. Having 'resigned' as John Drake, the loss of its star meant that the entire *Danger Man* production crew would be looking for new employment. 'I had the whole unit waiting to go onto the new programme,' McGoohan said afterwards. 'Everything was ready. So he gave me the green light. We shook hands – we never had a contract – and I went ahead and did it. He never bothered me, gave me anything I wanted, crazy or not. It was a deal. That's the sort of man Lew Grade is.' (This is slightly untrue. Director of Photography, Brendan Stafford, recalls that ITC officials occasionally came onto the set attempting to cut the budget and interfere with McGoohan's ideas. They were promptly told where to go).

If we are to believe McGoohan's version of events, (and why not?) – in all probability it is as close to the truth as we will ever come (certainly Lew – now Lord Grade, has never cast doubt upon McGoohan's story although, as we will learn, script editor George Markstein would) – then the programme's origins are as remarkable as its content. But a million dollar series, clinched on a handshake?! It is far more likely that Grade, at the time one of the most powerful and astute men in the industry, fully aware that McGoohan was a highly bankable commodity, simply acceded to the actor's request in order to keep a valuable asset on the books.

The finance to produce the new series came from ATV, who were no doubt relying on the programme to sustain the popularity McGoohan had won with his highly successful portrayal of Danger Man John Drake. They were not to be disappointed – although it would take several years before the series recouped its high production outlay. By July 1966, the programme was up and running. It had a budget allocation per story reputed to be in excess of £75,000 – not a lot by today's standards, but then the highest ever assigned to produce a television series. Everyman Films, a subsidiary of ATV formed on 18 August 1960 by McGoohan, David Tomblin and others,

David Tomblin talking to Patrick McGoohan on the set of Living In Harmony

under its original name of Keystone Films, was chosen to produce the series. McGoohan elected to become Executive Producer, while Tomblin, a man with whom the actor had shared a long and fruitful relationship, donned the hat of Producer. George Markstein, who had worked in the same capacity on some of the hour-long *Danger Man* stories, was appointed Story Editor for the new programme – and almost immediately laid claim to creating the series' original concept!

Having been attached to British Intelligence in his capacity as the London correspondent for *Overseas Weekly*, a news magazine for the US forces in Europe (as a journalist he had attended over 400 court martial trials, which led to him being engaged as technical co-ordinator on ITC's *Court Martial* series), Markstein had gathered first-hand knowledge of an institution that existed in Inverness, Scotland (Inverlair Lodge, in Glen Spean). During World War II ex-spies who had served their usefulness as agents – together with other people who 'knew too much', people who had been compromised and had reached a point in their careers when they knew too many secrets to be let loose, but had not actually done anything *wrong* – were sent there on permanent 'holiday' by the State. Although well-treated, the detainees were nevertheless to all intents and purposes, prisoners. Inspired by this knowledge, the writer turned it to his advantage and used it as a basis for his Prisoner concept.

According to Markstein (who was introduced to McGoohan by scriptwriter Lewis Greifer when the then *Danger Man* star was shopping around for a script editor to knock some story synopses McGoohan had written into shape) what happened was this. Close to the end of the *Danger Man* production, McGoohan had approached him to 'come up with an idea that would retain the popularity of *Danger Man*, and keep the production team together.' Exploiting his knowledge of the Inverness real-life situation, Markstein merged fact with fiction and hit upon the idea of combining McGoohan's 'resignation' as John Drake from the spy game, with his concept of a self-contained world where a man with such knowledge could be locked away from prying eyes. Expanding the concept to suit his belief that anyone detained in such a place would be of obvious interest to both sides, the writer proposed the idea to McGoohan. Delighted with the concept, the actor accepted the proposal. However, when Markstein indicated that he intended to pursue the premise that the man locked away was John Drake, McGoohan categorically refused to have the character named and gave him a number – acknowledging to Markstein that if they used the name 'Drake' the character's creator, Ralph Smart, would have to be paid healthy royalties! The first that Markstein knew about the star selling the idea as his own, was when he read about it in a newspaper sometime later. By then the damage was done. Accepting the inevitable, that someone has to take the credit for originating an idea, the writer shrugged things off by stating 'Nobody wants to know about scriptwriters. It is actors who sell a series to the public' – but he never overlooked an opportunity to pursue his claim that McGoohan was taking sole credit for 'his' idea and concept. As to who actually did create the format, I for my part, offer no opinion other than saying that, at the height of his career, I find it doubtful that McGoohan had either the necessity or inclination to 'lift' someone else's idea. However, it is fair to say that, as things turned out, the concept used was not a million miles away from Markstein's original Kafkaesque idea. Of course, there is always another version to be considered. Interviewed by the *Six Of One, Prisoner Society*, director Pat Jackson said 'The germ of the idea was certainly McGoohan's – after hearing from a Home Office official (slightly the worse for drink) that a place such as the Village did exist.' Fuelling the fires of controversy, it is my belief that Markstein provided the canvas (the Village, with its overtones of Orwell's 'Big Brother' and 24-hour surveillance), while McGoohan added the brushstrokes (the numbers, the costumes, and so on).

Despite the actor's protestations to the contrary, I remain convinced that the man numbered '6' was indeed John Drake – a 'fact' confirmed by Frank Maher, the stunt arranger for *The Prisoner* who, when interviewed in 1987 on behalf of the Prisoner Society told Larry Hall and Arabella McIntyre Brown, that one evening after he and McGoohan had played a game of squash, the star gave him a synopsis of the series and confirmed that the man who had been kidnapped and taken to the Village was John Drake.

What is beyond doubt, is that well before the production got under way, Markstein produced a four-page writer's brief, the 'bible' that was necessary to acquaint potential scriptwriters with the vagaries of the plot, action and situations with which the 'man with no name' would eventually be faced – the blueprint which, under McGoohan's control, would develop into the now familiar Prisoner concept. A series that one critic dubbed 'a meaningless muddle of weird, science-fiction orientated twaddle' and another 'an irrelevant load of piffle'!

While McGoohan devoted his attention to the preparatory stages; the design of sets and costumes, the booking of actors who he wished to appear in the programme (his choice of thespians was described by leading casting director Rose Tobias-Shaw as 'off beat') Markstein and Tomblin set about penning the pilot story. Meanwhile, other positions were being filled. In common with other members of the production crew, Brendan J. Stafford had enjoyed a long working relationship with McGoohan during his tenure as *Danger Man*. Having filmed all the original half-hour and hour-long John Drake stories, he was chosen as Director of Photography. (In fact, Stafford was half-way through recording a television series in Hollywood when he got a call from McGoohan asking him to come back to England to photograph *The Prisoner*.) Jack Shampan, another member of the *Danger Man* team was appointed Art Director, and Don Chaffey, a man for whom McGoohan had great respect, was brought in to direct the first story. Chaffey, too, had a story to tell. Having recently completed the Ray Harryhausen fantasy film *Jason and the Argonauts*, Chaffey was about to do another feature in Ireland, when McGoohan, a close friend of Chaffey's family, arrived at the director's home and said he had this idea for a new series and he wanted his friend to direct the first stories. Chaffey refused McGoohan's request and went off to Ireland. In the meantime, however, the actor handed some script synopses to Chaffey's daughter – asking her to show them to her father. Intrigued by what she read, the girl told her father to look at them, insisting that the series was going to make compulsive viewing, and would have people loving to hate him when the series was shown. Chaffey did so, and was hooked. Within days he had called McGoohan and agreed to direct the first episodes.

Approximately one month later, Tomblin and Markstein presented McGoohan with their script for *Arrival* – or, as it was then known, *The Arrival*. Delighted with the result, particularly as Tomblin had never written a screenplay before, the star directed his story editor to brief his writing team, while he and Tomblin mapped out the location shooting schedule at Portmeirion – the 'perfect' locale McGoohan had had in mind from his very first visit to the place several years previously. (One of the stories that has circulated regarding the selection of Portmeirion as 'The Village' originated from Markstein's lips. Disputing McGoohan's claim that he had stored away the locale as 'somewhere to be used again,' according to Markstein, the location was selected by him, having read about the place in a *Sunday Times* magazine supplement. On the one hand, this can readily be discounted as being inconsistent with the fact that, as Markstein did not actually join the *Danger Man* production team until the second (hour-long) series, his claim was out of sync by quite a few years – McGoohan and his second-unit location crew having visited the locale some seven years earlier in 1959! On the other hand, it could well be that having read the magazine, Markstein *reminded* McGoohan about Portmeirion, the actor claiming that he first thought about the locale when he went there on holiday with his family, some time *after* filming his *Danger Man* stories.

Elsewhere, the runaway success of *Secret Agent* in America, had allowed Lew Grade the opportunity to negotiate both financial and commercial deals with the American buyer, Michael Dann, head of CBS, with the deal to buy *The Prisoner*, being made for a year ahead.

Location filming for the series began in Portmeirion on 6 September 1966, with architect Clough Williams-Ellis, owner and creator of the place, allowing the production team access only on the condition that the hotel's location remained a closely guarded secret. Only members of the public lucky enough to be visiting there were allowed to enjoy the thrill of seeing, at first hand, a film production unit going through its paces.

The initial episodes shot back-to-back were *Arrival* and *Free For All*, a script written by McGoohan, under the pseudonym Paddy Fitz (adapted from his mother's maiden name, Fitzpatrick). With the arrival of Chaffey and the second-unit location team, the serene surroundings of Portmeirion underwent a dramatic change. New notices were erected, strange 'information' kiosks appeared on street corners, canopied mini-mokes (Village buggy taxis) plied their make-believe trade (their presence there was, no doubt, a mystery to the day-trippers who attempted to hire them – only four were used, with usually no more than two appearing on screen at any one time). New arrivals in the shape of local residents, employed as extras (at 50 shillings – £2.50 per day) added colour to the proceedings as they tripped around in their brightly-hued costumes of boaters, frock-coats and top hats which, according to George Markstein, were meant to suggest a holiday camp atmosphere. A penny farthing bicycle (only one was used) tested the nerve of anyone foolish enough to attempt to ride it (in the series, the machine is always *wheeled* around), and a helicopter booked for the series soared low over the golden sands. Within days, Portmeirion had become 'The Village', a far from idyllic haven for its make-believe occupant.

The location shoot lasted for four weeks, during which time the unit worked flat-out to secure enough material for their purpose. As Portmeirion would be closing its doors in October, they worked a seven-day week, 16-hour-a-day schedule. Serendipity allowed them to put several of the location's inanimate objects to specific use: the Stone Boat finding its way into many of the stories; the Green Dome eventually becoming the permanent residence of Number 2 (the original choice for the Village superior was The Georgian House, ie Portmeirion's Unicorn Cottage); the locale's main hotel being transformed into the Old People's Home, while Portmeirion's Town Hall doubled in the same capacity in the series for the transaction of official Village business, and one building (Battery Cottage) became residence 'Number 6'.

Location material to be used in several other stories was shot during this period. *Checkmate* and *Dance of the Dead* contain scenes filmed at Portmeirion, as does *The Chimes of Big Ben*. Details of the shoot were kept quiet from the media, with McGoohan and Tomblin throwing a veil of secrecy over the location. (Not until *Fall Out*, the final story, was transmitted did the name of Portmeirion appear on the credits).

Rushes – the developed and unedited film shot on the previous day – were viewed at the Coliseum Cinema in nearby Porthmadog, allowing the team to judge their early footage as the cinema's projectionist, Bob Piercy, screened the silent footage every night, including weekends, throughout the four-week period (he would be employed in the same capacity again, when the team paid their second visit to Portmeirion in 1967). As Bob told *Six of One* co-ordinators David Jones and Julie Benson, 'The crew would sit at the front of the stalls, joined sometimes by local extras. Each day's filming was usually about five to eight minutes long. When it had finished, it was sometimes run again. They would sometimes watch it seven or eight times – taking anywhere between 15 minutes and two hours. We used to start at about 10 pm, which sometimes meant that we would not be out until after midnight. Patrick McGoohan would sometimes nip out to the pub. He'd bring little Angelo Muscat up to the projection room and say "Can I leave him here?" and he would sit on a high chair looking out through the projection hole at the film. The highlight for Bob, was when Sir Clough Williams-Ellis arranged a preview of the first episode, *Arrival*. Although the Coliseum only had a six-day licence, and was not officially allowed to show films on a Sunday, they went ahead and did so anyway (without too much concern it appears, the Chief Constable of Caernarvon, being one of the guests). 'It was a great success,' Bob Piercy recalled, confirming that this was the *first* showing of *The Prisoner* anywhere. 'I remember that I had a note inside the film cannister saying something like "Don't scratch this print as it is the only copy." I had to clean the projector first and put Vaseline on all the moving parts. I was quite worried.' Bob remembered that many well-known local characters appeared as extras during the series. 'They picked some good people. One of them, Tecwyn Williams, was employed to recover the balloons when they went astray, and he got wet through running into the sea after them! My son was an extra, doubling for Patrick McGoohan in one scene. They were good wages too!'

The 'balloons' to which Bob Piercy referred were, of course, the now immortal Village guardians, but apparently these came about by chance. An early casualty of the first week's shooting was as an experimental version of Rover, the dreaded Village patrolman, the lighter-than-air membrane bubble-sphere, which served as the community policeman. A prototype machine, designed by art director Jack Shampan to travel over land and water, it came under the influence of Murphy's Law and sank to a watery grave. As McGoohan told it, 'We had this thing designed to be the be-all and end-all of mechanical things.

Number 6 is ushered away by the giant menacing bubble

It would go under water, as in submarine, and was supposed to come out of the water onto dry land as in hovercraft. It was supposed to climb up the side of a wall and do all sorts of wonderful things. Valiant efforts were made. We were on location and about to shoot, and there came the day when we needed this thing called Rover, which had a light on top of it – a red blinking eye (the *Arrival* script gives the colour as blue), and issued a horrendous sound. Anyway, we tested it out in the ocean and it didn't come out. It stayed there. So we had to think of something else, and in desperation, Bernard Williams (the series' production manager) and myself were standing there not knowing what to do – we had to have a Rover to shoot on. We were looking up in agony at the heavens, and we saw this white thing, way up in the blue, and he said it must be a meteorological ballon. I said 'Do you think that thing would do? What size is it? Find out . . .' He took off and arrived back with the station wagon full of these balloons in varying sizes, from six inches in diameter up to eight feet in diameter, as well as cylinders of oxygen and helium and various other things. That's how we got what turned out to be the best possible Rover that one could have.' Version one. A second version was put forward by director Don Chaffey who, interviewed for the *Six Into One: The Prisoner File*, (a special Channel 4 documentary, shown in January 1984, immediately after *Fall Out*) expressed the wish to take credit for the Rover balloons. According to Chaffey, the original Rover was going to be a motor bike, with a sort of igloo stuck over it with a light on the top, which struck the director as not being too effective. 'Rover to me,' he said, 'had to be a sort of abstract thing, it represented bureaucracy, it represented that nameless, faceless lot "out there" who tell you what to do, how to do it and when to do it.' According to Chaffey, what happened was this. At the time he was having arguments in trying to get a telephone installed at his squash court. He had filled out the requisite forms twice, and on both occasions the documents had been mislaid by the Post Office. Finally, in exasperation, he telephoned one of the 'faceless ones' and told him that if he supplied him with his name and address, Chaffey could send the next lot of forms directly to him. When the person on the other end of the telephone told Chaffey that this was not allowed – civil servants had to remain anonymous, the director accused the bureaucrat and his colleagues of being a lot of white balloons. My God, thought Chaffey: 'White balloons!' So he telephoned McGoohan and said: 'Pat, this is it – white balloons! That's what that lot are out there, they're not motor bikes!' Version two. When summing up the 'facts', one must take into account the following: there is certainly *no* meteorological station anywhere near Portmeirion (nor was there at the time the series was being filmed); *no* photographs of the land/sea version of Rover exist, and *no* extras ever saw it! In fact, many people, including noted Prisoner authority and editor of the Prisoner Society magazine, Howard Foy, believe that it never actually existed, or if it did, was rejected at the planning stages. Which version is correct? Who cares. Of such things legends are made. What really counts is that, filled with air, helium and water, the balloons worked amazingly well although, as we will learn, they sometimes had to be motivated by a thin nylon cord attached to a fishing rod, which was tied to McGoohan's heels to make them give chase or, on one occasion at least, were made to earn their supper by camera tricks.

Markstein, meanwhile, having elected to commission scripts from totally different writers than those who had worked on *Danger Man* (he had already received scripts from Anthony Skene, Gerald Kelsey and Vincent Tilsley), approached other scribes to put forward their ideas for storylines. As McGoohan had already promised to write the final story, the script editor commissioned screenplays from writers he believed had the right sort of ideas and attitudes for a series such as *The Prisoner*. Among these were Terence Feely, Michael Cramoy, Roger Woddis and Lewis Greifer. Among the scripts commissioned but not used were ones by Morris Farhi and John Kruse. (History has it that Markstein also approached a number of well-known novelists but none were interested).

In early October, the crew were back at the MGM Studios in Boreham Wood, ready to begin work on the interiors for *Arrival*. At McGoohan's insistence, the set was closed to everyone but the production team. While the location unit had been filming in Portmeirion, permanent sets had been constructed on the sound stages: Number 6's cottage (which, with relatively small changes, also served as his London home); Number 2's Green Dome 'office', with its huge television screen (referred to by Shampan as 'The Living Space') and the Control Room, which, with the addition of ornate arches, also served as the Village Labour Exchange. It was now that McGoohan began to put his stamp of authority on the show. Day after day he would ask to view the previous day's takes, often supervising the editing and, wherever he believed a story could be improved, asking for changes to the script – his habit was to write his alernative ideas on paper which would then be handed over to Markstein for inclusion in that day's filming. To some, his reputation was becoming that of a fearsome ogre, described variously as 'dedicated' and 'difficult'. Flinging his heart and soul into the product, the actor worked long and difficult hours – and expected everyone around him to share his enthusiasm. He replied to the charges by saying 'I know what they're saying and it's true that I have been unpredictable and impatient. You get that way when you're working at high pressure. But I haven't lost a friend in the unit.' Assistant director Gino Marotta said: 'Pat makes strong demands on everyone, and if you try to raise objections all he says is "Get it done!" and you get it done. But I've never known a director like him, because he does his homework so far in advance.' Art director Jack Shampan, concurred: 'He knows what he wants down to the smallest detail. One of the trickiest problems we faced was the control room, with its furniture popping up out of nowhere, and floors that opened. Pat outlined what he had in mind, and left me to work it out. I couldn't see at first how some of the things could be done.' The answer came from a large tank beneath the studio set. It was like a powerhouse, with activators, winches and electrically-controlled hydraulic equipment.

Apart from the prisoner numbered '6', the only other recurring characters were actor Peter Swanwick, who appeared regularly as the Supervisor, and the enigmatic Butler, who tended to Number 2's every whim without so much as a word of complaint – but then he could not complain – the man was mute. But things could have been different. It appears that the draft script for *Arrival* pictured the Butler as being the archetypal Gentleman's Gentleman, a tall, well-spoken, very formal man in obviously good physical shape who would be at home in an E-type Jaguar car. As to why this was changed, who knows? Personally selected by McGoohan after studying 'a vast number of photographs', Angelo Muscat's dimunitive stature became one of the most intriguing characters in the enterprise, leading many viwers to suspect that the black-coated, stocky little servant, who was often hidden beneath a large umbrella was, perhaps, the unidentified, all-powerful 'Number 1'.

After a two-week studio shoot, the pilot story was in the can – although it had still to be edited (both visual and sound) and have the music score added. Hearsay has it that it was McGoohan's original intention that the opener should run to feature length of around 76 minutes (90 minutes when combined with commercials), but the idea was shelved in favour of the standard 52/54 minute transmission time. (See addendum to *Arrival* synopsis). No such mystery surrounds the episode's opening sequence. During an interview, George Markstein had this to say: 'In that episode I set out to define the framework of the whole series – to establish the theme, the mood, the story foundation, and above all, the *characters*. The hub of *Arrival*, was to lay the foundations of the entire concept: to show who the Prisoner was (a man with too many secrets); why they want to put him away (he knows too much); and the place to which he is banished (the Village). The episode is a cry against surveillance, the encroachment of computers, the rubber-stamping of individuals.' His plot device works wonderfully. The opening title sequence (which recurs, in edited form, throughout the remainder of the series – except in *Living In Harmony* and *Fall Out*) is guaranteed to send a shiver down the spine. The Prisoner's fate, when it arrives, has just the right amount of power to make the viewer wish to hang on and await the denouement. However, as Prisoner authority Roger Langley points out in his well-researched *The Making of The Prisoner* souvenir booklet, the opening and closing sequences of the series were originally in different form. As filmed, the original opening titles showed the Prisoner being chased from the beach by a Rover. The guardian finally catches up with him in the Village, bowls him over and sucks the air out of his lungs. In the closing sequence (which was used twice only – see addendum following *Arrival* and *The Chimes of Big Ben* synopses), the penny farthing bicycle motif fades away until the planet earth is viewed in close-up (the large wheel turning into the universe and the small wheel into the earth). The world then explodes with a giant POP, the word emerging from Somalia! Incidentally, the star background was obtained from the makers of *2001 – A Space Odyssey*, which was being filmed at Borehamwood at the same time.

With the pilot story in the can, McGoohan turned his attention to the music. Bearing in mind his admiration for the work of those who had already served their time with him on his *Danger Man* programme, one could have expected the actor to renew his working relationship with composer Edwin Astley, who had scored all the John Drake stories, but it was not to be. At this juncture, Astley was already contracted to provide the theme and incidental music for Roger Moore's *The Saint* television series, as well as composing some incidental music for ITC's *The Champions*. Composer Robert Farnon was the first to be approached to write the title music, but his version of the theme – a zingy, strident Western theme, based on *The Big Country* – did not reflect what McGoohan was looking for. Wilfred Josephs came next, but again McGoohan was not pleased with the result (although a great deal of the music Josephs composed at this time appears throughout the series – notably in *Arrival*). By the year's end the programme was still without a regular title theme. It was at this point that composer Ron Grainer entered the scene. With a track record of popular television themes behind him, *Doctor Who* and *Maigret* to name but two, the musician set to work composing his version of the title music. Although not entirely disatisfied with Grainer's composition, McGoohan nevertheless felt that it was not quite right – it needed 'beefing up'. He explained what he was looking for and the composer went away and revamped his original composition, eventually succeeding in supplying McGoohan with what he wanted. It appears, however, that Grainer was irritated that McGoohan, an actor, had told him, a composer, to change a composition which he believed was right for the series, so when Grainer issued the theme music commercially, he recorded a more 'pop' version of his *original* composition, and not the one heard on the programme! (Incidentally, the majority of the harpsichord music heard in the story *Dance of the Dead*, is composed by Grainer.)

Albert Elms was added to the roster to compose the remaining incidental music, and music editor, Eric Mival, who had recently joined the team to replace Bob Dearberg, was sent along to the Chappell Music Library to, as he put it, 'get to know the library backwards' because, although there would obviously be original music composed for the show, Mival would have to select some previously recorded library music as 'fills'. Mival, whose first story was *Free For All*, was responsible for adding some additional music to the first two stories when they were re-cut. On record as saying that he, for one, understood McGoohan's 'ruffling a few feathers' by telling experienced editors to change this, or alter that, after they believed that they had given their best, Mival said 'Perhaps, as directors are prone to doing, McGoohan changed his mind and perceived what he saw as a better way of presenting the shot – to give the scene more *impact*, by shortening or lengthening the action.' He added that the first story in particular, went through at least one re-cut of the negative after it had been reprinted, and it is partly because of this that the episode is exciting. (As seen on screen, *Arrival* does have at least one plot flaw, namely that Number 6 claims he saw the woman leave Number 2's residence when in fact – on screen – he sees no such thing. This could be explained by a cut, because the *Arrival* script matches the on-screen action).

McGoohan flexes his muscles behind the camera

After a Christmas break – a nice touch here being that each of the production crew received a Christmas card featuring the Butler with the penny farthing bicycle in a seasonal scene, the crew returned to the studio ready to face new rigours. By this stage, seven stories had been filmed and it was filmsmith Robert Asher's turn to occupy the director's chair, turning his cameras on McGoohan and company for the story called *It's Your Funeral* – the episode that saw the introduction of the Kosho game, a novel idea dreamed up by McGoohan and developed with input from master stunt arranger Frank Maher. According to Maher, the game was conjured up out of necessity, because McGoohan wanted to use trampolines: 'You're going to *love* what I've got for you in the next episode,' McGoohan told Maher, who went away with Tomblin and came up with the crazy idea. Maher, who had worked with McGoohan throughout the entire hour-long *Danger Man* series, had never been known to bat an eyelid when the actor's fertile imagination came up with yet another complex action sequence that he, as stunt co-ordinator would have to execute. He said of McGoohan: 'He has the nearest approach to a stuntman you'll ever get among straight actors. He is certainly better at action work than any other actor I know. He works just like a good stuntman: everything is perfectly balanced and co-ordinated.' Told what type of fight was required, Maher would work on the fight scenes with the scientific approach of a movie director. Every moment, every punch, every inch of footwork being carefully mapped out on paper. His 'script' would be shown to McGoohan, and each piece of action was then rehearsed, almost in slow motion, until the movements were right. 'Some of them,' Maher said, 'are so dangerous that the slightest mis-timing could cause injury.' The action is then speeded up during rehearsals until it reaches the dizzy rapidity of the final, spectacular shots that reach the screen, with camera angles (also mapped out by Maher) that were as ingenious and imaginative as the fight arrangements themselves.

In March 1967, the second unit team returned to Portmeirion to complete shots for episodes already filmed. Using doubles, pick up shots were obtained as inserts for episodes yet to be made, with some of the footage actually ending up in *Fall Out*. Further location work, including the scenes from *Many Happy Returns*, in which Number 6 arrives at his home from Trafalgar Square, to find Mrs Butterworth driving KAR 120C up to his front door, were filmed in and around London and Borehamwood.

As guardian of the Prisoner's secrets, it could be expected that McGoohan, the only person who knew what was going on, would have kept his crew aware of what he had in mind. It appears that this was not the case. When asked to explain the increasingly bizzare plot, or tell them the identity of the mysterious unseen character, Number 1, he blatantly refused to clarify what he had in mind Indeed, when asked anything about the production, he invariably gave half-answers and refused to reveal any of his secrets. After a period of disagreements over the way McGoohan was approaching the series, and frustrated that 'his' original concept was in danger of being buried under a barrage of science-fiction abnormality, Markstein – the man who had elected to play the man seated behind the desk to whom McGoohan repeatedly handed in *his* resignation in the programme's opening title credits and in *Many Happy Returns* – reversed the roles and left the series after 13 episodes. So did most of the production team who had, after all, only been booked to work on the first 13 episodes. To the chagrin of those left behind (among whom numbered several ITC executives who were beginning to show concern that the programme was already way over budget), this allowed McGoohan to flex his muscles and take almost total control of the series by overseeing nearly every aspect of the production. Scenes filmed by well-known directors, including Roy Rossotti and Michael Truman, were thrown out and reshot – usually by McGoohan himself. Unhappy with several of the completed stories, the actor ordered them to be changed, his habit being to edit out the scenes he felt could be improved and replacing them with newly-shot material. Ignoring the protests of his writing team, he began to revise scripts, usually working throughout the night to have the rewrites ready for the following morning. The atmosphere on the studio floor was fraught with tension, and the strain was beginning to tell. Unwilling to relinquish his position, or delegate responsibility to others, McGoohan was beginning to look tired and drawn. Interviewed later, he said 'I worked my way through three nervous breakdowns. First time the doctor ordered three weeks off. Last time he suggested three months. There was only one answer – to keep on working. You can't let up when you're in charge.' (McGoohan, it seemed, was far from prepared to step down off his high horse, but within weeks he was about to climb down from his saddle and hand the reins over to David Tomblin). Meanwhile, however, his commitment to the job knew no bounds. He would work a full day, usually from 7 o'clock in the morning to well into the night, but was always the first to arrive at the studio and be available for the cameras the following morning. Producer David Tomblin said: 'When you're making a television series, you reckon to get through between 15 and 20 set-ups a day. Pat often averaged 33 a day, and in one two-day spell achieved 104!'

Nevertheless, the series was weeks behind schedule and something had to be done. After talks between Everyman Films and ITC, a decision was taken to produce a further four stories and to aim for a season of 17 episodes – an unusual number, but one that would slot neatly into the USA summer schedules. (In his *The Making of The Prisoner* booklet, noted Prisoner authority, Roger Langley, commented that, in a flush of enthusiasm for the series, Lew Grade had originally envisaged 30 episodes, but after almost two years' work, increasingly hostile criticism and the outlay of over £1¼ million, it was decided to call a halt at episode 17. While I defer to Roger's infinitely superior knowledge of the subject, I would suggest that a full season of *26* episodes was far more likely, Roger's assertion seemingly based solely on a press interview that Lew Grade gave at the time. Even shrewd entrepreneurs have been known to be misquoted!

As unlikely as it seems, the next episode to be made, *Do Not Forsake Me Oh My Darling*, would have to be produced without McGoohan taking part – at least, for the majority of the story. Having decided to accept an offer to go to Hollywood to play the role of Jones, the British agent sent to the polar wastes to crack a conspiracy in director John Sturges' version of Alastair McLean's *Ice Station Zebra* (a role not far away from the actor's earlier persona of John Drake), McGoohan, thankful no doubt for any break the filming would allow, decided to hand over his brainchild to David Tomblin. By the time the actor had returned to the studio, his partner had produced the story – a cleverly-woven tale that was scripted by Vincent Tilsley to take into account the absence of Number 6 (although Tilsley's script was heavily rewritten before filming). Feeling infinitely better for his break, McGoohan was soon back in front of the cameras filming his few scenes – with doubles standing in for the actors who, having completed their input prior to McGoohan's return, had left the studio. It was not long, however, before the actor rediscovered his thirst for leadership and he soon slipped back into his old habit of believing that 24-hour days are made for mortals. Within days, he was back at the tiller, steering his ship through the stormy waters that lay ahead.

It was as though he had never been away. Working at a frantic pace, McGoohan once again found himself appearing before the camera during the day and spending each evening consolidating his vision of the next day's shoot – not to mention, one assumes, devoting whatever time he had left to working out the screening order for the programme's imminent debut on television. Barely weeks after his return to the studio, the star and his production team were at each other's throats, the head-to-head spectacle rivalling the fictitious on-screen confrontations between Numbers 2 and 6 – an event that was hardly encouraging to a crew who had seen and heard it all before. Lew Grade, meanwhile, though not overtly worried about the production falling behind schedule (true to his word he had continued to back McGoohan to the hilt) was nevertheless concerned that there would not be a final story ready in time for transmission. 'I knew there *would* be an ending,' he told everyone, 'because Pat *told* me there would.' But the man who refused to be 'pushed, filed, stamped, indexed, briefed, debriefed or numbered' was becoming increasingly intolerant of the charge that he had lost sight of his perspective. With neither the time, finance or inclination to return to Portmeirion for further filming, he threw himself into the

McGoohan rehearses a scene from* The Girl Who Was Death, *which was made almost entirely on a backlot at MGM studios

next two stories *Living In Harmony* and *The Girl Who Was Death*. The former broke with tradition by being made almost entirely on a backlot at MGM studios, with location work being restricted to a couple of exterior sequences shot in and around the Borehamwood countryside, the Portmeirion 'Village' footage being courtesy of stock film (as were scenes of the Village used in the episodes *The General*, *The Schizoid Man* and *A Change of Mind*, among others.)

In October 1967, to coincide with the series being premiered on British television, a pre-launch Press conference was arranged, with reporters being invited to question McGoohan about the programme as he sat in the cage used as the Embyro room in *Once Upon a Time* – a story that, though completed many months earlier, had been pulled to serve as the penultimate episode. Dressed in Kosho uniform and a Cossack hat (after a Press screening of *Arrival*, the star would return dressed in *Harmony* western garb), the enigmatic McGoohan, determined to confound and confuse, turned the tables on the media by not only refusing to give straight answers to their questions, but actually asking them questions of his own! A nice anecdote is attached to the *Living In Harmony* episode. Actor Alexis Kanner, contracted to play 'The Kid', received a telegram from McGoohan, who at the time was filming the Alastair McLean story, saying that he was taking quick-draw shooting lessons from Sammy Davis Junior and Steve McQueen. 'So I realised,' Kanner recalled, 'that Patrick was in earnest, and meant this to be shoot-out to end all shoot-outs – the fight wasn't going to be faked by a cut or an edit – and we were really going to have to shoot it out. So I eventually found a gun and practised my own quick draw. Then I wired back the trigger, which was a very dangerous thing to do, because when the trigger is wired off, there is nothing to stop the trigger going off. So the day finally came when we had to film the showdown in *Harmony*, and bets had been placed as to who was the quicker draw, myself or Patrick McGoohan. What actually happened, was that we both drew, but only one shot was heard. So the bets weren't paid out until the next day when the film had been processed and by counting the frames, Patrick had taken 11 frames to draw, while I had taken 7 – a difference of a sixth of a second or something. So after that the healthy competitiveness and respect between us became greater and greater.' (Stunt arranger Frank Maher recalls that when he read McGoohan's cable saying Steve McQueen was teaching him to draw, he had some pencils ready for the star's return, teasing McGoohan by suggesting that the Hollywood actor had been teaching him to draw *pictures*!)

It was during the filming of *The Girl Who Was Death* (in which, incidentally, Kanner made an uncredited appearance) that McGoohan announced that he would be writing the long-awaited finale – but not before he marched into Lew Grade's office and said 'I can't find an ending ... I've become too confused with the project!' Given the fact that the majority of the ITV regions had already transmitted 12 of the episodes, an ending *had* to be found. As McGoohan had always claimed to have had the idea for the finale from the outset, he alone was obliged to deliver the goods. (With the wrap-up story originally due to be screened in January 1968, the final two Prisoner stories were pre-empted, with some ITV regions running the two *Danger Man* colour episodes *Koroshi* and *Shinda Shima* on consecutive weeks, in black and white). Having locked himself away for the weekend, 36 hours

McGoohan attends a Press conference, dressed in Kosho uniform and Cossack hat ....

.... and returns dressed in Harmony Western Garb

later McGoohan presented his crew with the script for *Fall Out*, a tale so wildly ambitious, surreal and pretentious, that neither his allies or the viewing public were prepared for the extraordinary conclusion. Put together at the eleventh hour (the filming and editing were completed with barely days to spare). McGoohan's promise that the story would solve all the mysteries, only served to fuel the fires of controversy. To the disappointment of many fans – not to mention the actor's colleagues – far from being resolved, the questions that had permeated the programme were forgotten, to be replaced by even more questions. The actor's promise to explain everything was wrapped up in a confusing mixture of ambiguous symbolic imagery which shattered the expectations of just about everyone. *Why* had the one numbered 6 resigned? *Would* he finally throw off the shackles of his captors? Who exactly *were* his gaolers? And perhaps most important of all, *who* was Number 1? The episode answered nothing, beyond, perhaps, adding to the mystery. If the doyen of the court was looking for controversy by providing neither a neat resolution or a simple, easy-to-understand answer, he had achieved his aim; the preceding 16 remarkable stories were washed away in a disorderly mixture of pantomimic design that deliberately avoided a tidy conclusion. Viewers who had expected the denouement to answer everything were dumbfounded, with predictable results. During and immediately after *Fall Out* had been transmitted, the ATV duty officer logged well over 150 calls from a confused public.

***McGoohan directs actor Leo McKern and Alexis Kanner during his extraordinary conclusion story* Fall Out**

The following day the mail began to flood in, though strangely enough, the trends of the previous evening were reversed with the majority of the correspondence in favour of the series. The Press were more cautious – their reactions were a mixed bag with some critics asking whether *The Prisoner* was all hokum, while others drew their own conclusion that the programme had been the most vivid of comment on modern civilisation in the history of British television. McGoohan, it seemed was prepared for the outcry. As he told the Press afterwards, 'I *wanted* controversy, arguments and discussion. I was *delighted* with the reaction. It was the intention of the exercise.' Mind you, he was equally liable to claim that the series had reached its perfectly logical and finite conclusion. Answering his critics, he remarked 'I've done a job. I set out to make a specific number of films. I've made them. The series has come to an end. It is just the end of a job, that's all.' Then, with a leprechaunish grin, he invited anyone who failed to appreciate the result of his labours to say, 'Nuts to you, Paddy boy!'

But the job was far from finished, and the actor would experience further hardships before he could slam shut the doors on his creation. As the person responsible for devising the product, there can be little doubt that, despite his claims to the contrary, the man who had strived for perfection in every facet of his career, *must* have been scarred deeply by the initial reaction of both the viewers and critics. Many people regarded the wrap-up story as a betrayal of the established views of the essence of television making: questions are *supposed* to be answered. The good and the bad guys are *supposed* to be defined as such. Programmes are *supposed* to have a beginning, a middle and – in this case in particular – an *end*. They felt let down, hurt and alienated by the actor's total disregard for the established institution of creative television. Many, who seeing the show for the first time had recorded their verdict that the programme was doomed to failure, had long since become hooked on the series and were uniformly unprepared for – to their minds – McGoohan's shocking ending. When the actor came in for a barrage of acidulous Press, many of his former workmates deserted him, only to comment over the years that, with hindsight, they could now understand what McGoohan was about and why he wanted it that way.

Two decades on, it appears that McGoohan's attitude remains resolute. Interviewed for *Six Into One: The Prisoner File* (a 50-minute documentary commissioned by Channel 4 and shown in January 1984, immediately after *Fall Out*), and asked if he had realised that the episode would cause such an outcry, he replied 'Well, I hoped that there would be a bit of an outcry – I *knew* there would be something going on, because it wasn't the conventional ending. People may say "Let's see something original" but basically people like a good solid story that ends up the way it should. This one didn't, of course. There was an outcry – I nearly got lynched and had to go into hiding. They thought they had been cheated, they still had the idea, God love 'em, that it was still John Drake, a secret agent story – *Danger Man* or *The Saint*, or *James Bond*. It had nothing whatsoever to do with any of these. People go to see a James Bond story because they know precisely what they are going to get for their money – a very stylish, bad, bad villain. This had nothing to do with that. This was *not* an action adventure show. It was an allegory. An allegory is a story in which people, places and happenings hide and conceal a message. There is symbolism, therefore there is enormous latitude with what one can do. The main outcry was the evil that had been there throughout, had never been seen. When it turned out to be the evil side of myself, for 12 frames of film in one shot and 18 in another, they were outraged. But what is the greatest evil? If you are going to epitomise evil, what is it? Is it the bomb? The greatest evil that one has to fight constantly, every minute of the day until one dies, is the worser part of oneself. And that is what I did. And I would do the same again.'

But *did* the Prisoner ever *escape*? 'In the final episode,' McGoohan said later in the same programme, 'they all get away, singing "The hip bone's connected to the thigh bone", and he goes back to his house – and the door opens on its own. And he goes in, and the car is there, and you *know* it's going to start all over again. Because we continue to be prisoners. When the door opens on its own – and there is no one behind it – exactly as the doors in the Village open, you *know* that someone's waiting in there, to start it all over again. He has no freedom. Freedom is a myth. There is no *final* conclusion to *The Prisoner*. We were fortunate enough to do something as audacious as that, because people do want the words "The End" put up there. Now, the final two words for *this* should have been "The Beginning"!'

Did McGoohan take the easy way out? Was the ending inconclusive? In retrospect, it is not too difficult to imagine why the actor decided to pull the plug in such an extreme manner. Such a radically innovative series *demanded* an equally radical conclusion. Only much later would the series become accepted as the classic it undoubtedly is – a slice of television history that defies all efforts to catergorise its unique qualities. As Roger Langley sums it up so well: '*The Prisoner* can be appreciated for its high standards of creativity, original ideas, direction, acting, scripts, music, camerawork and sets, placing it many years ahead of the time in which it was made. Much of its appeal lies in its unanswered questions. Alternatively, it can be seen as a challenging epic, allegory, parable, fantasy or thriller. It combines Orwell, Kafka and even, when considering Shampan's sketches and set designs, Fritz Lang.'

Another writer, (unnamed) working for the *ATV Newsheet*, the staff newspaper of the (then) ATV network, prepared the following man-in-the-street's guide to *The Prisoner*, in the issue dated February 1968:

The Village	It did not exist in any materialistic form. It symbolised the prison that is man's own mind.
The Numbers, No. 6, etc.	This represents man's lack of freedom – the stifling of individual liberty by authority.
The Balloon – Rover	Symbolises repression and the guardianship of corrupt authority which, when corruption is finally overcome, disintegrates.
The Penny Farthing	Represents the slowness of progress in our modern civilisation.
The Hippy Character (as played by Alexis Kanner)	Symbolises youth in rebellion against the establishment and, as in the closing sequence of the young man trying to thumb a lift first in one direction and then in another on a motorway, youth not knowing, or caring, in which direction it goes.
The Former No. 2 (as played by Leo McKern)	A former trusted member of the establishment who, having broken away, is accused of having bitten the hand that fed him and is being made by authority to pay for his failures.
The Little Butler	He represents the little men of every community, prepared to follow faithfully, like sheep, any established leader.
The 'break-out' sequence, guns, firing – overlaid by the theme 'love, love, love'	This was a protest against the paradoxes which exist in modern civilisation. Man, preaching love, love, love against the holocaust of war. A penetrating comment on the world situation – Vietnam, the Middle East, etc.
No. 1	The unveiling of No. 1 as Patrick McGoohan himself is representative of every man's desire to be No. 1 – to be the top dog.
The 'shouting down' of McGoohan by the hooded assembly	The inability of the ordinary man to make his voice heard – to put forward his viewpoint to the world.

Whatever its ultimate aim, *The Prisoner* is a series that demands to be seen over and over again – but not in an attempt to unravel its hidden meaning. In my humble opinion there isn't one – but purely to serve its intended purpose, that of an hour of *entertainment* which has never been equalled for its sheer fortitude in daring to keep the viewer both amused and *alert*. One cannot help being appreciative of its creativity, originality and pure, unabashed excellence!

Before entering into the chronological history behind the making of *The Prisoner*, we should perhaps, look at the picture painted by the *ITC Press Book* for the series, a document that was prepared as the series was still being produced. What follows is reprinted exactly as it appears in the brochure, with only biographical details – not pertinent to the subject matter – being omitted.

THE PRISONER

After John Drake – what?

This was the question asked on all sides when Patrick McGoohan came to an end of the *Danger Man* series – a series acclaimed in almost every corner of the world and one which turned McGoohan into one of the greatest names in television.

It is a question which Patrick McGoohan asked himself. And he himself provided the answer. The answer is **The Prisoner**.

The idea for the series is Patrick McGoohan's own, and it is probably the most original idea ever conceived for a television series. It has so many unique aspects that when the production began, McGoohan insisted that it should be filmed on closed sets, banned to interviewers and other visitors, in a bid to prevent its secrets from leaking out.

The secrets are revealed as the series progresses. Each segment, a complete story in itself, paves the way to intriguing new aspects of the drama. Suspense builds up from the very opening scene in the initial episode.

Patrick McGoohan is not only the star of the series. He is executive producer. He has elected to direct several of the segments. He has written some of the stories and has been closely involved in the scripting of each one that appears on the screen. No actor has ever been more closely identified with a programme.

Who is **The Prisoner**? He has no name. Only a number – Number 6. All references to him in the stories are simply by that number. In the scripts and on the programme billing he is just 'The Prisoner'. Few of the other characters have names either. They, too, are numbers except when story developments demand identification by name – occasions when anonymity is deliberately discarded.

Apart from Number 6, there are no other regular running characters, although some do appear several times. Identification of the characters is probably much simpler for the viewer than when they have names because all wear a numbered disc in their lapels or attached to their clothes.

The Prisoner's background is a mystery. He is a man who has held a highly confidential job of the most secret nature. He has retired, but retirement brings increased vulnerability to men in his position. They still have their secrets – secrets which, in many cases, they have kept even from those who employed them. They are secrets which many, many people, whether friends or enemies, would like to have and, in this new series, are determined to have.

This is why the central character in **The Prisoner** has been abducted. He is among others who have equally vital secrets locked away in their own minds and which only brain-washing can extract . . . and among those who have imparted their secrets and, having done so, can never be allowed freedom again.

He has no idea who abducted him. They could be his own people. They could be enemies. Perhaps both. And he has no idea where he is, except that the compound is a completely self-contained village. It could be anywhere in the world, and there is no way of knowing. He is given a cottage with maid service and every conceivable amenity. But every inch is bugged. His every move is watched constantly on close circuit television. There is a detailed map of the village with all the exits clearly marked – but they are cut off by a deadly ray barrier.

The action is on three levels. The Prisoner is constantly probing to discover the identity of his captors and why they have seized him. He is striving by all means and at risk of death to escape. And he becomes involved with his captors and takes an active part in situations arising in their lives.

Some of the village's residents encourage him to try to escape. Others attempt to dissuade him. He has no way of distinguishing between a possible ally and a potential enemy. He has no idea who are the other prisoners any more than he knows who the captors are. They all speak English, but sometimes a foreign language is heard in distant conversation but ceases upon his approach.

He has no idea if it is the West training him up to top indoctrination resistance, or if it is the East trying to break him. But he does know that he has got to resist every effort to make him talk. The efforts to break him are both physical and mental; but he is a man of integrity, determination and willpower, with an inflexibility of purpose that cannot be defeated.

Suspense is the keynote of the series. The action is electrifying but, more than anything, these are stories of a man's personal courage and convictions. The emotional impact is intensely moving. 'It tears at your heart,' one member of the unit declared after seeing a rough-cut of the first episode.

The Prisoner is *not* John Drake. Patrick McGoohan is emphatic on that point. But there is one thing in common with the *Danger Man* hero, and this is in keeping with Patrick McGoohan's well-known refusal to introduce anything of a nature which cannot be viewed by family audiences. There is no sadism. There is no flamboyant sex.

The Prisoner will not become emotionally involved with girls, but this does not mean that there is any lack of feminine appeal. On the contrary, the series introduces some of the most excitingly glamorous and talented of Britain's actresses; and women do, in fact, play a much more vital part in the stories than they did in *Danger Man*.

But Number 6 can trust no-one, not even those he believes to be friends and particularly the girls who display their femine appeal . . .

McGoohan refuses to reveal, except for an undertaking to do so at a later date, where *The Prisoner* was filmed while on location. A large amount of the action takes place out of doors in and around the mysterious village, and the programmes have been filmed in one of the most fascinating and colourful villages in the world – a village which is unique in that it is privately owned and has no permanent residents.

Interior scenes have been filmed at the Metro-Goldwyn-Mayer Studios in England, where some of the most imaginative and ingenious sets ever devised for a television series have been created by set designer Jack Shampan. Nothing like them has ever before been seen on the screen, and it is part of McGoohan's puckish sense of mystery that they will convey to the viewer no indication of the time in which the stories are set. They could be taking place today or tomorrow.

The hour-long stories have been filmed in colour, but whether in black-and-white or colour, they introduce a new element into the making of television films, with their unusual settings, intriguing costumes and fresh, vital ideas.

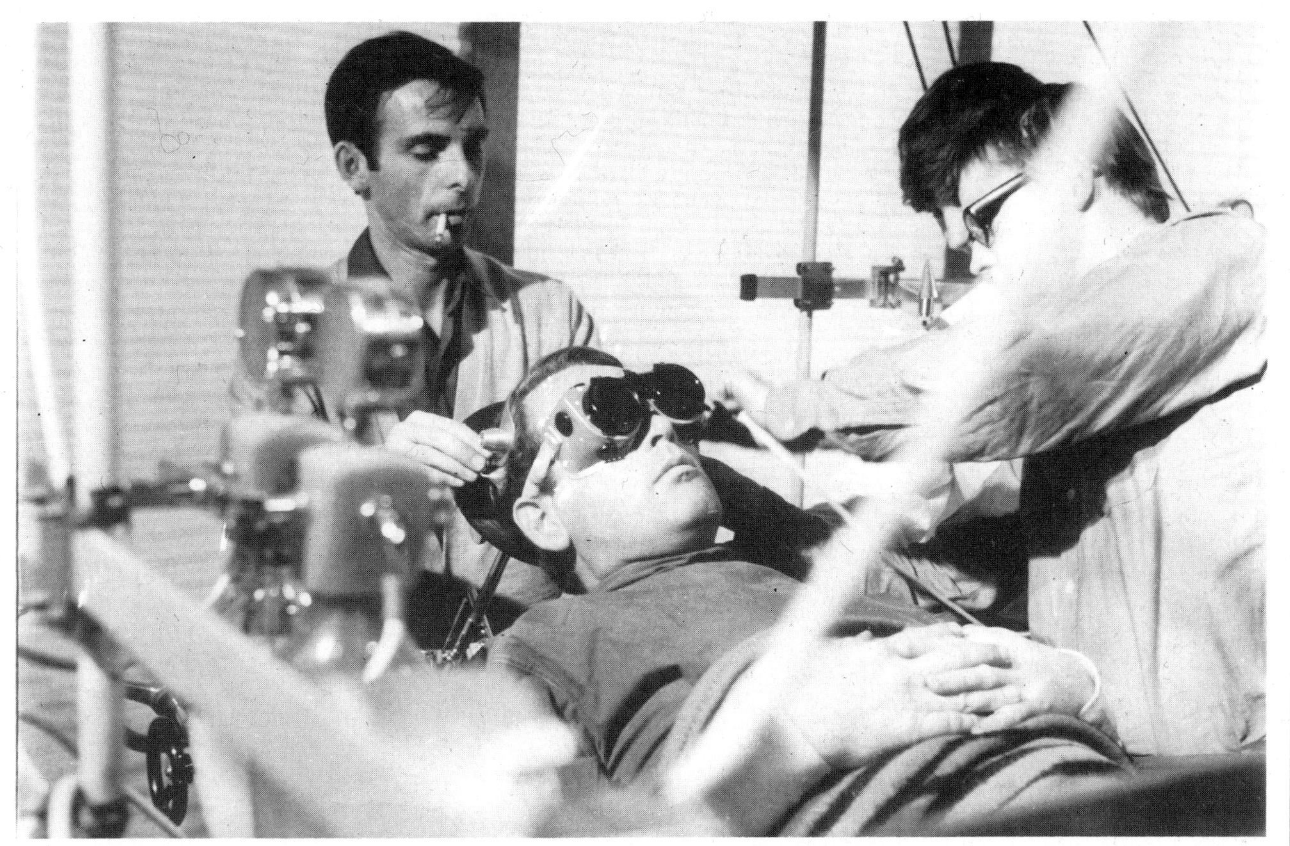

Studio technicians prepare Number 6 for the reversal process in Do Not Forsake Me Oh My Darling

THE VILLAGE

It is known simply as The Village. It has no name. Its occupants have no idea where it is, and they no longer have names themselves: they have become numbers. But they have one thing in common. All are prisoners of one sort or another, and all have been associated with highly confidential jobs of the most secret nature for one country or another. Some have been brainwashed and have accepted their new life. Others are still fighting for survival as individuals.

The Prisoner is one of the fighters, and this is the role Patrick McGoohan plays in his new series of one-hour episodes in colour, **The Prisoner**.

The village to which he finds himself abducted is fascinating. It's colourful, unusual to a high degree, and entirely self-contained. Geographically beautiful, it is built on a hilly peninsula, isolated by a range of mountains, dense forests and the sea. It could be anywhere in the world. Its buildings suggest that it might be in Italy, but everything about it refutes this. It could be a village built especially for the grim purpose for which it exists, but it could be one that has been taken over completely for this purpose.

Viewers might well imagine that it is a vast film set built especially for the series. But it is not. The village really does exist, and all the location scenes for *The Prisoner* were filmed there. Its very existence, known personally to McGoohan for some years, was partly responsible for inspiring the idea for the series, devised by Patrick McGoohan himself.

But what it is, and even which country it is in, is a secret which Pat McGoohan is hoping to keep during the initial airing of the episodes, at any rate, not only because secrecy will add provocative interest to the programme but because further scenes might have to be filmed there and the presence of the public would hinder production.

Fact and fiction have been skilfully blended. The village, and what it stands for, is an integral part of the story construction, and The Prisoner's efforts to discover its secrets are thwarted at every turn.

He has a map, but there are no place names. The map is detailed. There is 'The Sea' – but what sea? There is 'The Beach'. There are 'The Mountains'.

The Village has two kinds of inmates – those who have been taken there and those who run it. But it is almost impossible to tell who is who. Surveillance is constant. Television cameras record every move and activity, both indoors and outside. Every type of modern electronic watching device is used to keep tabs on everyone.

Standing in a clearing by itself is the Castle, which is used as a hospital. It is also, in actual fact, a conditioning centre using the latest methods to break down the prisoners. But the prisoners, except when being brain-washed, are well catered for. There are entertainment facilities of all kinds, from chess, dancing, gambling and film shows to a Palace of Fun and amateur theatricals.

There are shops, a Citizens Advice Bureau, cafes, an hotel, a village square; the village has its own Council, its own water supply, electricity, telephone exchange and, ominously, its own graveyard. It even has its own newspaper and local TV and radio service.

There is no single industry, but the people are kept busy doing all kinds of work, with a factory manufacturing local requisites. There is a Labour Exchange which assigns people varied tasks, drafts them to wherever they are needed, and organises the inhabitants. And there is a Town Hall which is the municipal office and headquarters of the chairman. No-one can get away from The Village, which has flying strip facilities for helicopters but no railway station. A local taxi service is run for the benefit of the inhabitants, and consists of mini-mokes driven by girls.

Life is self-contained and, for those who have accepted what they feel is the inevitable, it is leisurely and even enjoyable. But for those who have accepted there is no longer self-respect and no freedom. The Prisoner is one man who is determined not to be broken. Over it all hangs a menacing shadow . . . a threat that provides **The Prisoner** series with spine-tingling suspense and seat-riveting excitement. And the Village itself is part of its unusual appeal.

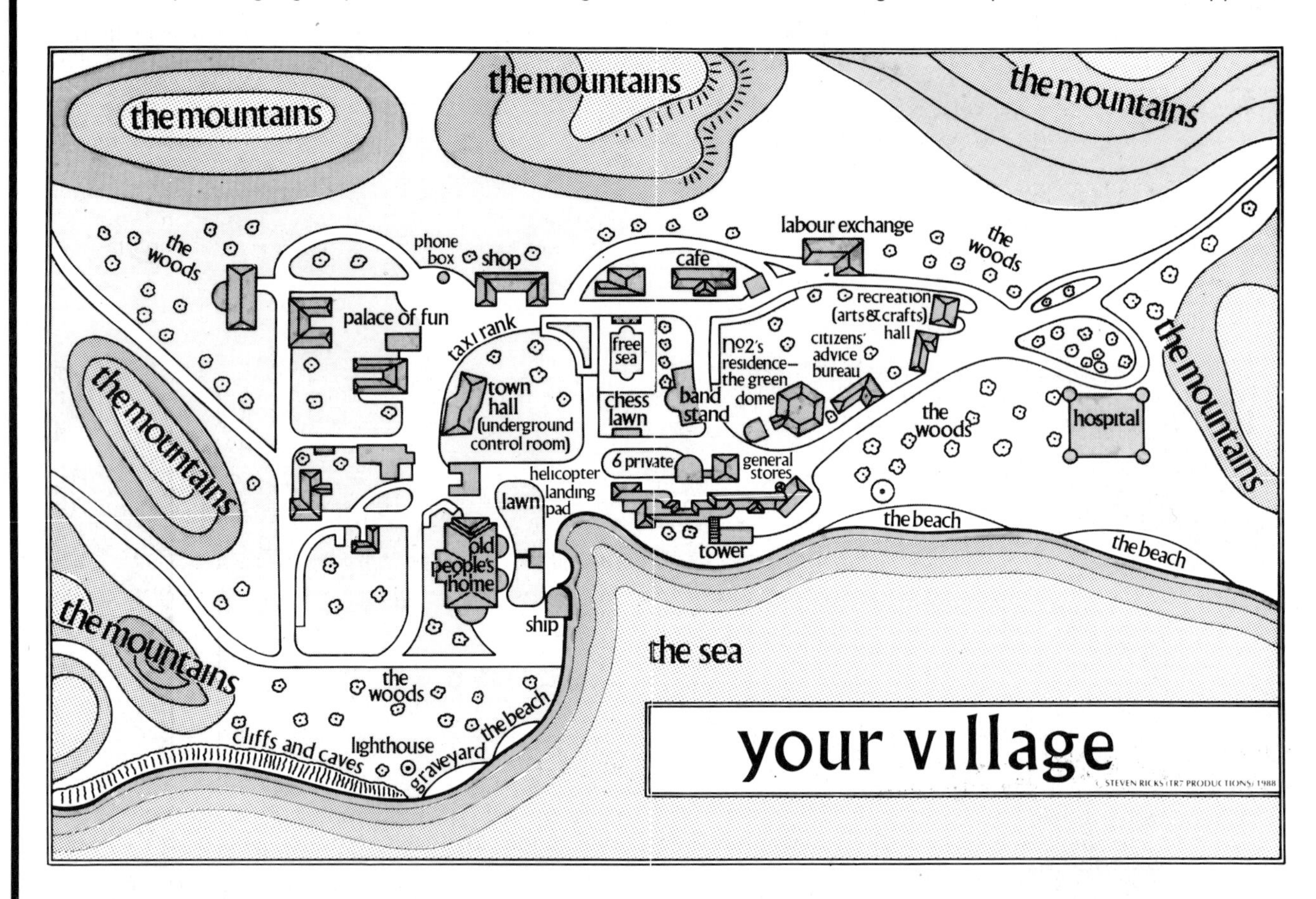

PAT MCGOOHAN IS A PRISONER OF HIS OWN SECRETS

The Irish in Patrick McGoohan surges to the surface when asked about his new television series **The Prisoner**. A leprechaunish smile creeps over his face as he admits that he is the only person in the world who knows the answer to all the questions that are going to be fired at him when the programme is shown.

The Prisoner is Pat McGoohan's first series since his phenomenally successful *Danger Man* (*Secret Agent*). He has conceived the idea himself. And originality is the keynote of the most off-beat stories ever filmed for television.

Who is The Prisoner and what is his name? 'Wait and see,' is McGoohan's enigmatic retort to this initial question, and all he will say about this is that the character is not John Drake of *Danger Man* and that he is a man who has retired from a highly confidential job. And this makes him vulnerable: there are many who want to learn his secrets.

McGoohan reveals that The Prisoner (he is simply known as that or as 'Number Six') has been abducted from his home and taken, unconscious, to a mysterious village.

Where is The Village? Again no answer; viewers will have to wait, and follow the series, to find out.

Who has captured him and why? 'The Prisoner,' McGoohan explains, 'has no idea. This is one of the main points of the series – something he himself is trying to find out. But the reasons are fairly clear: he has secrets they want to get out of him. What isn't so clear, though, is if this is just a method of training him to top indoctrination resistance . . . to see how far he can go without breaking.'

The man behind the organisation is known simply as 'Number One'. Who is he and will he ever be seen?

McGoohan grins impishly. 'The scriptwriters, directors and every single member of the unit have been plying me with these questions,' he comments, 'and I am hoping that viewers will be sufficiently intrigued to follow the series until they find out!'

The Prisoner's direct contact is 'Number Two'. But 'Number Two' is never the same man twice running. This position in the organisation changes regularly, with the Prisoner himself put forward as a candidate in one segment. By why? Just watch the series to find out! It's a hot seat for anyone to occupy.

The Village emblem is an old-fashioned Penny Farthing bicycle with a colourful, modernistic canopy. Once again, this is something Patrick McGoohan has dreamed up, but when asked if there is anything symbolic about it, he just smiles mysteriously. It has no personal associations with his private life and he admits: 'I've never been on one, and it's going to take a lot to get me on one!'

Who is the strange dwarf who wanders in and out of the stories, oddly garbed and frequently with an umbrella over his head? Could he be 'Number One'? A lot of the members of the unit believe he might be, and viewers will undoubtedly wonder as well.

Here again, McGoohan is giving nothing away. There is a good reason for the dwarf's presence, just as there is a good reason for the presence of other unusual characters and for the odd things that happen. Beyond that, McGoohan refuses to be drawn.

What is the Rover? What is the significance of the salute everyone gives? Again . . . wait and see!

Within a short time of **The Prisoner** becoming established on the air, a new slogan is likely to catch on among the viewers. It is, 'Be seeing you.' Why? 'Just watch, and you'll find out!' McGoohan exclaims.

Throughout the production of *Danger Man*, it was widely publicised that Patrick McGoohan would have nothing to do with the opposite sex in a romantic manner. McGoohan still feels that sex, as such, has no place in a popular television series intended for family viewing. There are, however, plenty of girls in **The Prisoner**, but what they will be doing is McGoohan's secret.

Actresses Mary Morris and Norma West pictured with McGoohan during a break from filming Dance Of The Dead

The series will have viewers asking one question after another, and McGoohan will assure you that he knows all the answers. They are locked in his own head and interviewing him presents problems: he is a prisoner of his own secrets.

He will not even reveal where the location scenes for the programme have been filmed. 'It's a real village,' he says, 'and it's one of the most unusual villages in the world.' He is not, he avers, simply trying to puzzle viewers. Each story is complete in itself, and the unanswered questions are part of the developing theme: 'Questions the Prisoner himself is asking, and once he finds the answers he will be well on his way towards solving the mysteries that are baffling him.'

Inevitably, he is repeatedly asked if **The Prisoner** has anything in common with *The Fugitive*? His answer to that is emphatic. It has not. It has nothing in common with any other television series ever filmed. It's new . . . unusual . . . and challengingly intriguing!

PATRICK MCGOOHAN

Three of the most important men attending a production conference on a film are the executive producer, the director and the star.

In the case of **The Prisoner** series, one man sometimes represents all three. Patrick McGoohan is not only starring but is executive producer, and is personally directing several of the episodes.

It is a challengingly formidable undertaking for one man, even if only on the grounds of physical stamina. Few actors would accept such a challenge, but Patrick McGoohan does so with an air of undisguised enjoyment and restless energy.

'If things go wrong,' he exclaims, 'I am the only one to shoulder the blame!'

The idea for **The Prisoner** is his own, and in playing the title role he is taking over a brand new character to follow the long-running and phenomenally successful John Drake of *Danger Man (Secret Agent)* and certainly in stories which bear no resemblance to any series previously filmed for television.

McGoohan has never disputed the fact that he entered television because he wanted to prove that a film series could attain the quality of the best in feature film production and the theatre, with a distinctive flavour of its own. He also wanted to prove that action-filled adventure could be presented without sadism and sex.

The success of *Danger Man*, even though it kept him away from the theatre and film projects he had in mind, was so great that, the moment the series came to an end, he began work on the preparation of *The Prisoner*.

Now he continues his television career in his most provocative role yet.

THE PRISONER

17 colour
52–minute episodes

ARRIVAL

Written by George Markstein and David Tomblin

Guest stars

The Woman	**Virginia Maskell**
Number 2	**Guy Doleman**
Cobb	**Paul Eddington**
The New Number 2	**George Baker**

with

The Butler	**Angelo Muscat**
Taxi Driver	**Barbara Yu Ling**
Maid	**Stephanie Randall**
Doctor	**Jack Allen**
Welfare Worker	**Fabia Drake**
Shopkeeper	**Denis Shaw**
Gardener/Electrician	**Oliver MacGreevy**

and

Ex-Admiral	**Frederick Piper**
Waitress	**Patsy Smart**
Labour Exchange Manager	**Christopher Benjamin**
Supervisor	**Peter Swanick**
Hospital Attendant	**David Garfield**
1st Croquet player	**Peter Brace**
2nd Croquet player	**Keith Peacock**

Directed by Don Chaffey

AS THE mid-morning sunlight gives way to slow-moving storm clouds and thunder shatters the heavens, from a distant horizon, an open-topped, yellow and green Lotus 7 sports car appears, racing at speed down a deserted airport runway. Its driver, clad entirely in black, his face set in determination, steers the machine into the busy London streets, proceeding at speed across the city's Westminster Bridge, and weaving its way past the Houses of Parliament. Making a right turn, the vehicle descends into a dimly-lit underground car park, its driver pausing only to snatch a ticket from the building's automatic ticket dispenser before impatiently driving the car at speed beneath the ascending checkout barrier. Grinding to a halt before two closed doors marked 'Way Out', the man climbs from his seat and strides purposefully along an empty corridor towards a second set of doors, his footsteps punctuated by the pulsating musical accompaniment. Throwing the barriers aside, he enters an ante-room furnished to serve as an office. Seated impassively before him is his bespectacled superior, his squat body framed against a large wall map of the world. Pacing angrily before the man (his words lost in repeated thunder claps) the intruder slaps down a white envelope from his inside suit pocket. Then, bringing his fist forcefully down onto the desk, upsetting a cup and saucer in the process, the man turns on his heel and storms back to his car; back into the sunlight and *clean* morning air.

Simultaneously, we see a sterile room, empty save for lengthy rows of metal filing cabinets, above which glides a mechanical arm. Plucking a computer-identity card adorned with the man's photograph from a file, the machine methodically types a row of X's across the man's picture, before depositing the card into a drawer marked 'Resigned'. Driving home, the man mysteriously finds himself behind the hearse he passed earlier. Watched by its driver, who is dressed in mortician's garb, the man overtakes and enters a nearby residential street. Bringing the Lotus to a stop outside a genteel Victorian house, the driver springs from the vehicle and enters his home. Unseen by the man, the hearse draws silently to the pavement behind him. Inside the house, the man selects a suitcase and begins to pack. (He is identified now, by the on-screen title *The Prisoner*.) Outside, the driver of the hearse climbs the three concrete steps leading to the tenant's front door. Stowing travel brochures on top of his clothes, the man snaps shut his luggage, then, as clouds of billowing gas begin to seep into the room through a keyhole, he pauses, a quizzical look on his face. Blurred visions of spinning sky-scrapers float across his face as, finally overcome by the gas, the man falls backwards onto his studio couch. Waking, he sits up dazed. His surroundings seem familiar – and yet? Climbing to his feet, he crosses to the window, draws back the venetian curtain and stares in disbelief at . . . The London view he knows so well has disappeared. His eyes stare out at a village he has never seen before. Onto the screen comes just one word: 'Arrival'.

His eyes stare out at a village he has never seen before

The place is so architecturally puzzling and difficult to identify that, confused, he looks again at his room, before he realises that it is an exact replica of his London home. Uncertainly he paces to the veranda outside to take stock of his surroundings. He now stands outside a small cottage. London's landmark, Big Ben, has been replaced by a lofty bell tower, perched high on a rocky tor. Believing he sees a figure staring down at him, the man races upwards. The 'person' is just a statue and, glancing downwards, the man sees no sign of activity. Just then the bells begin to chime and in the distance he sees the figure of a woman erecting a colourful sun canopy over a cafe table. Racing to the spot, the girl informs him that the establishment will open shortly. Demanding to know where he is, the girl makes small talk. 'Where is this?' (The Village?) 'Where's the police station?' (There isn't one). 'Can I use your phone?' (She doesn't have one, but there is a phone box around the corner.) He locates the device, an odd-looking telephone booth marked 'For information lift and press,' it carries a white circle containing a canopied penny farthing bicycle motif. The stranger lifts the cordless telephone receiver. (A chance to learn his whereabouts?) It is not to be. After some verbal banter about exchanges and numbers, a female voice cuts the line dead when the man is unable to give her his number. Resuming his walk, he passes quaint little buildings of elaborate design, before arriving at a roadside board displaying a map denoted 'Free Information'. Selecting a category from the dozen or so listed, he presses one of its many buttons, and the machine clicks into life. Within seconds, he is picked up by an Oriental girl driving a Village taxi (a motorised buggy, topped with a colourful canopy). She, too, refuses to answer his questions and, telling the newcomer that the taxi is for local use only, refuses to take him to the nearest town as requested, dropping him instead outside a charming little village shop sign-posted 'General Stores'. The charge for the journey is two units. Realising the man does not have the fare the girl says that he can pay next time. Entering the shop, which has a large penny farthing emblem in its window and stocks only one brand of goods – Village Food, each can bearing the penny farthing motif (a symbol he is now growing used to, having seen it worn in badge-form by every Village inhabitant he has encountered, each of whom appears to have their own individual number printed over the bicycle's large wheel). The stranger finds the shopkeeper, a rotund man wearing an apron and straw boater, talking to a female customer. As he enters, they are speaking in some foreign language but, catching sight of the newcomer, they revert to English. 'Be seeing you,' the shopkeeper calls as the woman leaves. Requesting a map of the area, the stranger is asked if he requires colour or black and white? Handed the latter, its cover titled 'Map of your Village,' the man becomes further disillusioned. The chart provides no additional information to the one he had seen earlier at the Free Information directory: useless detail, with vague names. The colour version, containing slightly more detail, proves just as vague: an 'Old People's Home', the sea, the beach, and again 'the mountains', which appear to dominate the region on all four sides of the map. Learning that there is no demand for a map of the larger area, the newcomer leaves in disgust, the shopkeeper's 'Be seeing you,' and forefinger-and-thumb-together salute ringing in his ears.

Walking back to the cottage in which he awoke, the man hears a message being transmitted on the public address system: a woman's voice wishing everyone 'Good morning all. It's another beautiful day.' Approaching 'his' home, and seeing a maid shaking her dust cloth from 'his' verandah, he breaks into a run, arriving at the cottage to find a newly-erected sign pointing to his front door. It reads '6 Private'. The door opens automatically, he enters and it closes behind him with a gentle hum. The girl is winding her way down the steps outside the cottage. Looking around the room, he spots a stick-like doll resting on his writing bureau. It holds a message card, 'Welcome to your home from home.' At that moment a telephone, its subscriber exchange and number dial bearing the solitary numeral '6', purrs into life. It is an invitation to join someone for breakfast, 'Number 2, the Green Dome' – an opportunity, perhaps, to learn more about his strange surroundings?

Climbing the building's ornamental rock-garden steps, where a gardener is tending some plants, the visitor approaches its large white door and tugs at the bell push. Once again the door opens of its own volition, beckoning the man into a richly-furnished room where, as the door swings shut behind him, he is led across the room to another set of doors, steel ones this time, by a mute dwarf Butler wearing a tailcoat. Stepping inside the dimly-lit chamber, the man takes stock of the room. The chamber is huge. Rising vertically from the centre of the floor is a large black orb, before which rests a console of switches, colourful glowing lights and buttons. Seconds later, as the black sphere revolves, he notices that its rear side is hollow. Inside it sits a middle-aged man, dressed in a dark blazer, roll neck jumper, flannels and plimsoles. In his hands rests a furled-up umbrella, and draped around his neck is a long woollen scarf. Pinned to his blazer, he wears a penny farthing badge, boasting a red numeral '2'. Approaching his host, the visitor notices that one entire wall of the chamber consists of a giant television screen, with soft psychedelic patterns floating across its surface. 'Do sit down,' invites the host, the absence of a second seat being remedied by the man extending his umbrella to press a control button on the console before him. A circular floor aperture opens and a small chair and table rise at the visitor's feet. The dwarf Butler enters pushing a breakfast trolley. To the visitor's bemusement, his request for China tea with lemon, plus bacon and two eggs, is served instantly. (Did they already have knowledge of his preferences?) The giant metal doors open and close as the Butler leaves, and the question-and-answer session begins in earnest. 'I suppose you're wondering what you are doing here?' (It has crossed the visitor's mind.) 'It's a question of your resignation.' (Go on.) 'The information in your head is priceless. I don't think you realise what a valuable property you've become.' (The visitor paces the floor, refusing the offer of another seat.) 'A man like you is worth a great deal on the open market.' (The pacing stops.) 'Who brought me here?' demands the visitor. (I know how you feel, believe me, they have taken quite a liberty.) 'Who are *they*?' Whoever they are, they are apparently curious about what lies behind the man's resignation. He had a brilliant career. His record is impeccable and *they* want to know why he suddenly left? The bout continues until, realising that the session has turned into an interrogation, the visitor, making to leave, announces 'I don't know who you are or who you work for and I don't care. I'm leaving.' Reaching the top of the ramp, the doors slam in his face. Stepping out of the globe, Number '2' leans towards his control panel, on the top of which sit a row of coloured telephones – green, yellow, red, all cordless – and reaches for a black-covered book. As this is opened, the wall screen begins to flash pictures of moments from the visitor's life – large reproductions of those in the album. Snatching the book the visitor begins to flick through its pages ('Oh, feel free,' snorts his host.) The large screen now shows the man in his London home, getting ready to meet a colleague named Chambers. ('A nice guy, Chambers – and so talkative,' comments his host.) Slamming the book shut, the visitor ponders his position, realising now that every facet of his former life is accessible to his enemy: his former life has been monitored and filmed. Reopening the book brings further images from his past career, revealing that not a single moment of his life has been overlooked, entered and filed. 'The time of my birth is missing,' observes the man. 'Well there you are!' exclaims the other, feigning surprise. 'Now let's bring it all up to date. 4.31 am, 19th of March, 1928. 'I've nothing to say. Is that clear? Absolutely nothing!' replies the visitor, throwing the book to the floor. His interrogator whines on that it is just a matter of time before he does tell them what they wish to know and, who knows, if he co-operates, he might even be given a position of authority. It is finally out in the open. The man has been captured by an unknown power who are after the priceless information stored in his head. He will be kept in this place until he divulges his secrets. His response is immediate. Pacing angrily before his host, he tells him that he refuses to make any deals. He has resigned! And he will not be pushed, filed, stamped, indexed, briefed, debriefed or numbered! His life is his own. 'Is it?' asks Number 2. 'Yes, you won't hold *me*' retorts his guest. '*Won't we*,' the other replies confidently. To prove that they will, he leads the man from the room. The time has arrived to show the newcomer exactly what he is up against.

With the dwarf Butler at its controls, a Village helicopter takes off with the two men as passengers, for an aerial tour. From aloft, the Village can be seen as a self-contained area. With pride, Number 2 shows the newcomer the community. 'Quite a beautiful place, really, isn't it? Almost like a world of its own.' (I shall miss it when I'm gone) quips the other. Number 2 pinpoints the Council Building, the restaurant, commentating that they even have their own newspaper. (You must send me a copy.) And their own graveyard. A social club – members only, of course, but Number 2 will see what he can do . . . If the new man has any problems, he should visit their Citizens Advice Bureau. 'They do a marvellous job. Everybody's very nice. You might even meet people you know!' The helicopter lands and the newcomer is shown a group of senior citizens, several of whom are climbing the rigging of a stationary stone boat moored by the

'They're our senior citizens. Of course, they have every comfort'

beach. Then it's off in a taxi to the Village square. A band is playing, and the now familiar female voice reports over the public address system that strawberry ice cream is on sale, and there is a possibility of intermittent showers later. Everyone appears to be enjoying themselves, all save the newcomer who, frowning, is urged forward by Number 2 to approach the Town Hall's balcony, on which he stands, a megaphone is his hands ready to address the Villagers. Bidding the newcomer a beautiful day, an elderly couple salute the man as they pass. 'They didn't settle in for ages. Now they wouldn't leave for the world,' says Number 2. Suddenly Number 2 repeats the word 'wait'. All save the new man stop dead in their tracks. He continues to walk forward, until he sees a small white circular ball spinning on top of a jet of water in the fountain nearby. In the wink of an eye, it has increased its girth a hundred fold and has soared upwards to nestle between two ornamental stone pillars overlooking the square. Setting eyes on the apparition from his position by the Village pool, a man wearing sun-glasses lets out a scream, and races between the immobile villagers. Ignoring the warning by Number 2 to 'Stop – Come back,' the man races away. A mistake. Watched by the newcomer, the vibrating white sphere glides down from its perch and propels itself after the running man, homing in on its victim to suck the life from his lungs. The thing departs as quickly as it came and the Village returns to normal. Watching the amoeba-like thing bounce away, the newcomer asks 'What was that?' '*That* would be telling,' replies Number 2, through his megaphone.

The next initiation takes place at the Labour Exchange. Passing two rows of villagers waiting outside, one formed by men, the other by women, Number 2 and his guest venture inside. Greeted by an official, who eyes the new man with disapproval, Number 2 is told to go straight through. Placards adorn the walls: 'A still tongue makes a happy life'; 'Questions are a burden to others, answers a prison for oneself'. Eyeing these with amusement, the man follows Number 2 into a huge hall, adorned with ornate arches. Everything is ready, and the new man is given an aptitude test. Placed before a display panel showing a square hole, the man's attempts to frustrate Number 2 by selecting a round peg, fail to materialise: the hole magically shrinking to accommodate the round peg like a glove. Like it or not, he has passed. The questionnaire is next, the man being asked to fill in details of his race, religion, hobbies, reading matter, food preferences, what he was, what he wishes to be, any

'Any family illnesses? Any politics?'

family illnesses – any politics . . .? The last phrase spurs the newcomer into action. Smashing a contraption consisting of wheels, cogs and spokes which sits upon the Exchange Manager's desk, he storms out of the building – leaving Number 2 to console his colleague with the words, 'Never mind, you can get all you need from this.' Handing the man the black book we saw earlier, he adds 'I think we have a challenge.'

Back at 'his' cottage, the man finds a lovely blonde girl working there, sent by the Labour Exchange. 'That's another mistake *they* have made. Get out!' Alarmed by the man's demeanour, the girl leaves. Immediately she does so, a central wall panel in the lounge rises with a hum, revealing a part of the accommodation which has hitherto remained hidden: a bedroom, a bathroom, and a kitchen stocked with tins of Village Food, each bearing the ubiquitous penny farthing motif. Examining everything as he paces the room, he confirms that it is an exact replica of his London home – with two additions. Music is being piped into the room from a loudspeaker, and a lamp containing floating globules of oil immersed in liquid, rests upon his furniture. Opening 'his' writing bureau, he produces a day-by-day memo/diary – with neatly written pre-printed daily entries. Things to do: TODAY 'Don't forget to send thank you note for flowers at earliest.' TODAY'S Memoranda: 'Arrived today. Made very welcome.' Another drawer contains a bound volume of the 'Map of your Village,' but again this offers no further clues to the ones he has seen earlier. Finally, when his aimless pacing before the speaker turns to annoyance, he angrily crosses to the device and throws it to the floor. Disintegrating, it nevertheless continues to pour out its music, despite being kicked and trampled on by the man. As he does this, a voice from the speaker announces: 'Attention Electrics Department, please go to Number 6 where adjustment is needed.' At that moment, the maid returns on the pretext of having forgotten something. Demanding to know how to stop the music, the man is told that they cannot. It's automatic. 'Who controls it?' (She doesn't know – she *really* doesn't know.) 'Have you never tried to find out?' Relenting a little, he questions her further, but she does not have, or refuses to give, the answers he is seeking. (We have a saying here, a still tongue makes for a happy life.) The man moves on. People must have tried to get away from the Village 'How many have succeeded?' (Don't ask.) 'Has *anyone* ever escaped?' (Some have tried, but have been brought back – not always alive.) At that point the girl breaks down and begins to cry. Eventually confessing that she was ordered to gain his confidence, in exchange for her freedom, the man mocks her by saying 'You believe that. With all that knowledge in your head, you really believe that they would let you go?' (They might – if he gave her some sort of information.) Her words find no sympathy. 'Your services will *not* be required tomorrow!' he exclaims. Tearfully, the girl leaves.

Every move and word of this scene has been watched and monitored on a closed circuit television by Number 2 and his Supervisor, a bald-headed, bespectacled official, who stand side-by-side in the enormous control room – an impressive place, laid out with ultra-modern machinery. Banks of monitors are punching out ticker-tape messages. An enormous rotating shaft with an observer seated at each end manning surveillance cameras, spins backwards and forwards before a huge map of the world and a star chart. The Village nerve-centre. An all-knowing, endlessly-watching operations room which controls everything outside. Staring impassively at the monitor screen, the Supervisor confesses that the girl was most convincing. He was sure that she would pull it off. 'He's no ordinary man,' observes Number 2. 'This one has got to be handled very differently.' Pointing out that that could be dangerous, the Supervisor takes solace when his colleague reminds him, 'You know how important this is.' Back in 'his' cottage, the new man receives a visit from an electrician carrying a replacement speaker unit – the tenant is neither chided for breaking the original, or asked if he wants a replacement! After several minutes of small talk, the occupier decides to take a stroll. 'Be seeing you,' he smirks. 'And you,' returns the repair man. Reaching the gardens the man acknowledges a passing cyclist and bumps into a gardener – an exact double of the man he left repairing his speaker unit! Startled by the likeness, the newcomer makes for the nearby woods, passing rows of stone statues during his progress. Suddenly he is forced to drop behind a bush when he sees one of the huge white balloons, patroling a nearby road. Changing direction, the man reverses back towards the column statues, whose heads turn to follow his progress, their 'eyes' emitting flashes of light. Back in the control room, the Supervisor is watching the man's every move. Sensing that he is under surveillance, the newcomer breaks into a run, but his progress is blocked by the return of the bouncing white sphere which, uttering a fearsome roar, pursues the man. Back in the control room, the Supervisor speaks into a red telephone: 'Attention Post 14 – Yellow Alert. Now leaving Northern perimeter, Number 6 – Repeat, Number 6.' Hearing the approaching wail of sirens, the pursued man keeps going. Observing the man's progress on his monitor screen, the Supervisor adds: 'Now approaching, contact imminent.' A motorised buggy takes to the beach and pursues the running man who, zig-zagging, races along the sands to evade his pursuers. He falls, then quickly regains his feet to engage the man leaping from the vehicle. They fight and the buggy's passenger is knocked to the ground. Leaping onto the back of the speeding machine, the would-be escaper tosses its driver overboard and drives away at speed. 'Number 6, heading for Outer Zone, in our vehicle. Orange Alert,' warns the Supervisor. As if by magic, an obstruction now appears before the racing buggy – the quivering white balloon. Approaching at speed, the man leaps from the vehicle and attacks the glutinous thing with his fists, but his adversary engulfs him. Immobilising the man, the Village guardian bounces away, then sits on guard beside the prostrate figure as a second mini-vehicle, summoned by the Supervisor, arrives and carts the unconscious man away.

Wearing pyjamas, the prisoner awakes in a hospital bed. An old woman sits before him, knitting as she rocks back and forth in her chair. Asking how he feels after his nasty experience, his immediate response is to ask where he is. 'You're in the hospital, son,' she retorts, feigning sympathy. As the woman leaves to fetch the doctor, he recognises the face of a patient in an adjacent bed. He slips from his bed and crosses to the figure. The man is Cobb, an old colleague. The figure stirs as the man questions him. 'Cobb. What are you doing here?' he asks. 'And you?' says the other, recognising his vistor. His story matches that of his friend. 'How long have you been here?' (Days? Weeks? Months? Cobb cannot be certain.) 'Who brought you here?' (The patient remembers nothing beyond returning to his hotel room in Germany, climbing into bed, and waking up in the Village.) Any further conversation between the two is cut short by the arrival of the doctor who, handing the new patient a dressing gown, leads him on a tour of the hospital. Perusing the corridor outside his ward, the newcomer stares through an observation window in a door. In a passage flooded with red light, he sees two rows of people, each attired in dressing gowns, each apparently doing nothing. 'Group therapy,' explains the doctor. 'Counteracts obsessional guilt complexes producing neurosis.' As they walk away, an infantile man with electrodes taped to his shaven head is being led to a room, his expression blank. Accompanying the doctor to a medical room, the patient is invited to sit in an examination chair. At its base are a pair of slippers, his

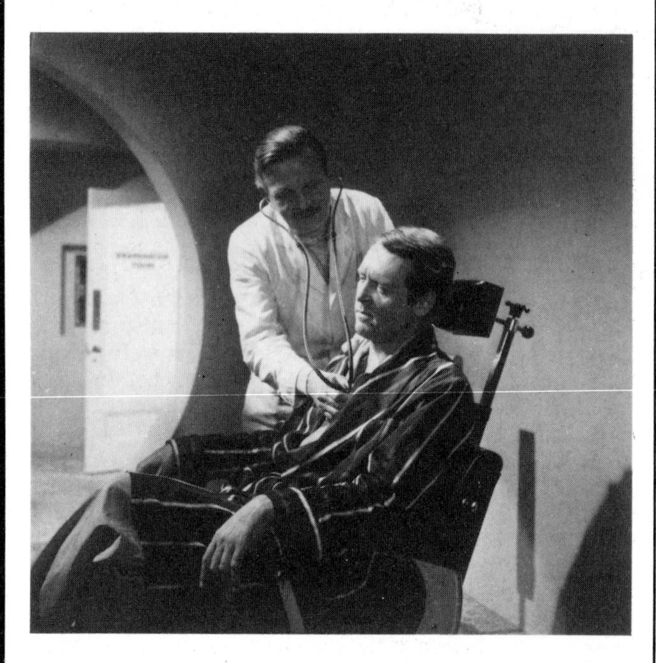

'. . . Just listen to the old ticker'

size! The patient is examined and a machine produces a perforated card pronouncing the man absolutely fit. In the control room sits Number 2, engaged in conversation on a red telephone. 'He's having a medical. Mmm, no, course I don't mind. One has to make sure of these things.' Telling his patient that he is free to leave the following morning, whereupon he will be issued with new clothes (his own have been burned), the trip back to his ward allows the patient to catch sight of the infantile man again. Looking into the man's room, he sees the figure watching a small white ball dancing gaily on a water fountain, a demented look upon his face as he sings in time with the bubbling water jets. An alarm bell sounds, and the doctor's assistant races forward to announce that Çobb, the amnesia case, has jumped to his death from a window. Back in his ward, staring at his deceased colleague's bed, the newcomer ponders what the future holds for him.

The following morning, wearing his newly-acquired clothes, the patient is discharged and escorted from the hospital by a male nurse. The man now looks very different. He is wearing a dark blazer with white piping lapel trims, fawn-coloured slacks, and thick black plimsoles with white rubber soles. A straw boater adorns his head and he is carrying an umbrella. Most notable of all is the fact that he now wears a badge pinned to his jacket's left lapel, a badge identical to the ones worn by every Village inhabitant, save for one small diference, the man's badge is numbered '6'. Handing the man a folder containing his employment, identity, health, welfare and credit card, the medico returns to the hospital. As he does so, the new Number 6, casts his hat, umbrella and badge into the back of the taxi waiting to take him 'home'. Glancing back at the hospital as he is driven away, to the female driver's consternation, the man abruptly jerks back the vehicle's handbrake and runs up the steps leading to the Green Dome. As before, the door marked '2' opens of its own volition and the mechanical steel doors are thrown back by the mute drawf. Marching down the

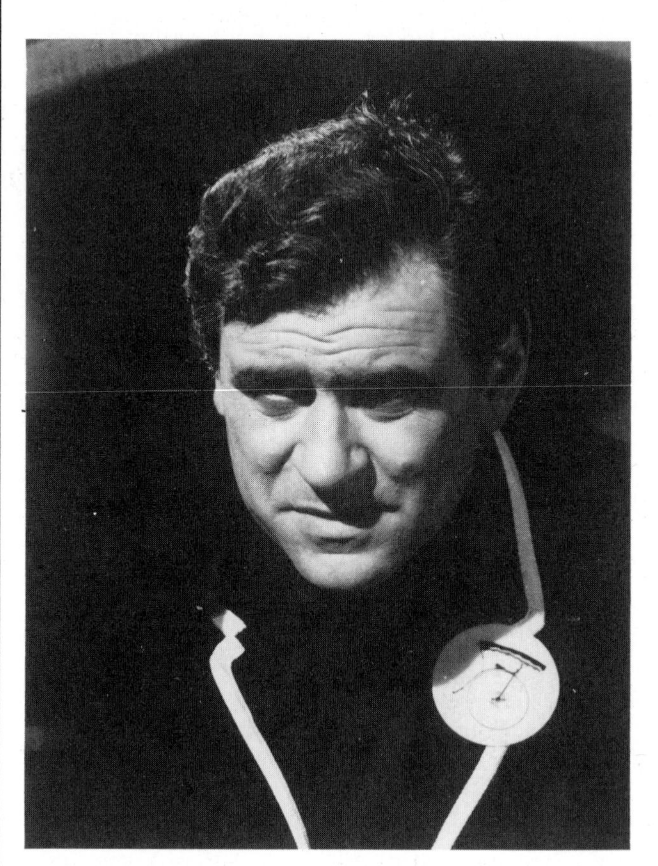

'I have taken his place. I am the new Number 2'

interior ramp towards the figure seated in the oval shaped chair, he is astonished to see a new face. 'Get him,' he shouts to the seated figure. 'I have taken his place. I am the new Number 2!' (Get Number 1.) 'As far as you are concerned I'm in charge! What can I do for you?' (Cobb!) 'What we do here has to be done. It's the law of survival. It's either them or us.' (Imprison people. Steal their minds. Destroy them!) 'Depends on whose side you're on, doesn't it?' (I'm on our side.) 'Then we'll have to find out where your sympathies lie,' retorts the new Number 2, leaning forward to pick up a black book. (You know where they lie.) Reading from the book, the man in the chair recites the intruder's record: the subject shows great enthusiasm for his work. He is utterly loyal. Pausing he comments 'Is this a man who suddenly walks out?' (I didn't walk out – I *resigned*!) 'People change, exactly, as do loyalties.' (Not mine!) Telling the intruder that his words are all very commendable, but he is interested only in the facts, and the only chance the man has of getting out is to give him the facts. 'If you don't give them, I'll take them. It's up to you.' The new Number 2 dismisses the intruder with a flippant 'Good day – Number 6.' Number what? Quizzes the man. 'Six,' replies his tormentor, 'For official purposes everyone has a number. Yours is Number Six!' 'I am not a number. I am a person,' the intruder throws back defiantly. 'Six of one, half-a-dozen of the other!' exclaims Number 2, as the so-called Number 6, exits through the steel doors. Staring at the man, Number 2 dictates an addition to the man's file. 'Report on Number 6. Normal classification. On arrival subject showed shock symptoms, followed by accepted behaviour pattern. Since then has been unco-operative and distinctly aggressive. Attempted to escape. Subject proving exceptionally difficult, but in view of his importance, no extreme measure to be used yet.'

At 'home' again, the man denoted Number 6 paces his room. Hearing the sound of a band approaching his cottage, he steps out onto the balcony. A procession of villagers, some carrying umbrellas, are marching up the hill towards him. At the rear is a flower covered coffin, towed in a trailer by a buggy. Some way behind walks the solitary figure of a woman, her face a mask of sorrow. Leaving the balcony, the man follows the procession to where the woman stands alone. She is looking at a section of the beach where gravestones mark a small cemetry, towards which pallbearers are carrying the coffin. His intuition tells him that the casket contains his ex-colleague Cobb. The man crosses to the woman, who wears a badge numbered '9'. Seeing the tears clouding her eyes, he tells her that he was a friend of the dead man, and offers to help. Expressing some doubt as to whether she can trust him, she says that she knew Cobb but a short time. Told by the man the cause of his death, she flinches, turning her head away. A bell chimes and she warns him to leave. Grabbing the woman's arm and explaining that they must talk further, the woman agrees to meet him at the concert centre at 12 o'clock.

Shortly after the appointed hour, the woman joins him before the grandstand on which a band is playing. This time she is more forthcoming. Pretending to read a book, she explains that Cobb had been planning to escape from the Village. They had an escape route planned but 'they' came sooner than Cobb had expected them to. In order to use Cobb's method of escape, he will need to fly a helicopter (one is due at two o'clock) and will need an electropass which, synchronised with the alarm system, will allow them to reach the machine. (She can supply this. She knew the last pilot.) Agreeing to meet again by the stone boat at two o'clock, they leave – the man watching her climb the steps to the Green Dome.

Inside his home, Number 2 is dictating a further report on the new Number 6, up to and including his attendance at the concert just a few minutes earlier. Looking up, he offers the woman sitting opposite him a congratulatory 'Thank you, my dear. More tea?' Then, adding that she has done well and should not worry too much about Cobb, it was not her fault, he hands Number 9 a black-fronted folder containing details of her new assignment. Turning back its cover, the photograph of Number 6 stares back from the page!

Later that day, Number 6 is playing chess with Number 66, an ex-Admiral, but his mind is not on the game for. As a helicopter approaches and lands nearby, his attention is distracted further by the arrival of Number 9. His partner cries 'Checkmate!' Refusing the offer of a second game in favour of a stroll, the ancient mariner recommends the boat. 'She's great in any weather. Sailed her myself many a time. Have a good trip.' Leaving the seadog humming the melody of 'The Drunken Sailor', Number 6 joins the woman inside the mock stone boat. Handing over the electropass (a kind of wristwatch, with rather more dials than usual), the woman is taken aback when he intimates that it was sent by her 'boss' Number 2. Confirming that she has been assigned to him, and was previously assigned to Cobb, Number 9 denies that she has betrayed either of them. 'We *were* trying to get out, before it was too late. Soon it will be too late for you.' Declining his offer to join him, she leaves, instructing the man to go right away. Watching her depart, the man begins his long walk to the helicopter pad. Passing merrymakers swimming in the pool, and the mute dwarf Butler, he arrives unseen to where the flying machine waits unmanned, guarded only by the hovering white sphere. Flicking on the electro device, its hands being to rotate, punctuating a flashing light on its dial. Hesitantly, he approaches the helicopter. The device works and the guardian withdraws. Climbing into the pilot's seat, he slips the device into his pocket, starts the machine and roars skywards. Back in the control room, Number 2 observes the man's departure with a smile. He nods, and one of his staff coaxes back a lever. Inside the helicopter, Number 6 loses control of the machine: the control stick freezing in his hands as, of its own accord, the helicopter banks sharply and heads back to base. Resigned to his fate, the pilot removes his hands from the controls.

Below on the lawn, Number 9 looks concerned when, having told the chess-playing seadog that she does not play his game, he advises 'You should. We're all pawns m'dear.' Within minutes, the helicopter makes a gentle landing at the very point from where only moments before, escape looked assured. Watching the touch-down with glee, Number 2 turns to his companion (Cobb, now very much alive and dressed in a businessman's suit, ready to meet his new masters in London), and tells him 'I think I'll let him keep the watch, just to remind him that escape

Hesitantly, he climbs into the helicopter

is not possible.' Then, assuring his companion that the woman will be well taken care of, he bids Cobb au revoir. 'They'll be delighted with you,' he calls after the retreating figure. 'Give them our compliments.' Promising to tell his new masters that there are no loopholes, Cobb gives the familiar hand salute and bids his colleagues 'auf wiedersehen.'

Ushered away by the giant menacing bubble, Number 6 walks, defeated, across the lawn, the bouncing glutinous bodyguard following close behind him. As he walks to his fate, the mute Butler, his umbrella raised above him, watches the *prisoner's* return!

The prisoner's face zooms from a panoramic aerial view of the Village. Filling the screen, bars snap closed across the face with a deafening thud. The man is now THE PRISONER.

AUTHOR'S NOTE: Originally filmed as *The Arrival,* this story features the only full version of the title sequence and theme music.

To achieve the effect of the Rover *closing in* to smother its victim, the production staff sometimes used a fishing rod with a thin line tied to Rover's 'neck'. On other occasions, the film was shot in reverse, with people walking *backwards* to give the impression that the balloons were passing them when the film was played projected *forwards*. In an alternative version of *Arrival* (a pre-broadcast print, shipped to America for the early 1970s syndicated run of *The Prisoner*) Rover had a mechanised 'heartbeat' and its progress was accompanied by 'heavy breathing'.

As mentioned earlier, the alternative version (which probably still exists, but has yet to be found – although an *audio-taped* recording of the episode does exist, courtesy of USA Prisoner enthusiast Christopher Campbell, who had the presence of mind to make a reel-to-reel recording of the story when it was transmitted by WHDH Channel 5, in Boston, Massachusetts on 10 May 1974) also contains the POP closing credits.

FREE FOR ALL

Written by Paddy Fitz (Patrick McGoohan)

Guest star

Number 2 **Eric Portman**

with

Number Fifty Eight **Rachel Herbert**
Labour Exchange Manager **George Benson**
The Butler **Angelo Muscat**
Reporter **Harold Berens**
Man in Cave **John Cazabon**

and

Photographer **Dene Cooper**
Supervisor **Kenneth Benda**
Waitress **Holly Doone**
1st Mechanic **Peter Brace**
2nd Mechanic **Alf Joint**

Directed by Patrick McGoohan

'WHERE AM I?' (In the Village.) 'What do you want?' (Information.) 'Whose side are you on?' (That would be telling. We want information, information . . . *information*.) 'You won't get it!' (By hook or by crook, we will.) 'Who are you?' (The new Number 2.) 'Who is Number 1?' (*You* are Number 6.) 'I am not a *number* I am a free man!' (Laughter).

The telephone marked 6 purrs into life: an early morning call from Number 2. 'Good morning, good morning. Any complaints?' (I'd like to mind my own business!) 'Fancy a chat?' (The mountain can come to Mohammed!) Almost immediately, Number 2, sporting a light-coloured blazer and his long woollen scarf piped with white trims, walks into the man's cottage. 'Mohammed?' (Everest, I presume?) 'I've never had a head for heights.' (How's Number 1?) 'Past the summit.' (Play it according to Hoyle?) 'Oh, all cards on the table. They rely on that.' (Whose move?) 'Your turn next. Confide and we concede. Breakfast?' As the words leave the elder man's lips, Number 58, dressed as a maid, walks into the cottage, carrying a breakfast tray. Introduced to the reluctant host, she is addressed by Number 2 in a foreign language, then leaves. Informing Number 6 that the woman used to work in records and has a great variety of information, the elder adds that she has a wonderful gift, a photographic memory. She has done well during her stay and should not be with them for long. Over breakfast – international cuisine – Number 2 turns the conversation to the forthcoming election campaign beginning that day. 'Are you going to run?' quizzes Number 2. (Like blazes – the first chance I get.) 'I meant run for office,' retorts the elder. (Whose?) 'Mine, for instance.' (You have a delicate sense of humour.) 'Naturally,' replies Number 2. 'Humour is the very essence of a democratic society.' Their conversation is interrupted by a fanfare of trumpets broadcast over the host's loudspeaker unit. Then, hearing campaign music being played outside, they rise: the one known as 6 follows his guest to the door. Stepping out onto the veranda, the elder man returns the salute from the crowd gathered in the street below the cottage, many of whom carry colourful

Numbers 2 and 6 relax during a break in the filming

umbrellas. A placard bearing the man's photograph and the words 'Vote – No 2' is being held aloft. Passing comment that it appears as if his guest has a unanimous majority, Number 6 is told by Number 2 that that is why he is worried – 'It's bad for morale. The good people don't seem to appreciate the value of *free* elections.' Told that he, Number 6, is the sort of candidate they need, the younger man asks what the outcome would be if he chose to run against Number 2 – 'What *physically* happens, if *I* win?' 'Then you're the boss!' answers the elder, inviting Number 6 to step back into the cottage. 'If you win,' suggests Number 2, 'Number 1 will no longer be a mystery to you. I'll introduce you properly, and we'll see how you feel after accessing the maddening crowd.' Leading Number 6 outside, they climb into a taxi and are driven to the Village square. Entering the Town Hall, they emerge onto a balcony and Number 2 calls for silence. Informing the congregation that the lack of opposition in the matter of the pre-election is not good for the community and reflects an acceptance of things as they are, he adds that they are, however, fortunate in having among them a recent recruit whose outlook is particularly militant and individualistic; he hopes that the man will not deny his duty to the community by refusing to take up the challenge. Turning to his guest, he introduces Number 6 to the congregation. The younger man's opening announcement that he is *not* a number, but a person, is greeted with great amusement. 'In some place, at some time,' he continues unabashed, 'all of you, held positions of a secret nature, and had knowledge that was invaluable to an enemy. Like me, you are here to have that knowledge protected or extracted.' 'That's the stuff to give them,' smiles Number 2. 'Unlike me,' the younger man continues, 'many of you have accepted the situation of your imprisonment and will die here like rotting cabbages.' 'Keeping going. They love it,' goads Number 2. 'The rest of you have gone over to the side of our keepers. Which is which? How many of each? Who's standing beside you now?' continues Number 6, informing the onlookers that he intends to discover who are the prisoners, and who are the warders. 'I shall be running for office in this . . . *election*?' he ends, purposefully. Asking the crowd to applaud a 'citizen of character', Number 2 barely raises an eyebrow as 'Vote for 6' placards appear throughout the crowd, as if by magic. 'Be seeing you,' grins Number 2, as the candidate finds himself hustled by his newly-won supporters into his election vehicle, a Village taxi, decked out with placards bearing his image.

Leaving his cottage at sunrise, Number 6 is angry to find Number 58 waiting for him in a taxi. Ringing Number 2, he is informed that the girl has been selected as his aide, because she, too, is new. She will be at his disposal for the election period – and for anything he might desire, within reason, of course. Number 6 is expected to attend the dissolution of the outgoing council in 30 minutes' time in the Town Hall chambers. The girl can speak no English and cannot, therefore, understand him when he requests to be driven to the establishment, so he determines to walk. Leaving the girl behind, he crosses the Village green and arrives at the 'Free Information' board. Seconds later, he is joined by Number 58 who, witnessing him selecting a number from the board's control panel, joins him and presses the button marked 6. Babbling in some foreign language, the girl heads back to her vehicle, beckoning her unwilling passenger to join her. As he does so, two Village reporters race after the taxi and bombard the man with questions. Introducing himself as Number 113, and his photographic colleague as Number 113B, one of them states that they work for the Village newspaper, the *Tally Ho*. The reporter asks how the candidate will handle his campaign? 'No comment,' comes the reply. Further questions bring the same response, but undeterred, the journalist makes up his own answers for each question asked: 'Intends to fight for freedom at all costs. Will tighten up on Village security etc.' Arriving at their destination, the newspaper team move away, thanking the candidate for his answers as they go. Paged by an announcement over the public address system, Number 6 is about to enter the building when a voice causes him to turn. Standing a few feet away, is a young man selling newspapers – a man looking remarkably similar to the newspaper photographer now racing away to develop his pictures! Crossing to a printing device signposted 'The Tally Ho', the candidate is astonished to be handed a hot-off-the-press edition of the newspaper carrying the headline 'Number 6 Speaks His Mind' – barely seconds after he gave the reporter *no* story! Puzzling over the headline, it takes a split second before the man becomes aware that a Village guardian is approaching his position. Ushering the candidate towards the Town Hall entrance, the bouncing monster departs once the man is safely inside.

Directed by Number 2's voice, the candidate enters a vast subterranean chamber, akin in size to a circular aircraft hanger. Before him sits Number 2, surrounded by 12 candidates, each of whom wears a top hat. All stare blankly before them. Asked by the elder man if he wishes to question the council, the candidate nods. The dais on which he stands begins to rotate and the interrogation begins. 'Who do you represent? Who elected you? To what place and public do you owe your allegiance? Whose side are you on?' he asks. No reply is forthcoming and the dais ceases to revolve. 'Any further questions?' mocks Number 2. The candidate retaliates. 'This *farce*. This 20th-century bastille that pretends to be a pocket democracy . . . Why don't you put us all into solitary confinement until you get what you're after and have done with it!' Furious, Number 2 bangs his gavel, calling the man to order. 'Brainwashed imbeciles,' continues the candidate, ignoring the man's fury. Then, staring at the rows of blank faces, 'Can you laugh? Can you cry? Can you think?' Holding aloft the *Tally Ho* headline purporting to contain his words, he berates the silent onlookers, ignoring the elder man's attempts to silence him. With the push of a button, the dais occupied by Number 6 begins to rotate again. Gaining in momentum, faster and faster it whirls as Number 2 orders that the man undergoes the 'test'. Deposited with a thud into a strangely-lit corridor, the man struggles against dizziness to rise to his feet. Traversing the corridor by clutching straps suspended from the ceiling, the fear-stricken man stumbles into a room, to be greeted by the manager of the Village Labour Exchange. Purporting to be a friend, the bespectacled man offers the new arrival tea – unsweetened, he declares, acknowledging that he is aware of the man's preferences: the records show that the man gave up sugar four years and three months earlier on medical advice, which shows that he is afraid – afraid of death. 'I'm afraid of nothing!' exclaims the guest. 'You're afraid of yourself,' comes the reply. 'You're aware of that? Good. Honesty attracts confidence, and confidences are the core of our business.' In the Green Dome, Number 2 receives a telephone call from Number 1. Apologising that his experiment got out of hand and, yes, he is aware of how valuable Number 6 is to them, he offers to be more careful in the future. Then, telephoning Number 6's companion, he informs him that the Prisoner must be taken to the first stage only, the tissue must not be damaged. Looking sideways at his guest, the interrogator presses a button on the control panel before him. The chair occupied by Number 6 is now electrofied and its occupant is forced to grip its arm rests for support. On a screen behind him appears a silhouette of the man's head, with two triangular lines running from the shadow's eye-line. Questioned as to why he wishes to run for electorial office, Number 6 stares impassively ahead. The question is repeated. The man's eyelids flicker and a circular black spot appears on the screen, moving along the top line towards the silhouette's face. The man is lying. Informed that everything he thinks there is treated in the strictest confidence, a black square moves inwards on the bottom line. The man being interrogated understands: he is ackowledging the truth. Asked again why he is running for office, both objects move, leading the interrogator to postulate that he believes that had the man won and took over the Village, he would be able to control an organised breakout – correct? The black square moves forward. That was a mistake, wasn't it, asks the interrogator. The circular spot urges forward. Told to think only of his responsibility, both objects reverse. A challenge. Fighting to regain control of his thoughts, the man in the chair makes an all-out attempt to defeat the device. Within seconds, both objects being to move forward and converge. As they enter the head on the screen, Number 6 slumps into unconsciousness. Having witnessed these events on the control room monitor screen, Number 2 orders Central Area to stand by. Staring at his helpless prisoner, the interrogator remarks, 'Good. Simply splendid.' Seconds later, the prisoners awakes and rises cautiously from his chair. Looking around him, he acknowledges his gratitude for the tea. He shakes hands with his interrogator, thanks the man for voting for him and with a cheery 'Be seeing you' leaves the chamber, a changed man. Outside the establishment, he acknowledges the cheers of the villagers and willingly gives answers to a reporter from the *Tally Ho* newspaper.

Back in the residence marked '6 – Private', in the company of Number 58, the man watches his televised election speech with pride. He advises the girl to learn her lesson quickly; if she obeys the rules, *they* will take good care of her. Gradually, however, he begins to struggle for clarity of thought and runs away from the girl, driving off in a buggy parked outside. Weaving his way through throngs of villagers, he slams the vehicle to a halt and races away towards the beach – pursued on all sides by Number 58, people carrying 'Vote 6' placards, an helicopter and the mute Butler. Jumping into a small powerboat, he guns its motor and heads out to sea at speed. Staving off attempts by two engineers who try to impede his progress, the man regains control and races away at full throttle – ignoring the warnings from Number 2 in his helicopter to stop being foolish and to turn back before it is too late. Alerted by the control room Supervisor, a guardian rises from its anchor point on the ocean floor. The white sphere looms before him and he is forced to leap overboard as the pulsating mass heads directly for the boat. Too late. The swimmer's attempts to forge ahead are doomed. Exhausted, he is soon overtaken and the guardian engulfs him in its glutinous mass, suffocating the man into submission. Carried to the shore, the man recites his election speech in delirium as an ambulance arrives to carry him away. Its mission over, the guardian returns to its undersea lair.

Staving off attempts to impede him, Number 6 throttles away at speed

Disturbed by dreams of the election, Number 6 regains consciousness back in his room, as a pulsating lamp above his bed flashes into his eyes. He is conditioned by messages flashed to his brain: perched on the stone boat he addresses the Villagers with words put into his mouth by Number 2: give *them* information and the community will be a better place to live. *He* can fulfil their dreams. Whatever they require *he* can supply it: winter, spring, summer or fall, all can be theirs. Apply to *him*, and it will be easier and better. Number 2 makes an alternative campaign speech. Beware, be careful. There are those among them with a fresh face and an enthusiasm that cannot be denied. *Their* promises ring richly in their ears. Number 6 has explained his record. He has adapted admirably, but he has no experience whatsoever of the manipulation of a community such as theirs. Beware. Ask yourselves if he has got the administrational ability to implement his priorities? Can you trust *him*? The prisoner's slogan '6 for 2, and 2 for nothing, 6 for free for all, for free for *all*. Vote, vote for *6*.' Watching his opponent whipping the crowd into a frenzy, Number 2 opens a debate about spare time, stating that *he* cannot afford such a luxury. Telling *his* supporters that *everyone* is entitled to spare time, Number 6 proposes that should *he* win the contest, he will make spare time for 'less work and more play.' Hearing this, the people roar, 6, 6, 6!

Evening finds the junior candidate in a bar. The beverage on offer is supposed to be non-alcoholic, but Number 6 puts on a good display of being intoxicated. Screaming for drink, he is led outside by Number 58, who he accuses of spying on him. Driven by her to a secluded spot in the woods, she indicates that real alcohol can be found in a cave, kisses him and departs. Entering, he finds a still – and an intoxicated Number 2 sprawled out on a makeshift cot. The man confesses the need to keep his nerves steady: he is worried about the forthcoming election and what will happen to Number 6 during it. Handed drinks by a brewer and confirming that they are not under surveillance in the therapy zone, the older man sits up. Told by Number 6 that he does not approve of the Village, Number 2 exclaims: 'To hell with the Village!' Then, leading the other into an ante-room, he shows his guest a large blackboard on which is written a complicated equation. The brewer, he is told, was once a brilliant scientist. He now brews his brew, plays with his chalk and, once a week, they come down to photograph what he has written, then clean it away so that the man can begin over again. 'Clever', says Number 6, keeling over at the man's feet. 'Quicker than usual,' remarks the brewer entering the room, to which a now sober Number 2 replies that he warned the man not to make it too strong – 'we must not damage the tissue.' Telling his superior not to worry, the brewer explains that Number 6 has been given just enough to take him through the election: he will remember nothing.

The beverage is non-alcoholic, but Number 6 puts on a great display of being intoxicated

'6 for 2, 6 for 2' chant the villagers outside the election hall. Inside, the votes for Number 6 overflow the ballot box. Conceding defeat, removing his opponent's rosette and replacing it with that of his own – one bearing the number 2 – the older candidate leads the victor outside. Acknowledging the bemused and silent faces of the crowd, the men are driven by Number 58 to the Green Dome. Beckoning the victor into his new home, the defeated candidate makes to leave, pausing for a moment to tell the new man 'Anything you need to know, press a button. You're the boss.' As the door glides shut behind him, the new Number 2 and his aide enter the building's vast circular chamber. A press of a button by Number 58 and the recently-vacated oval-shaped chair rises from the floor. A telephone purrs. It is the Labour Exchange Manager, asking if there is anything he can do for them. 'Be seeing you,' gloats Number 2. 'And you,' comes the reply. In a moment of mad exhilaration, Number 2 follows the woman's lead and experiments by pushing buttons. Chairs rise from the floor and retreat to their nests. The monitor screen flashes into life. Further equipment appears from all corners of the room until, at the touch of a button, a piercing blue and white light

'Anything you want to know, press a button'

begins to pulsate in front of the man's eyes. He stiffens, unsure of his surroundings. Led by Number 58 he is placed before the psychedelic patterns flitting across the monitor screen. Turning the man around, his eyes remain glazed as the woman tears off his rosette and slaps him forcibly across the face. The hypnotic trance broken, the man reels backwards, landing awkwardly in the oval-shaped seat. It revolves, bringing him back to the woman's icy stare. Terrified, he regains his feet and races to the bank of telephones – his babbling words being piped around the Village cause barely a second of interest. Two security men rise from beneath the floor and attempt to pin his arms by his side. He escapes to an ante-room, but the men follow him and rain vicious blows to his body. Within minutes his bruised and battered body is carried back into the room to face the new Number 2 – the girl he left behind just a few minutes previously. Speaking in perfect English, the woman tells him that this is only the beginning: they have ways and means of getting the information they require, but have no wish to harm him permanently. Is he ready to talk? Silence is her answer as, falling backwards on a stretcher provided for him, the prisoner is returned to his residence.

At the controls of his helicopter, the out-going Number 2 telephones his replacement. 'Just on my way. Everything go according to plan?' 'Don't worry, all was satisfactory in the end. Give my regards to the homeland,' replies Number 2. Leaving the Village behind, the helicopter rises skywards.

AUTHOR'S NOTE: The violent, some say sadistic, fight between Number 6 and the two 'guardians' which takes place in the Rover cave was deleted when the episode was first broadcast in the UK. This was later restored, and appears intact in the *Channel 5* video cassettes. Stuntmen Alf Joint and Peter Brace played the 'guardians', with the former being responsible for choreography.

Although not credited in the story, the Supervisor was played by Peter Swanwick, who is seen courtesy of some stock footage from 'Arrival'.

This was the only view of the Cat and Mouse nightspot.

CHECKMATE

Written by Gerald Kelsey

Guest stars

Rook	**Ronald Radd**
1st Psychiatrist	**Patricia Jessel**
Number Two	**Peter Wyngarde**
Queen	**Rosalie Crutchley**
Man with the stick	**George Coulouris**

with

The Butler	**Angelo Muscat**
2nd Psychiatrist	**Bee Duffell**
Supervisor	**Basil Dignam**
Painter	**Danvers Walker**
Shopkeeper	**Denis Shaw**

and

Ass. Supervisor	**Victor Platt**
Nurse	**Shivaun O'Casey**
Skipper	**Geoffrey Reed**
Sailor	**Terence Donovan**
1st Tower Guard	**Joe Dunne**
2nd Tower Guard	**Romo Gorrara**

Directed by Don Chaffey

A BEAUTIFUL SUNNY morning in the Village. Its inhabitants go about their business as usual until, emitting a fearful roar, a guardian bounces into view. Moving aside to allow the gelatinous thing to pass, the Villagers freeze in their tracks – all save one, an elderly gentleman who hobbles along on his walking stick without so much as a glance at the malign beast. Watched by Number 6, whose curiosity is aroused by the man's apparant unconcern, the man disappears through an archway leading to the gardens. The guardian continues its progress and the Prisoner races after the man as the community returns to their normal activities. Catching up with his quarry in a courtyard, the floor of which has been designed to represent a giant chessboard, the man with the stick invites Number 6 to take part in the unusual game. Joined by the Queen, a woman dressed to represent a chesspiece who invites the Prisoner to be her pawn, it becomes clear that this is no ordinary game of chess. Only the man with the stick and his opponent actually play while others, dressed in colourful costumes which represent chessmen, 'move' across the board as indicated by the two players. Taking up his position as the Queen's pawn, Number 6 begins to question the woman as to the man's identity. He is the champion, she replies as the man climbs into his high chair to commence play. 'Who *was* he?' he urges. The woman has heard that the man is an ex-Count, whose ancestors are supposed to have played chess using their retainers: rumour has it that they were beheaded as they were wiped off the board. 'Charming,' quips Number 6. 'Oh, don't worry,' says the Queen 'that's not allowed here.' The game continues, as do the pawn's questions. 'Who is Number 1?' (It doesn't do to ask questions.) 'Why were you brought here?' Keeping her eyes on the play, the girl repliies, 'That was a good move, wasn't it?' 'I know a better one,' says he. (Oh?) 'Away from this place.' (Oh, that's impossible.) 'For chessmen – not for *me*,' he retorts. (They told me there wasn't a hope.) '*I* don't believe what they tell me. Are you surprised?' he continues, missing his cue to move as the man with the stick orders the Queen's pawn to another square. 'Maybe I could help,' offers the woman. 'How? ... How? ... HOW?' he shouts, as the address speakers surrounding the chessboard bark out the player's request for the Queen's pawn to move to Queen's 4. Urged on by other 'chessmen', he finally moves as ordered and a Bishop from the opposing side tells him not to worry, he is quite safe, protected by the Queen. The game proceeds, observed from the Control Room by Number 2 and the Supervisor, who have the Queen and her pawn under surveillance. Passing comment that Number 6 looks placid, the Supervisor is reminded by his colleague that the man is just a pawn – one false move and he will be wiped out. 'Not while the Queen is protecting him,' the Supervisor replies. 'The Queen!' exclaims Number 2. 'She'll take no risks to help him.' Reminding his colleague that he knows where he will be if he needs him, Number 2 leaves. The chess game continues until, confused by the bombardment of moves indicated by the players, the Rook, standing in the next square to Number 6, walks off the board in disgust. Entering an unoccupied square, he yells 'Check!' Informing Number 2 that the White Queen's Rook has moved without orders, the Supervisor is told to bring him in for treatment. In seconds, the 'chesspiece' has been carried away to the hospital and the game proceeds with a substitute chesspiece. Asking the Queen why the man has been removed, Number 6 is told 'for using his initiatve' – the forbidden cult of the individual. Four moves later and the game is over, won convincingly by the man with the stick. Congratulating the winner on his performance, Number 6 joins the man for a stroll. Inquiring why the man uses people for his game, the elderly man replies that, according to psychiatrists, it satisfies his desire for power. As they walk, Number 6 turns the conversation to the possibility

'Psychiatrists say it satisfies my desire for power'

of escape. Admitting that he has given it some thought, the other says that he has now learned to distinguish between the blacks and the whites – indicating that the attitudes of the villagers gives away the difference between the prisoners and the warders. Everybody has an attempt, but they all fail, the Prisoner is told. Leaving the man behind, Number 6 walks off alone, but is soon overtaken by the Queen, who wishes to know how he plans to escape. If he will tell her his plan, she will be willing to help: she likes Number 6, and if it is a good plan she would be willing to join him. Unsure as to whether he can trust the woman, he tells her as much and returns to his residence.

At sunrise the following morning, as Number 6 is taking a stroll, he is greeted by Number 2, who wishes to know if the Prisoner enjoyed the chess game? 'Don't tell me you care?' comes the reply. (But of course, *we* want you to be happy.) 'Fine. Just give me a one-way ticket home!' barks Number 6. 'Won't you ever give up?' asks the superior, indicating that they have ways of making him see sense – ways that are carried out under the strictest medical supervision, of course. 'I can guess what,' the Prisoner retorts, pointing to the hospital, 'from the state of the man you took yesterday.' 'The Rook? Oh he'll come to no harm, he's been put on a rehabilitation course.' 'You make it sound very attractive – what do you want me to do, envy him?' replies the other. The outburst is greeted with a smile and Number 2 offers to drive the man to see the patient. At the hospital they see the Rook being wheeled into a room. It contains three coloured water coolers, and Number 2 explains that the patient has been dehydrated: when he awakes he will be suffering from an insatiable thirst. As they watch, a woman psychiatrist enters the room, administers an injection into the sleeping man's arm and leaves as the patient stirs. Joined by the woman, the men watch as the Rook rises from his chair and attempts to quench his thirst from the first of the water dispensers. A voice piped over the room's public address system tells him to wait, but his thirst is too great. Ignoring the command he picks up a cup and turns on the dispenser. The container is empty. In desperation, he sidles along to the second dispenser. Again the voice orders him to desist. Failing to heed the advice, he receives an electric shock and falls to the floor, his body racked with pain. Viewing this in disgust, Number 6 turns to his host. 'Don't tell me,' he growls, 'it hurts *you* more than it hurts him.' The superior sighs. 'In a society, one must learn to conform.' Regaining his feet, the Rook staggers around the room pleading for an end to the ordeal. Do as you are told and you will be given water, he is scolded. He is directed by the voice to the dispenser coloured blue. Approaching the container with caution, after further coaxing the Rook turns on its tap. It yields water and the patient drinks, refilling his cup several times over. According to the psychiatrist, the man is now cured. 'You must be proud of yourself,' snaps a disgusted Number 6 to the man at his side, leading Number 2 to quip that they are proud of the patient: in future, the man will be fully cooperative, a statement which leads the doctor to observe that she, for one, is glad, the patient had proved troublesome. Marching to the door, Number 6 warns them that their troubles are only just beginning, a comment that spurs the woman to ask her superior if he, Number 6, is there for treatment. His negative response bringing forth the comment that it is a shame, the man is an interesting case – one whose breaking point she would love to discover. 'You could make that your life's ambition,' throws back Number 6, departing with a grin.

Later that day, as he is wandering through the Village, filling out chess moves in the *Tally Ho* newspaper chess competition, Number 6 comes across the Rook sitting alone on the steps of a fountain. Seeing the man staring at him, the Rook races away, but he is overtaken and questioned by the stranger. He learns that the man was brought to the Village after a new electronic defence system he had invented was stolen. Believing that the man can be trusted, despite the treatment he has received, Number 6 tells him they will meet again. In the Green Dome, Number 2, informed by the Supervisor that his prize subject is getting friendly with the Rook, orders his colleague to give him vision. Within seconds his monitor screen glows into life, showing the two men sitting together on a veranda, deep in conversation. Unable to decipher their words, Number 2 asks the control room to connect the audio link. However, having noticed the head of a statue nearby turning in their direction and aware that their conversation is being monitored, Number 6 is ready for them. When the audio link buzzes into life, the two men are discussing nothing more suspicious than chess moves. Reassured by the doctor that the Rook is cured and content that anything Number 6 learns from the man will only serve to teach him that there is no point in rebellion, Number 2 orders the surveillance to be closed down. Free from observation, the men continue their talk of escape. Informing the Rook that they must determine who they can trust, the Prisoner and his new ally circulate through the Village to discover a nucleus of prisoners who could be reliable allies. A gardener ignores them, but others show more promise.

'I'd like a word with you.' (Then you'll have to wait.)

Observing the men talking to several villagers, Number 2 orders the audio link to be reconnected: it is not working, having been sabotaged by the Rook. Concerned that the men may be planning something, he has Number 6 taken to hospital for psychiatric examination. Interrogated by a woman doctor, the question-and-answer session produces nothing significant. But a second test, conducted by the doctor who attended the Rook's ordeal shows that Number 6 shows positive signs of an abnormality: a total disregard for his personal safety, and a negative reaction to pain – something no prisoner could fake, unless he possessed superhuman willpower. Elsewhere, the Queen is brought before Number 2. Hypnotised, she is ready to undergo a new experiment, one which if it works, will prove invaluable to the superior: a development of studies carried out on dolphins which, when performed on humans could prove highly effective for Number 2's purpose. Delighted by what is planned, the superior watches with interest as the psychiatrist implants in the patient's brain the belief that she is in love with Number 6: she will do anything for him, even betray him to save him from his own folly. She is given a necklace which she is told is a gift from her sweetheart – a locket that contains a detection transmitter which will relay all her emotions to Control. She will now dote on Number 6, follow him like a lap dog. When her true love is out of sight she will sigh, when she sees him her pulses will quicken and if she thinks she is about to lose him – if he attempts to escape – she will be frantic and her emotions will send an alarm to the control room, the device is foolproof. Released from hospital, the Queen follows Number 6 everywhere, observed by the doctor and the control room Supervisor on their monitor screen. Each time the woman catches sight of the Prisoner, her pulse-rate quickens and the detector in the locket keeps the onlookers informed of their whereabouts. Meanwhile, handed a report of the tests carried out on Number 6 by her medical colleague, the doctor's suspicions are confirmed. She suggests to Number 2 that she be allowed to perform an operation on the man in order to lock out the aggressive tendencies in his brain. Telling her that the man is too valuable to take such a risk, her superior refuses her request. Meanwhile, the man they are discussing steals a buggy and drives away from the Village. The Queen follows suit, racing after her *beau*, honking her buggy's horn as she tears after him. Informed of this event, Number 2 orders the control room to take no action: he wishes the device to be given a proper test. The couple should be kept under observation, but no further action is to be taken unless it reaches a Yellow Alert situation. Giving the woman the slip, Number 6 picks up the Rook and drives into the woods. Concerned that the girl has lost her quarry, the doctor urges the Controller to try to locate her on the monitors, but camera 34 is not working, the Rook has ripped out its innards. Together with Number 6, he steals a cordless telephone and an electronic device from the tool kit belonging to the repair man sent to repair the broken camera. Driving away, the men are spotted by the girl, her pulse-rate quickening as she spies Number 6. Leaving the Rook to drive away with the stolen equipment, the Prisoner joins the girl in her buggy. When the woman confesses her love for him, he tells her she is crazy: they hardly know each other. The woman begins to sob: he is waterproof and a slight drizzle will not wash away his doubts. 'But I want you near me,' she sobs. 'Everybody's near in this place – far too near,' he replies, climbing out of the vehicle. Try as he may, he cannot shake his lap dog. That evening she appears at his cottage, singing merrily as she prepares to brew him a hot cup of chocolate. Their conversation continues as before: she vowing her love, he distrusting her words. Eventually, as curfew beckons and the girl refuses to tell him who sent her, he orders her to leave. She begins to sob and he softens. Asking if she can see him again, he replies dryly 'Oh, I'm here all the time.'

'I'm waterproof. A slight drizzle won't wash away my doubts'

Number 6 sees the Rook safely out to sea

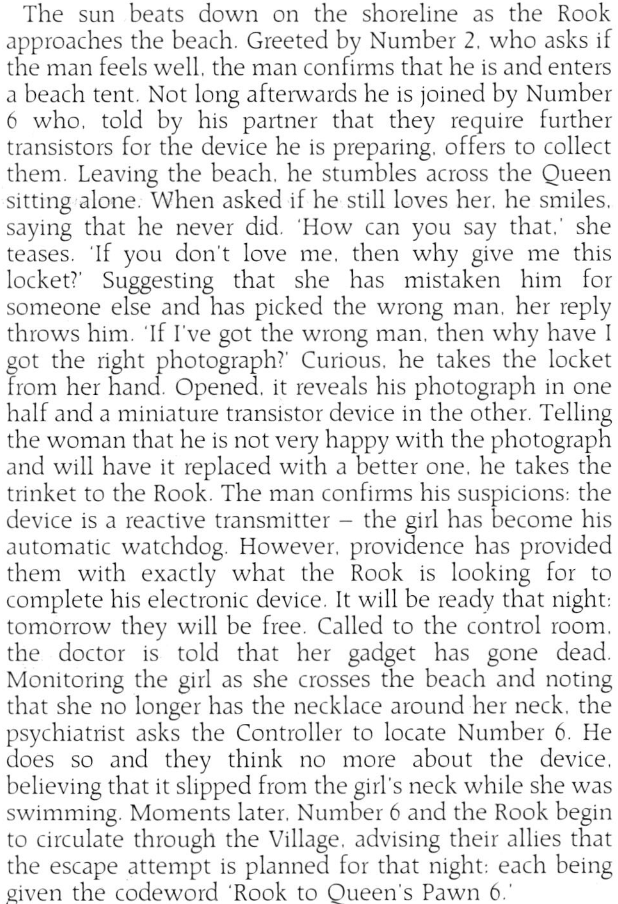

The sun beats down on the shoreline as the Rook approaches the beach. Greeted by Number 2, who asks if the man feels well, the man confirms that he is and enters a beach tent. Not long afterwards he is joined by Number 6 who, told by his partner that they require further transistors for the device he is preparing, offers to collect them. Leaving the beach, he stumbles across the Queen sitting alone. When asked if he still loves her, he smiles, saying that he never did. 'How can you say that,' she teases. 'If you don't love me, then why give me this locket?' Suggesting that she has mistaken him for someone else and has picked the wrong man, her reply throws him. 'If I've got the wrong man, then why have I got the right photograph?' Curious, he takes the locket from her hand. Opened, it reveals his photograph in one half and a miniature transistor device in the other. Telling the woman that he is not very happy with the photograph and will have it replaced with a better one, he takes the trinket to the Rook. The man confirms his suspicions: the device is a reactive transmitter – the girl has become his automatic watchdog. However, providence has provided them with exactly what the Rook is looking for to complete his electronic device. It will be ready that night: tomorrow they will be free. Called to the control room, the doctor is told that her gadget has gone dead. Monitoring the girl as she crosses the beach and noting that she no longer has the necklace around her neck, the psychiatrist asks the Controller to locate Number 6. He does so and they think no more about the device, believing that it slipped from the girl's neck while she was swimming. Moments later, Number 6 and the Rook begin to circulate through the Village, advising their allies that the escape attempt is planned for that night: each being given the codeword 'Rook to Queen's Pawn 6.'

As darkness falls, Number 6 transmits a mayday signal on the device put together by the Rook. The weak signal is picked up by the *Polotska*, a ship somewhere out at sea. Receiving the message that 'Trans-Ocean flight D-for Delta 250 Zero, is on fire and losing height,' the ship asks the mayday caller to give his position. Unaware of the Village coordinates, Number 6 transmits a garbled reply. Crumpling paper into the transmitter's mouthpiece to convince the *Polotska* that static is responsible for breaking up the signal, he breaks off in mid-sentence. Picked up by the control room, the mayday call is ignored on the advice of Number 2. Number 6 joins his colleague on the beach and, before seeing his partner safely out to sea, fixes a bleeper device onto the Rook's makeshift raft. Hearing the distress signal, the men in the control room, suspicious that the signal is coming from close to the shore, telephone to the radio tower in the mountains to give them a cross-reference. Number 6, meanwhile, having arrived at the stone boat, which harbours prisoners waiting to escape, is aware that they will need to knock out the radio tower's searchlight and sets out to head an attack on the observation post. The guards are quickly overpowered and the lamp is doused. Number 2, meanwhile, angry that his hour for meditation has been interrupted, becomes interested when his control room staff telephone him with an emergency alert. Too late. By the time the man is ready to leave his home, Number 6 and his friends are waiting at his door – not wishing to leave without thanking the man for having had them as his 'guests'. Bound by the men, Number 2 retains his reserve: he is disappointed that Number 6 in particular could not devise a more original escape attempt. Crossing to the Green Dome's master control panel, the subject of his indignation is about to switch off the Village surveillance cameras when the Rook's distress signal ceases its transmission. Suspicious that it has stopped too soon, Number 6 races to the beach alone. Finding his colleague's empty raft and spying a boat a few hundred yards from the shore, he uses the makeshift structure to reach the *Polotska*. Helped aboard by its captain, the would-be escapee stops dead in his tracks when he comes face to face with a grinning Number 2! No longer bound, the man's face stares at him from a television monitor in the captain's cabin. Taunting Number 6, the Village superior smiles with satisfaction as he confirms that the ship belongs to the Village – and besides, the weather report was unfavourable. Number 6 would not have stood a chance of escaping in such a frail craft. As the control room camera pans to the man standing at Number 2's side, the Prisoner learns what went wrong with the plan. Believing Number 6 to be a *warder*, and suspicious when he was not given the psychiatric treatment that the Rook was subjected to, his ally had convinced the others that their leader was a traitor: the Prisoner's air of authority convincing the Rook that Number 6 was one of *them*. 'You only have yourself to blame,' gloats the triumphant Number 2, stating that the others will be back tomorrow – on the chessboard, as pawns! Spotting a single yellow chesspiece, a Queen's pawn, standing solitary on the control unit before Number 2, the Prisoner snatches up an ashtray from the bulkhead beside him and throws it through the television screen. Watched by an unconcerned Number 2, the Prisoner turns on his heel and fights off the attempts of the captain and his crew to detain him. One by one the men are thrown overboard. Bored with this entertainment, Number 2 reaches out with his umbrella and selects a button on the display panel before him. Called to alert, a guardian rises from the depths, bursts to the surface in an eddy of bubbles and bounces its way towards the ship. On board, the Prisoner attempts to steer the vessel away from the beast, but the *Polotska's* controls have a mind of their own and refuse to respond. Growing in size, the guardian draws alongside. Watched with caution by the helpless Number 6, the shimmering spectre bounces to the vessel's stern to push the *Polotska* back to the Village. In the control room, the mute Butler, his face a mask of complacency, places a yellow-coloured pawn back onto its rightful position on his superior's chessboard!

AUTHOR'S NOTE: Originally made under the working title *The Queen's Pawn*.

This story contains the first (and only) interior view of the Watchtower.

The shots of the *Polotska* at sea and the mock-up of its deck were re-used in the gun-runner boat scenes of *Many Happy Returns*.

DANCE OF THE DEAD

Written by Anthony Skene

Guest stars

Number 2 — **Mary Morris**
Doctor — **Duncan Macrae**
Girl Bo-Peep — **Norma West**

with

The Butler — **Angelo Muscat**
Town Crier — **Aubrey Morris**
Psychiatrist — **Bee Duffell**
Day Supervisor — **Camilla Hasse**
Dutton — **Alan White**
Night Supervisor — **Michael Nightingale**

and

Night Maid — **Patsy Smart**
Maid — **Denise Buckley**
Postman — **George Merritt**
Floweman — **John Frawley**
Lady in Corridor — **Luck Griffiths**
2nd Doctor — **William Lyon Brown**

Directed by Don Chaffey

NIGHT. Observed by a doctor and his colleague from the control room, three men in white medical coats enter the Prisoner's residence. Straps are attached to the sleeping figure's wrists and a device with wires running from it is secured to the Prisoner's forehead. 'Shouldn't you be doing this in the hospital?' asks the man standing at the doctor's side. 'I know what I'm doing,' replies the doctor. 'What about Number 2? Has it been agreed?' queries the other. 'I'll take responsibility. If we wait for orders, we'll never get results,' snaps the doctor. Responding to a nod from the man strapping the devices to the sleeping man's body, the doctor crosses to a control unit and turns on a machine. 'I hope you *do* know what you're doing,' says the other, a look of concern crossing his

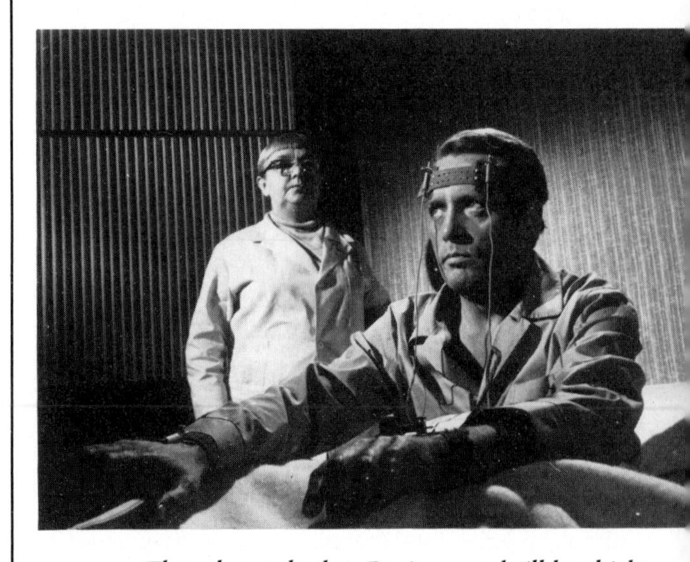

'They always do that. Don't worry, he'll be alright in a moment'

brow. Throwing back his arms for support, Number 6 suddenly sits up erect. 'Don't worry,' says the doctor, seeing the look of concern on his colleague's face. 'They always do that. He'll be alright in a moment.' Telling his associate that he is aware about the instructions for Number 6, if any damage is done . . . Silencing the man with a move of his finger, the doctor tells him that the man in the bed will talk before that happens. Viewed on the monitor screen, Number 6 blinks his eyes, shakes his head, then with a hint of a grin, looks around him. 'It's going to work. I knew it would!' exclaims the doctor, crossing to a third man, a zombie-like figure sitting upright in a chair, his left hand raised as if talking to someone on the telephone – but his hand is empty! Placing an L-shaped telephone in the man's right hand, the doctor puts the drugged figure's finger on its dialling button. The phone by the Prisoner's bed purrs. Placing the receiver to his ear, Number 6 listens as the man tells him that *they* want to break them down on everything they know: you, me, Arthur, the Colonel, everybody. Apparently it is a suspected security leak: all the files he has seen, the projects he knows about. Just headings, not details. The phone is scrambled and the man has a recorder: Number 6 may as well tell him now. Drawing a waist-high console towards him, the doctor switches on a tape machine. Pausing for an instant, Number 6 stammers 'You . . . you must . . . not . . . ask me about that . . .' The doctor advises the man in the chair to tell Number 6 that *he* is not asking the questions, it is the committee who require answers. Trembling now, Number 6 grasps the telphone tightly and stammers 'Who . . . is that? Who . . . is THAT?' Alarmed by the Prisoner's condition, Number 2's associate attempts to switch off the machine, but the doctor probes further, telling the drugged man to answer that it is Dutton. The man does so. Number 6 trembles and falls backwards in a helpless heap. 'Stop. Stop!' cries the associate. 'You'll damage the brain, then we'll all be . . .' 'Stop!' cries Number 2, as she enters the control room. 'Get that man to hospital.' Crossing to greet her, the doctor hastily interjects 'Number 6 was about to talk . . .' 'Don't you believe it,' she snaps. 'He'd have died first. You can't force it out of this man, he's not like the others.' '*I* would have made him talk – every man has his breaking point,' says the doctor staring at the monitor screen. 'I don't want him broken. He must be won over. It may seem a long process to your practical mind,' Number 2 tells him, 'but this man has a future with us.' As they talk, the zombie-like man is led away behind them. 'There are *other* ways,' Number 2 concludes.

As sunlight filters through his cottage window, Number 6 rises to the ubiquitous piped music and the Village Voice greeting everyone with a cheery good morning. Donning his dressing gown, he crosses to the window, peers outside and turns as his television monitor flickers into life. 'How did I sleep?' he asks Number 2, pictured in the Green Dome. 'Sound as a bell,' she replies. 'Have a nice day. Feel *free*.' Observed by the woman, the Prisoner crosses to his bathroom, sliding the door closed behind him. His ablutions complete, the man begins shaving. Number 2 speaks to someone on the telephone. 'Yes. Splendid,' she says, turning her chair to view Number 6 on her monitor screen. 'Oh he'll be no trouble. It's just a matter of time. Tomorrow night . . . we're preparing for it now. Yes, *I* wish you could come, too.' Transported in a trailer pulled by a Village buggy, a young woman attired in an old-fashioned dress enters the Prisoner's residence carrying a breakfast tray. 'Don't tell me that time-travel has been invented as well?' quips Number 6, catching sight of her dress. 'A woman is always impatient to wear a new dress,' the girl replies, pirouetting to display her finery. 'How do you like it?' 'Different from the others,' he replies, passing comment that maids come and go. 'I'll get along,' says the girl, passing the man on her way out. 'I'm sure you get along with everybody,' he returns. 'I've a good mind to report you,' the girl throws back. 'I'm new here,' quips Number 6, following the maid to the door, where a postman stands holding a special delivery for the resident. It is a card inviting him to attend the Village Carnival and Dance. Asked to sign with his number, the occupant replies by slamming the door in the postman's face. The Village is alive with people carrying their colourful parasols. A brass band marches through the streets and a bell-ringer rides past the Prisoner's cottage in a colourful buggy. While stroking a black cat, Number 6 views the festivities from a balcony overlooking the Village square. He is joined by Number 2, who informs him that the forthcoming festival is one of the Village traditions; each year they hold a fancy-dress party and a ball in the evening. This year, they are promised a cabaret. Will Number 6 be present? Has he a choice? Of course, she says, he can do as he wants. 'As long as it is what *you* want,' he sneers. 'As long as it's what the *majority* wants.

'We're democratic – in some ways' (Scene different to *tx* version)

We're democratic – in *some* ways,' replies the woman, joining Number 6 as he walks to a table on the cafe veranda. 'No game is worth playing if you can't win,' she continues, keeping apace with the man. 'That's not very English I know . . .' 'Are you – *English*?' he smiles. Advised that he is too independent, and should find himself a nice young lady, Number 6 spots a girl sitting alone towards the rear of the cafe. He teases, 'What about her?' Turning to the girl, Number 2 states that she is quite unsuitable. 'I'm independent, don't forget,' says the other, ignoring her advice by crossing over to the attractive blonde wearing a white cap. Seeing his approach, the girl makes to leave. 'Don't go,' he says, as the girl rises from her seat. 'I must,' she replies – indicating that Number 2 wants her to go. Pausing for a second to consider if, perhaps, he is entering a game with rules set by Number 2 (is he playing *her* game or his own? He tells the girl that she can leave if she likes and when she fails to do so, he plies her with questions. 'How long have you been here?' 'Questions are a burden to others. Answers a prison to oneself,' she replies, showing signs of being nervous. He tries again. 'What did you do, to have yourself brought here?' 'Questions are a burden . . .' she begins. Losing his temper, he finishes the quote. Upset by his outbursts the girl races away up some steps. He tries to follow her, but a guardian blocks his progress, and the girl vanishes into the Town Hall courtyard. Attempting to follow her, an electronic barrier halts him in his tracks as his body receives a mild electric shock. 'Are you alright?' asks a gardener. 'You tried to go in. By mistake? It's fussy about who it lets in – this is the Town Hall.'

In the control room, the girl he chased after is explaining to her colleague that it was not her fault that Number 6 tried to follow her. As she watches the man leave on her monitor screen her colleague replies, 'Funny though. You being his observer. Remember, keep a sharp watch.' Outside his residence, Number 6 finds the black cat he had befriended earlier. Carrying the animal inside, he is surprised to find the maid dusting his room. 'Where did you find it?' she asks. '*It* found me,' he replies, stroking the animal's ebony fur. Telling him that it is against the rules to have pets, and moving towards the cat to pick up the animal, the girl is shocked by his comment that *he* is not subject to *their* rules – besides, she may get scratched! In full-flow now, he bombards the girl with questions: where does *it* come from? How did it get here? The milk? The ice cream? The potatoes and the aspirins? Staggered by his onslaught, the girl leaves, his questions unanswered. 'At night? When everyone's asleep?' he throws after her, adding that he has never seen a night. Prowling his room, he picks up a cushion and places it over the television monitor screen, short-circuiting the device. A man is placing flowers in a window-box outside his room. He jovially answers the Prisoner's comment that he does not want any by stating that everyone has flowers during carnival time. With a Village salute and a cheery 'Be seeing you,' the man leaves. Later, an elderly maid brings Number 6 a nightcap. 'Drink it while it's hot,' he is told. Sniffing the drink suspiciously, he lays the cup to one side and enters his living room. Observed by the girl he had raced after earlier, he smiles when the lights go out.

'What is it?' (It's good for you.)

Number 2, meanwhile, is telling the doctor that his earlier attempts to condition Number 6 will not be reported: she will put it down to enthusiasm. Thanking the woman, the man asks her for a directive about Dutton – the man is being difficult. At 10.32, curfew time, Number 6 paces the floor, ignoring the fact that his cottage is in darkness. He crosses to his door: it refuses to open. Retreating to his bedroom and finding the cat stretched out on his bed, he returns to his living room and seats himself in a chair. In seconds, the light above his head begins to pulsate. His eyelids flicker as the soothing voice of Number 2 attempts to send him to sleep. 'Sleep, sleep. Sleep softly until tomorrow,' purrs the voice. The attempt to hypnotise him fails. Throwing back his curtains he races from the cottage – the door is open now – and steals off into the night. Seeing this, his observer telephones Number 2, who tells the girl not to worry, the man's actions will test their efficiency. On her control room wall screen, the woman watches the man's progress along the beach. Released from the depths, a guardian rises from the sea and shadows Number 6 as he races along the shoreline until, exhausted, he falls to his knees. Hovering a few feet away, at the flick of a switch the guardian is returned to its nest by a delighted Number 2 who, turning to the cat at her side, tells the animal that the man will eventually go back to his room, 'It's the only place he can ever go.' At dawn, waking on the beach, the Prisoner spots a body lying in shallow water. Turning it over he removes the dead man's wallet and a small leather pouch. The former contains some photographs, the latter a small transistor radio. He tests the receiver. It works.

A town crier proclaims that the carnival is decreed for that night. He informs the villagers that there will be music, dancing and happiness – by order, sending them into a frenzy of anticipation – a sight greeted with apathy by Number 6 who, walking into his cottage is informed by his maid that his bed has not been slept in. Replying that he thought he would save her the trouble, he shows little interest when the girl tells him that they have given her a new dress – something special. He asks about the cat. 'Gone,' the girl replies, adding that she played no part in its leaving. Passing the comment that everyone appears to be having a good time, the girl tells him to wait until evening. 'Do you mean we're allowed out after hours?' he mocks. Anyone would think they were locked in the way he talks, says the girl, informing Number 6 that his costume has arrived. It's not of the man's choice. 'Other people choose,' says the maid. 'It's a game.' Opening the box, the man produces his own evening suit, specially delivered for the occasion. 'What does that mean?' asks the girl, expecting to see fancy-dress. 'That I'm *still – myself*,' he suggests. 'Lucky you,' says the maid, leaving. Number 2 watches as the Prisoner attempts to tune in the radio he found earlier, and warns the doctor not to be so eager with his attempts to crush the Prisoner's reserve. His techniques are efficient, but not always beneficial and Number 6 will be of great value yet. 'He can't do as he likes,' says the doctor. 'He's an individual and *they* are always trying. Don't worry, his observer will ring me the moment he puts a bomb in your lovely hospital. Incidentally, how's Dutton?' Informing Number 2 that the man has given him lots of information, but he is reluctant to go any further, the medico confesses that he will have to use more extreme measures if he is to win in the end – as he always does. Commenting that Dutton is a small fish, the woman nevertheless agrees to allow her colleague to continue his work on the patient: it will of course, give him the opportunity to experiment. 'After all,' she adds, '*he* (meaning Dutton) is expendable.' In the meantime, Number 6 has climbed to the Bell Tower and managed to get the radio working. He has just picked up an English-speaking station when Number 2 approaches, followed by his observer. Asking Number 6 if it works, he contemptuously retunes the device, and an announcer invites listeners to take part in a shorthand typing exercise. 'Hardly useful,' grins Number 2, switching the radio off. Telling the man that she is sad and believed he was about to ... 'Give in?' fires back Number 6, anticipating her words. '... why not? Everything you ever wanted is here,' she suggests. 'Everything's elsewhere,' he replies. Told that they will only stand for so much, he adds, 'Yes, I know. I've been to the hospital and seen.' 'You've seen only a fraction,' threatens Number 2, as, glancing at the other woman, the man states that he knows where her loyalties lie. The superior explains that the girl is one of their best observers. 'We have one each?' queries Number 6. 'Only our more fractious children,' states the superior, inviting the man to return to the Village. When he fails to answer, she departs alone, taking the transistor radio with her. 'I have my duty,' says the girl, as Number 6 moves towards her. 'To whom?' he asks. 'To everyone,' comes the reply. 'It's the rules. *Of* the people, *by* the people, *for* the people.' 'It takes on a new meaning,' he counters. 'You're a wicked man,' states the girl. 'Wicked?' 'You have no values,' she says. '*Different* values,' he replies. 'You want to be helped!' she exclaims. '*Destroyed*.' 'You want to spoil things,' she snaps. He retaliates, stating that he won't be a goldfish in a bowl. 'I must go. I will see you later?' questions the girl, softly. 'Can you avoid it?' Indicating that his radio is alright, he questions her as to what she would do if she had found it? She would report it. Ask for instructions. 'From Number 1?' (Yes) 'Who ...?' (No) '... Tell me.' (That's all I know – all there is to know.) 'In the place where you work?' 'Don't keep asking me questions,' says the girl, leaving the man standing alone. Slipping out the wallet he took from the dead man, the Prisoner takes out a photograph of a father and child. Descending to the Village, on the pretext of joining a crew renovating the Stone Boat, he steals a lifebuoy and a length of cord. Racing down to a cave on the beach in which he had earlier placed the dead man's body, he removes his Village identity card and some paper from his pocket and begins to write a note: 'To whoever may find this ...' In the control room, his observer, scanning the Village for her ward, but unable to locate his whereabouts, telephones her superior to confess that she has lost contact with Number 6. 'Don't worry,' says an unconcerned Number 2, 'he'll turn up. It's only a matter of time, he's very undisciplined.' Turning to her colleague, the observer asks if she should watch Number 34 instead? 'No, he's dead,' reports the other. 'Dead! When?' exclaims the girl. 'That's none of our business,' snaps her colleague. 'I got to know him quite well,' sighs the girl. 'He didn't get to know *you*, did he?' comes the reply. Back in the cave, his message complete, Number 6 seals the wallet containing his own documents into a plastic envelope, puts them into the dead man's inside jacket pocket and drags the body out of the cave and into the sea. The lifebuoy strapped around the man's lifeless body carries the figure away on the outgoing tide. Turning back to the cave, the Prisoner sees a man observing him. It is Dutton, the man to whom the doctor handed the telephone in the opening sequence. 'You. You of all people. I'd never have believed it,' says the man, as the Prisoner approaches him. 'Roland ... Walter ... Dutton,' stammers Number 6. 'Who was he?' asks the other, indicating the body floating away on the tide. 'His body was washed up on the shore,' answers Number 6. 'How long have you been here?' 'You don't know?' asks Dutton. 'Would I ask?' The other, his face and body showing signs of interrogation, staggers to support himself by the rockface. 'It's difficult to say ... a couple of months? And you?' 'Quite recently,' Number 6 replies. 'How's London?' Dutton wishes to know. 'About the same.' 'Yes. Places don't change – only people,' sighs Dutton. '*Some* people,' suggests Number 6, helping the man into the cave. Safely inside, Dutton confesses that he has told them everything he knows, the irony being that they still do not believe that he told them the truth – that he never had access to the vital information. Telling Number 6 that they will take him back to the hospital and by the time they learn that he was telling them the truth it will be too late, he adds that he has been released for 72 hours, so that he can reconsider in the peaceful atmosphere of the Village. 'There's still hope,' the Prisoner tells him. 'No my friend, not for me,' Dutton replies. 'Such noble thoughts are long dead. Soon, Roland Walter Dutton will cease to exist.'

Later that evening, dressed in his tuxedo and looking out to sea, the Prisoner is joined on the beach by Number 2. 'You're waiting for someone, Mr Tuxedo?' she calls. 'Or expecting someone?' Turning, and catching sight of her costume, a skimpy pantomime outfit depicting the creation of author J.M. Barrie, he retorts 'Mr Peter Pan?' 'So it seems,' says the woman. 'With his *shadow*!' he mocks. 'You're being hostile again,' says the imp-like figure. 'What were you looking at?' 'A light?' (A star?) 'A boat?' (An insect?) 'A plane.' (A flying fish!) Bridging the gap between them, he quips 'Somebody who belongs to *my* world.' 'This is your world. *I* am your world,' says Peter Pan. 'If you insist on living a dream, you may be taken for mad.' 'I like my dream,' he replies. 'Then you *are* mad! Now go on up to the Town Hall.' 'May I?' he taunts. 'You *may* enter tonight – it's carnival.'

As deadly as the male

Entering the great hall, they find the place bedecked with rows of white masks, those in attendance dressed in a variety of colourful fancy dress costumes. 'What, no dancing?' shouts Number 2, to the rows of villagers who stand agape at the sight of Number 6 who, dressed in his tuxedo, is completely out of step with the spirit of the event. 'Tonight's for dancing!' exclaims Peter Pan. Then, with a glance in the Prisoner's direction, 'amongst other things.' As the man wearing the tuxedo strolls through the crowd, Number 2 signals to the orchestra to begin. Handed a glass of wine by his host, the Prisoner confesses that he rarely partakes. 'Then you'll enjoy it all the more,' she says. 'Self-denial is a great sweetner. It's undoctored, for the carnival.' She raises her glass. 'Your administration is effective, but you have no opposition,' he says, looking at his glass. 'An irritation we've dispensed with. Even at best, free democracy is remarkably inefficient,' she returns. After some small talk about the vintage of the wine, he asks why he has not been given a costume. 'Perhaps because you don't exist,' Number 2 replies, commenting how lovely his observer looks as she arrives dressed in her costume. 'Little Bo Peep,' says the girl proudly. 'Who always knows where to find her sheep,' Number 6 replies. While Number 2 offers the doctor, (dressed as Napoleon) a glass of wine, Bo Peep leads Mr Tuxedo to the dance floor; he stands with his arms crossed, while she sways before him. 'How many of these have you been to?' he asks, adding that this is his first – and last. 'Don't be silly,' Bo Peep replies, attempting to cajole him to dance. 'Who's saying that,' he replies, 'you or the computer?' 'Me!' she exclaims, stopping dead in her tracks. 'Oh, don't behave like a human being, it might confuse people.' 'Only you are confused,' says the girl, picking up the rythmn, 'but not for long. They have treatments for people like you.' Apologising for bumping into the doctor and Number 2, the couple continue to dance, he walking in time to the music, she attempting to persuade her partner to join in. The questions continue. '*She* must get instructions. Who do they come from?' asks Number 6, indicating Number 2. 'Is he here tonight . . . the man behind the big door?' 'There's no need to know,' says Bo-Peep, 'this place has been going for a long time.' 'Since the war? *Before* the war? *Which* war?' 'A *long* time,' replies the girl, storming off the dance floor. Brushing aside two doormen attending the hall's entrance, Number 6 dons a white hospital coat from a clothes stand in the corridor then, placing the pair of spectacles he finds in the coat's pocket onto the bridge of his nose he patrols the corridor until he finds an unlocked door. Mistaking him for a doctor, a woman wearing a similar white smock enquires if he has seen Number 2. 'I'll *be* seeing her,' he mocks, taking the urgent termination order from the woman's hand. 'Much obliged,' she says, reminding him that the matter is urgent. 'Right away,' states Number 6, giving the impression that he is on his way. Alone in the corridor, however, he opens the missive. In white lettering on a black background it contains just three words: 'Roland Walter Dutton'! Musing over his colleague's fate, the Prisoner enters a darkened room. The lights switch on automatically as he does so, and two doors, which swing open of their own volition, beckon the man into a second darkened room. As before, the lights come on and he finds himself standing in a huge room. Crossing to a third door, he tries to open it. It is locked, but entrance is secured when he notices a key hanging from a hook by the side of the door. Passing through, he finds himself in a vast ante-chamber, containing two rows of metal cabinets – a repository where, sliding open one of the drawers, he discovers the body of the dead sailor that he had cast out to sea! 'You make the most of your opportunities,' calls Number 2, entering with the cat at her heels. 'You don't blame us for doing the same.' Meowing its affection, the cat crosses to the man. 'Ah, she's taken to you,' grins Peter Pan. 'I'm jealous. Oh she's mine. She works here too. She's *very* efficient – almost ruthless.' 'Never trust a woman,' grins Number 6 weakly, 'even the four-legged variety.' 'You can trust everyone,' mocks Number 2, sliding the mortuary cabinet closed, 'and will – in time. Let's go back. The cabaret's beginning.' Indicating the body in the closed cabinet, Number 6 asks 'In his pocket . . . ' 'The wallet?' retorts Peter Pan, anticipating his question. 'It's still there – "amended" slightly. We'll amend him slightly. It's you who's died – in an accident at sea.' 'So the outside world . . .' says the Prisoner, removing his coat and handing her the keys to the room. ' . . . Which you only dream about,' reminds Number 2. ' . . . I'll be dead,' he concedes. 'A small confirmation of a known fact,' concludes Peter Pan. 'Don't blame me. It's a question of waste not, want not.' Leaving the mortuary, they rejoin the festivities in the dance hall. But the dancing has ended. All those in attendance are now gathered around a large circular platform placed in the centre of the dance area. 'I thought there was a cabaret?' asks the Prisoner, as Number 2 struts to her throne, a large chair positioned at the end of the room. 'There is. You are *it*!' says Peter Pan. Addressing the gathering, she brings the court to order. 'In the matter of the People versuses this person,' she begins, 'the court is now in session.' 'What is my crime?' asks Number 6. Telling the accused that they will come to that, Number 2 explains that their legal system is unusual. 'No jury?' mocks the Prisoner. 'Three judges decide here,' continues Peter Pan, ignoring the man. 'As in the French Revolution,' suggests the Prisoner. 'They got through the dead wood, didn't they,' retorts Number 2 unamused, adding that she has been appointed by the court to act as his defence and Bo-Peep will prosecute. The judges have been chosen: Marie Antoinette, Nero and Napoleon, take their seats on the circular platform. 'Proceed,' orders Peter Pan. The Town Crier opens the proceedings. 'You are charged with having on your person and using for unlawful purposes and against the interests of the community, an object the possession and use of which breaks our Rules. A radio set.' 'Don't you ask how I plead?' enquires the accused. Ignoring the man, the Town Crier orders the prosecution to proceed. Confirming that she saw the device twice, once in his room and again on the bell tower, Bo Peep gives way to the maid, who steps forward to say that she saw the device while dusting the man's residence. The accused was listening to the radio; as it is improper to listen, she has no idea as to the programme. 'Quite right,' confirms the Town Crier, turning to Number 2. 'Did you listen Madam?' 'How can my Defender be a prosecution witness?' asks the accused. 'No, my lords, but it did work,' says Peter Pan, ignoring her charge yet again. 'It is the duty of all of us to care for each other . . .' continues Bo-Peep, ' . . . and to see that the Rules are obeyed. Without their discipline we should exist in a state of anarchy.' 'Hear, hear,' mocks the Prisoner. 'You do yourself no good,' pipes up Napoleon. Stating that the accused had no radio of his own but, by acquiring one he made a positive effort against the community, indicating a malicious breaking of the Rules, the prosecution turns to the Prisoner. It is the duty of the court to pass the severest possible sentence. Number 6 joins Peter Pan in applauding the girl's words.

As the judges have no wish to question the Prosecution, the Defence can open its case. Number 2 takes the stand and tells everyone that the accused is a human being with the weaknesses and failings of his kind. The fact that he had the radio and has broken rule after rule cannot be denied, but she pleads with their Lordships for clemency. The accused is new and guilty only of folly. No more. They must treat folly with kindness, knowing that soon his wild spirit will quieten and the foolishness will fall away to reveal a model citizen. 'That day you will never see,' challenges the accused. 'The Prisoner will be silent . . . this is a serious matter.' says the Town Crier. 'Very serious,' mocks Number 6. Stating that both officers have presented their pleas with creditable simplicity, Nero suggests that they now consider their findings. 'I wish to call a witness,' says the accused. 'Witness?' quizzes Napoleon, a look of concern crossing his face. Looking at Bo-Peep, Number 2 states that they are the sole witnesses

'He was listening to a programme'

to the man's guilt. 'What manner of witness?' asks Marie Antoinette, indicating to the others that the accused has rights. 'A *character* witness,' states Number 6. 'I want the court to call Roland Walter Dutton!' A look of consternation crosses the judges faces. 'No names are used here,' states Nero. 'He's a man I think I knew. A man who is scheduled to die, and therefore better fitted than I to say the things that need to be said,' pleads the accused. Rising from her seat Peter Pan brings forth Dutton, dressed now in a jester's suit. The man shows signs of having become an imbecile: his head droops forward onto his chest, his eyes stare unseeing. 'Your *character* witness,' mocks Peter Pan, returning to her throne. The judges begin their deliberations. They find the accused guilty of a breach of the Rules, which his folly and inexperience cannot excuse. In accordance with the Rules, sentence is passed and Nero hands the mute Butler a proclamation. 'No. Stop it!' exclaims Bo-Peep, rising from her chair. 'It's the Rules my dear,' says Peter Pan, as Nero places a black cap on his head. The sentence is death! The accused has been sentenced in the name of the people. The people carry it out in the name of Justice. With a final stare at his friend Dutton, the Prisoner marches warily through the crowd. As he reaches the Town Hall's entrance, they surge forward after him, like a hungry pack of wolves howling for blood. Racing down the corridor, he runs through the doors he passed through earlier and enters the mortuary room, lights to each chamber coming on as he rushes through them. Entering the ante-room, he prises up a trapdoor in the floor and disappears into the blackness beyond, the howls of the villagers ringing in his ears. Traversing the underground vault, he ascends a staircase and slips back unseen, into the corridor through a concealed door. A second set of doors slide open to admit him into a lavishly-furnished room where, hidden behind a ticker-tape machine, its keyboard criss-crossing numerals onto a piece of blank paper beneath its platen, he attempts to switch off its staccato chattering by tearing out its electric wiring. Through a mirror set into a wall, he sees his pursuers still searching for him. 'It's a one-way mirror,' says Number 2, entering the room with Bo-Peep. 'They can't see you. They've never seen in here, and they never will. They lack initiative.' Turning to Bo-Peep, she tells the girl to deal with them. Nodding her approval, the girl leaves. 'Why are they trying to kill me?' asks Number 6, softly. 'They don't know you're already dead . . . locked up in a long box . . . in that little room,' replies Number 2, witnessing the crowd outside being dispersed by Bo-Peep. 'She's no longer your observer. Observers of life should never get involved.' 'You'll never win,' maintains the Prisoner. 'Then how very uncomfortable for you, old chap,' laughs Number 2, as the tele-printer behind Number 6 magically begins to chatter back into life. In unison with Peter Pan's cruel and mirthless laugh, the bars slam shut across the Prisoner's image.

AUTHOR'S NOTE: The part of Number 2 (played by Mary Morris) was originally written for a man, actor Trevor Howard, but due to ill-health the actor had to be replaced.

THE CHIMES OF BIG BEN

Written by Vincent Tilsley

Guest stars

Number 2	**Leo McKern**
Nadia	**Nadia Gray**
The General	**Finlay Currie**
Fotheringay	**Richard Wattis**

with

The Butler	**Angelo Muscat**
Colonel J	**Kevin Stoney**
Number 2 Asst	**Christopher Benjamin**
Karel	**David Arlen**
Supervisor	**Peter Swanwick**

and

Number 38	**Hilda Barry**
First Judge	**Jack Le-White**
Second Judge	**John Maxim**
Third Judge	**Lucy Griffiths**

Directed by Don Chaffey

THE VILLAGE is stirred into a new day by a fanfare of music piped over its personal address system: the Village voice, wishing everyone 'Good morning, good morning, and what a lovely day it is. Rise and shine. Rise and shine.' Inside the cottage signposted '6 – Private', its resident endeavours to sleep on. The strident announcement continues: a weather forecast, stating that the fine spell will continue for at least a month, and the local council – democratically elected by the villagers – has decided to organise a great new competition. 'Can you paint? Can you draw? Can you mould clay? If you can, then *your* day is just six weeks today!' The recumbent figure stirs, his eyelids flickering open to stare at the radio speaker in his room, struggling against this intrusion of his dreams. The voice gives way to music, a raucous brass band march. Resigned now, the figure turns back his sheets, slips into his slippers and dressing gown, and walks to his bathroom. Watching these proceedings from from his over-sized oval-shaped chair, sits a bearded, slightly balding, rotund figure dressed in the ubiquitous flannels and blazer, a badge denoting a red Number 2 pinned to its left lapel. 'He can make even the act of putting on his dressing gown appear as a gesture of defiance,' observes the man. Then, reacting to his duty officer's claim that there are methods they have not yet used, he rises from his seat, stating,'I want *him* with a whole heart, body and soul.' Crossing to his kitchen, the man being observed withdraws a food carton and two eggs from his refrigerator. 'He'll crack,' observes the man standing next to Number 2, watching the man select a saucepan from a shelf. 'Perhaps,' replies his superior, raising his morning cup of tea from his breakfast tray. 'One tiny piece at a time?! I don't want a man in *fragments!* Setting his breakfast aside, Number 6 crosses to the loudspeaker unit, clutches the device to his chest (it has no exterior wiring) and transports it to the refrigerator, placing it untidily on top of a chicken breast and a sliced roll of pastrami! 'Fascinating,' declares Number 2, sipping from his cup. 'He doesn't even *bend* a little,' observes his colleague dryly. 'That's why he'll break,' states the older man. 'It only needs one small thing. If he will answer one simple question, the rest will follow. WHY DID HE RESIGN?'

Attired in his Village uniform, Number 6 takes an early morning stroll. Observing this, Number 2 frowns as he is forced to respond to a flashing light on the red telephone sitting behind him on the console unit. It is a message from the Controller. The helicopter Number 2 is expecting has been sighted. Stating that he has no wish to make radio contact, Number 2 requests that he be informed when the machine lands: he wishes to meet it personally. Watching the helicopter's approach, Number 6, is sitting at a table on the terrace, playing a game of chess with an elderly gentleman wearing a military cap. He allows his attention to be distracted from the game, leaving his opponent to regain his attention by stating 'Your move, young man.' Turning half-heartedly back to the game, Number 6 makes a random move. 'Mmm,' says his opponent, perplexed by the man's foolishness, 'Know what I'll do.' 'Resign?' teases the younger man. 'No,' his opponent grumbles, picking up a chess piece and stating that he will make a new set for the Arts and Crafts exhibition. 'Are you entering? No! You're a fool Number 6, that's my opinion. You'll be here for as long as you live.' 'However long that is,' retorts his companion. 'Might as well try to settle down. No point in being uncooperative.' replies the military man. 'Was there ever a time when *you* were not cooperative?' queries his playing companion. 'No point in fighting battles you can't win.' 'Perhaps you came here of your own free will?' throws back the man denoted as 6. 'Wish I'd had you in my regiment for a few months,' states the chess player. 'Which regiment was that? Which Army?' counters his opponent. The helicopter lands nearby and the elderly man is rescued from further interrogation by the arrival of Number 2 and his dwarf Butler. Bidding the ex-soldier good morning, Number 2 appears non-plussed when the man nods expression of disapproval at Number 6, and departs in disgust at his playing companion's attitude. 'The General seems a little sour,' comments Number 2, selecting a chair opposite Number 6. 'Mate in 7 moves,' sneers the man, removing his hand from a chesspiece. 'How many more do you know?' inquires the newcomer. 'A few more,' comes the reply. '*We* must play sometime,' smiles Number 2. 'Certainly we must – by post!' retorts the other, rising from his seat and moving towards the helicopter. 'I must add humour to your file,' chuckles Number 2 behind him. 'They tend to leave out things like that. Very important.' An unconscious woman is being carried from the machine on a stretcher. Covered by a red blanket, she is young and attractive. 'What *crime* did she commit?' demands Number 6. 'Nervous tension,' calls back the elder. 'She's come here to recuperate.' 'How much are you charging her?' A hearty chuckle. The man's new file really must be brought up to date.

Having adjourned to Number 2's quarters, the mute Butler wheels in tea on a trolley as his master dictates an addendum to his visitor's file. Joining his guest, he enquires how many sugar lumps he takes. One lump or two? 'It's in the file,' snaps back Number 6 (Yes, but it would save time if the man answered.) 'Why? Are you running out of time?' quips his guest. Number 2 checks the man's file. (He does not take sugar – frightened of putting on weight perhaps?) 'No. Nor of being *reduced.*' (You really are a model.) 'But I don't run on clockwork.' (You will, my dear chap. You will!) 'Do you think so?' (Do you still think that you can escape, Number 6?) 'I'm going to do better than that!' (Oh?) 'I'm going to escape and come back . . .' (Come *back*!?) ' . . . Escape, come back, wipe this place off the face of the Earth, obliterate it, and you with it!' Seething now, Number 2 hastily dictates a sub-section six update on his guest's 'Persecution complex, amounting to mania – paranoid delusions of grandeur.' To add insult to injury, his guest calmly pours himself tea and, with great deliberation drops three sugar lumps into his cup. Apparently beaten, Number 2 sinks back in his chair. Then, renewing his resolve he adds, 'Don't worry, Number 6, you'll be cured. *I'll* see to it. No more nightmares. If you have so much as a bad dream, you will come *whimpering* to tell it to me. *Whimpering!* Watch, just watch!'

Viewing the giant monitor screen, the two men see the ambulance men leaving the cottage denoted '8 – Private'. 'Your new neighbour, the new Number 8,' the host tells his guest. 'What happened to the old one?' asks the listener. (Oh, he vacated the premises.) 'He escaped?' (A chuckle) 'There was no funeral?' (That's not always possible – you need a body.) 'Oh look, she's getting up,' begins Number 2. 'It's quite like old times, isn't it, Number 6? Do you remember *your* first day?' In her room – an exact replica of the one she lived in before she was kidnapped – the girl stirs. Taking her first faltering steps, she stares at her surroundings, then crosses to look out of the window. The view is a shock to her senses. Guffawing aloud, Number 2 reaches for his telephone and requests to be connected to Number 8. Their conversation is short, culminating with Number 2 inviting the girl to lunch. Distraught when the line goes dead, the woman trembles in fear. Sickened by his host's behaviour, Number 6 makes to leave. 'I trust you'll be neighbourly?' queries Number 2. 'I'll do a deal with you Number 6. You tell me one thing and I'll release you. *Why did you RESIGN?*' Unmoved by the man's false promise, the visitor turns his back and raps loudly on the giant metal doors before him. Number 2's plea that he should take part in community life, falling on deaf ears. 'At the age of fifteen, was top of the class in woodwork,' Number 2 reads from the man's file. 'Now that's the sort of thing I mean. Join in.' 'I'll make you a handle for this door,' quips back his guest, pacing determinedly through the now open doors. 'You'll be back,' echoes his host, 'Whimpering!'

Outside, further news of the Arts and Crafts competition is being broadcast by the Village voice. There are to be five categories to be judged, the winner to receive 2,000 work units. Outside his residence, Number 6 meets the new girl. She hails him, seeking directions to the Green Dome. 'Across the square, across the street, up the steps, you can't miss it,' he replies. 'I know it sounds crazy,' she stammers, 'but I don't know where I am.' 'In the Village,' he replies, as two villagers pass by, proferring the Village hand salute, which he returns. The woman is puzzled by the greeting and the stream of Village taxis plying their trade. At her request, Number 6 accompanies her to her destination, explaining as they walk that the taxi service is only local. 'Who are these people?' she asks. 'Why are they here?' 'Why are *you*?' he answers. At the door marked '2', the girl asks 'Who is Number 2?' 'Who is Number 1?' says he, as the door opens of its own volition. He makes to leave. Puzzled, she calls 'I've done nothing wrong. I've committed no crimes. All I did was resign.' 'No use telling me,' replies Number 6, with a hint of suspicion.

They meet again as the girl returns from her luncheon date. As curfew is approaching, the man offers her a nightcap: genuine non-alcoholic whisky, or would she prefer genuine non-alcoholic vodka, 24 and 16 work units respectively. 'Thank you, Mister . . .?' 'Sorry, no names,' he replies, pouring her drink. '*I* am Number 6. You are *Number* 8.' Inspecting his quarters, the woman informs him that she is Estonian. Commenting that she speaks good English, she explains that it was her job. 'From which you *resigned*?' he queries, a hint of suspicion in his voice. Remarking that Number 2 was a charming man and she would expect his assistant to be the same, he retaliates with: 'And what about *you* – Number 8?' 'I'm no Number 8, or number anything else,' she protests, adding that her name is Nadia Rakovski, and she has been interrogated enough for one day. Putting down her glass, she bids her host goodnight. 'Be seeing you,' he calls after the retreating figure.

'Taxis . . . local service only'

The following morning, the new girl joins the merry-makers on the beach. She selects a spot on the sand, immediately below the veranda on which her neighbour is sitting. Sipping coffee, she ignores the man's stare. 'May I join you?' asks Number 2, approaching the man's table. Indicating a vacant seat with a nod of his head, Number 6 peers over his shoulder at the girl. His reverie is broken when the man denoted '2' asks if he and the girl are now good neighbours? Imparting the comment that there are some people who leave this place and some who do *not* leave, Number 2 continues '*You* are obviously staying.' He awaits the man's reply. (Has it ever occured to Number 2 that he is just as much a prisoner as Number 6?) 'Ah, my dear chap, of course. I know too much. We're *both* lifers. *I* am definately an optimist, that's why it doesn't matter *who* Number 1 is.'

The woman rises and heads for the sea. 'It doesn't matter which *side* runs the Village,' continues the elder. (It's run by *one* side or the other?) 'Oh, certainly. But both sides are becoming identical.' Removing her sunglasses and bathing robe, the girl enters the water. 'What in fact has been created, is an *international* community, a perfect blueprint for world order. When the sides facing each other suddenly realise that they are looking into a mirror, they will see that *this* is the pattern for the future.' (The whole earth, as the Village?) 'That is my hope. What's yours?' (I'd like to be the first man on the moon.) Taking the joke agreeably, and thanking Number 6 for a delightful chat, Number 2 leaves his junior staring quizzically at the woman who has now entered the sea, and is pulling away from the shore using powerful swimming strokes. Back in the Green Dome, Number 2 open's the woman's file. Reading the entry 'International Swimmer: at the age of 17 was Olympic bronze medallist' with a mixture of interest and alarm, he telephones the control room Supervisor to ascertain what visual range he has out at sea. Two miles visual, comes the reply, radar after that. He joins his colleague in the control room, where Number 8's progress is being monitored on the wall screen. Aware that the woman is almost out of range, with a shrug of his shoulders the leader presses a button and orders 'Orange Alert'. Within the wink of an eye, a guardian is released from the bed of the ocean floor. Bursting to the surface with a high-pitched howl, the lighter-than-air monster rolls across the water after the girl. Watched knowingly by Number 6 from the beach, with a terrifying roar, the guardian overtakes the swimmer and engulfs her in its glutinous mass. Stretching its balloon-like fabric over her face, it sucks the air from her lungs and the swimmer is lost in a swirling eddy. Dividing into three (a 'parent' and its 'children') the grotesque creatures floats her body back to the shoreline where, watched by a quizzical Number 6, the limp body is carried away on a stretcher.

Told by Number 2 to meet him at the hospital, Number 6 is ushered into an observation room, and is treated to another demonstration of the interrogation methods of the Village. Looking through a one-sided observation window, he sees the woman sitting alone, being questioned by the Supervisor from the control room. 'What was the purpose of your swim? Were you attempting suicide?' drones the voice from a speaker placed in the room. 'Did you think you could escape?' Stating that he does not want to be hard on the girl – she is not that important, Number 2 asks the prisoner if he noticed any suicidal tendencies in the woman?' 'What are you doing to her?' demands Number 6. 'Oh, there's an alternating current in the floor, four seconds on, four seconds off,' replies the other. 'It takes just three seconds to get to the door. If she times it correctly, she can leave whenever she likes.' The woman's salvation is a glass of water on the table before her. By sprinkling a few drops upon the floor she can discover when the current is harmless and make her escape. Watched by the all-seeing mechanical eye positioned in the room, her every move is being monitored. 'I believe she's going to do it,' says Number 2, as the girl sprinkles further water droplets onto the floor's surface, counting the seconds that elapse between its evaporation. Suddenly, the girl makes her dash for freedom, but her bid comes to nothing. With the Supervisor's voice droning in her ears, she falters as she reaches the door, standing a split-second away from extinction. Falling helplessly to her knees she cries 'Kill me . . . kill me . . .' 'No!' screams Number 2. 'Switch off. Switch off!' Staring at the hapless figure, a distraught Number 2 turns to his fellow-observer. 'Well, well. We'll just have to try something else.' Outside in the corridor, he beseeches Number 6 to help; the lesson was very distasteful. 'Let her go!' demands the prisoner. (Looks like a suicidal tendency, doesn't it – but one must be sure.) 'Let her GO!' (Is that an order, Number 6?) 'All right,' says

'Alright, she's all yours'

Number 6. 'You wanted a deal. I'll make a deal with you.' He crosses to peer into a therapy room. 'Let her go and I'll collaborate.' (You'll what?) 'That's what you wanted.' (So obvious a weakness – in *you*?) 'Why not?" (For which you'll collaborate?) 'Don't get too excited. I'll tell you nothing. I'll join in, try to settle down, even carve something for the exhibition.' (If I turn her over to you, *you'll* do some woodwork for me. Is that your *deal*?) 'The best you'll get.' Amused by the man's arrogance, Number 2 dictates a further update on the prisoner's 'self-importance and egomania.' Turning to face the man, Number 6 asks 'Well?' 'All right! She's all yours,' concedes Number 2. 'Be seeing you,' smiles the other, leaving.

Preparing breakfast the following morning, Number 6, attired now in a zip-up anorak-type wind-cheater, with the ubiquitous white piping lapels, grins as Number 8 arrives and offers to complete his chore – a scene that is being observed by Number 2 and his aide from the control room. Commenting that things could not be going better, Number 2 decides to pay them a call. Meeting the couple as they leave the prisoner's residence, he bids them a joyful good moring, then asks if they are settling down. A nod from Number 6 brings the reply 'No swimming, I hope?' 'Off to the woods,' states the prisoner. 'Naughty, naughty,' chides Number 2.' Explaining that he has decided to do a series of abstracts, and is off to the woods to carve something with tools he has made himself, the prisoner leads the girl away.

Their progress through the trees is followed by the turning heads of the statues. Safe in the knowledge that they can see, but cannot hear, the man gives them a Village salute and tells the girl that they can talk freely; or does she still believe that it is a trap? Reaching the spot where he has buried his tools, he asks 'Were you sent here because you discovered the whereabouts of the Village?' Alarmed by his knowledge, the girls begs him not to tell them. Digging further by suggesting that she does know its location, the girl maintains that there is no escape. Not even by sea, he suggests, indicating that if he knew where he was sailing *from* he could calculate where he was sailing *to*. 'Sail?' queries the girl. 'By boat,' he replies.

commencing to chop down a tree with his home-made stone-headed axe – unaware that a delighted Number 2 sits watching them from his chair in the Green Dome. Before long the tree has been felled and hewn into the skeleton of a dug-out canoe. Intrigued, Number 2 leaves his residence and joins the woodcutter in the forest. 'I say, I say. What is it?' he asks. 'It doesn't make sense without the whole group. There'll be three pieces,' replies the wood carver. Reminding Number 6 that entries must by in by two weeks from the following day and that, technically, an axe and stone chisels are outside the pale of the law, the senior man asks the woodsman if he can give him a lift back to the Village. Declining the offer, Number 6 states that he wishes to continue his work while there is still daylight. 'Be seeing you,' says the departing Number 2. 'And you,' mocks Number 6 dryly, 'But not for long.'

'Were you sent here because you know the whereabouts of the Village?'

Curfew time. Sleep time,' says the Village voice. 'Allow us to lull you with . . .' A soft lullabye is transmitted through the speaker unit as Nadia calls on her neighbour. Signalling the man to speak softly, she takes him outside and sits close beside him at a table on his veranda. 'The language of love,' comments Number 2, seeing but unable to hear the man's words as he gently strokes the woman's hair. Walking arm in arm with her neighbour, Nadia finally concedes that she does know the Village coordinates. The government she worked for gave her access to a secret file on the place. Its location: Lithuania. The prisoner plans his escape route: from the Baltic, that means making for West Germany, then Denmark, 300 miles at least. Not so, says Nadia, offering her own plan. If he will take her along, they can travel to Danzig, in Poland. He tells the girl that although he cannot answer for the British authorities, he will give her his personal guarantee, for whatever that is worth, of her safety. Number 6 listens intently as she continues her story. They are only thirty miles away from the Polish border. Beyond that is a small village and her contact who will help them. Explaining that her greatest need is to hear the sounds of Big Bill – 'Big Ben', he corrects – as the curfew bell chimes, Nadia bids her comrade sleep well 'Goodnight, Big Ben.' 'Big *Bill*,' quips Number 6.

The day of the Arts and Crafts exhibition arrives with a fanfare from a brass band. A banner outside the exhibitors' hall proclaims the admission times. Together with other excited entrants, Numbers 6 and 8 arrive, to be greeted by an enthusiastic Number 2, shadowed as ever, by the mute dwarf Butler. Informing Number 6 that the Awards Committee are intrigued, though somewhat mystified by his exhibit, its creator promises to explain things. The room they enter contains paintings and sculptures, all of an obvious subject: Number 2. 'Remarkably high standard. Don't you agree?' boasts the leader proudly. 'Highly original,' throws back Number 6. Revolving merrily on a circular rostrum towards the back of the hall, sits the 'pride' of the exhibition, the younger man's abstract: a montage of three pieces, the dug-out canoe, a cross-member, and a long pole running through its centre. Introducing Number 6 as their 'very own Epstein', Number 2 takes credit for superior deductive powers when, asked by several visitors what the montage means, Number 6 replies 'It means what it is.' 'Brilliant,' echoes Number 2, 'It means what is *is*. Brilliant!' Then, realising, perhaps that he has spoken out of turn he quickly adds, 'Oh no! You mustn't let *me* influence you. *You* are the Awards Committee.' What puzzles a lady judge, however, is the fact that Number 6 has titled his work 'Escape'. Standing before his masterpiece, the creator, points out various portions of his work, stating that depending on how it is viewed, the structure represents freedom or a barrier. Popping his head through a circular hole in its rear, he proposes that the barrier is down, the door is open, you are free to go, *free* to escape, to escape . . . to this, the symbols of human aspirations, knowledge, freedom – escape. Moved by the man's words, the first judge removes his boater. 'But why the crosspiece?' he ventures. 'Why not!' fires back Number 6. 'Good. Splendid!' exclaims the lady judge. 'I was really quite worried for a moment.' The only thing she *really* does not understand, is the omission of any representation of Number 2! The subject of her consternation is at that moment waiting on the stage to hand out the prizes. Having presented the 'Over 60s' special award to Number 38, for her magnificient tapestry bearing his image, Number 2 announces the outright winner in all categories. The Awards Committee have selected Number 6. Stepping forward to receive his prize, the man proudly accepts his reward, but soberly airs his view that another is more worthy than he – Number 38, whose long life and work in the Village is a glowing example to them all. Offering his 2,000 work units in exchange for her tapestry, he proudly boasts that he will be honoured to hang it in his own home. To applause from the gathering, he joins Number 38 and leads the procession outside.

Night finds Nadia acting as a lookout while Number 6 carries his exhibit from the Arts centre. On the beach, they unroll a tarpaulin, which is in turn secured to the skeleton framework of the dug-out structure. The crosspiece and centre pole are added and the tapestry bought by Number 6 becomes a sail. Huddled together beneath the woven image of Number 2, the couple sail away under cover of darkness.

Their absence and location is soon pin-pointed by the control room's all-seeing eye. Requesting his superior's presence, the Supervisor picks out the vessel on his radar screen. 'There, almost out of range,' the bespectacled man tells Number 2. Advising his colleague to contact Post 5 as a precaution, the elder man turns to a map of the area behind him. Summoned into action by the Supervisor's orange alert command, a ghostly guardian rises from the depths and bounces off in pursuit of its quarry. Barely two miles from a welcoming shoreline, the would-be escapers fail to notice the white orb speeding towards them. Not so a man on the shore who, seeing their approach through his binoculars and aware that the guardian is almost upon them, raises his rifle and fires at the beast. Alerted now to the approaching danger, Number 6 orders Nadia to swim for it. As the rifleman's bullets bounce off the guardian's skin, the couple reach the beach unscathed. Scrambling to safety, they turn as, outwitted, with a terrifying roar, the guardian bounces away. 'Nadia,' calls her contact, conversing with her in a foreign language. Number 6 requests pencil and paper, wishing to write a coded message for the man to transmit to London. Asking what route they will be taking, the man tells him by sea to Gadansk, then Danzig; by air to Copenhagen and by air again to London. Asking the man for his watch, his own having been damaged by seawater, Number 6 straps the timepiece to his wrist and joins Nadia in a large wooden crate labelled 'London, via Danzig, Cophenhagen.' Aboard a lorry, the crate is transported to the docks and then by boat to its destination. During the long journey, the couple converse: Nadia asking if Big Ben has a wife, he telling her to hold out as she feels nauseous.

Fotheringay, a bespectacled civil servant answers his telephone. Confirming that he has seen a copy of the deciphered message, he adds that he cannot wait to see them. Simultaneously, the crate is being transported by plane. Consulting his watch, Number 6 tells his companion that there is less than an hour-and-a-half to go, adding that if his message has been properly received, they will land in a London office well-known to him. Jostled and bumped about, the packing case is unloaded, its occupants hearing a voice proclaiming 'Stone the crows, this one's a weight.' Back in Fotheringay's office, three smartly dressed men arrive, followed by other men carrying the packing case. 'Good evening, Colonel,' the civil servant greets the group's leader. Announcing that everything has gone according to schedule, the Colonel bids his men open the crate. Peering out at the face before him, Number 6 extends his hand to the man. To peals from Big Ben, Nadia is introduced. 'Is it . . .?' she queries. Pausing to listen to the chimes, her travelling companion confirms that it is. Politely asking the girl if she would wait in the next room, the Colonel turns to the newcomer. 'The return of the prodigal son.' 'I don't see any fatted calf,' returns his subordinate, stretching his legs. 'Did you expect one?' asks the other. 'No,' replies Number 6, as the Colonel slams the door behind him to a close. 'Who's *she*?' asks the man. Answering that the girl is named Nadia Rokovsky, the junior becomes annoyed when his superior fires back 'and what was her name before she left Peckham Rye to join the Bolshoi Ballet?' Aware now that nothing has changed, the junior man attempts to explain the details of his capture, Nadia's nationality, the Village, Number 2, and how the girl had known the location of the Village, thereby enabling him to escape. Telling the subordinate that *he* is there to answer questions, the Colonel nevertheless becomes interested when the man continues to mention the Village. 'What *Village*?' he asks. 'The *VILLAGE*,' snorts the newcomer, pacing the room. 'It's a place where people turn up. People who have resigned from a certain sort of job, have defected, or have been extracted, the specialised knowledge in their heads being of great value to one side or the other – are you sure you haven't got a village *here*?' (Where's the Village?) 'Lithuania, in the Baltic, thirty miles off the Polish border.' (How did you find out?) 'Nadia told me. I risked my life and hers to come back here, home, because I thought it was *different*! It is, isn't it? It's DIFFERENT!' Apologising, the Colonel asks the man if he would like a drink. 'Scotch?' '24 work units.' 'What?' asks the superior. 'That's how much it costs in the Village.' 'The Village!' scoffs the Colonel. 'Surely you know about it?' asks his junior. All the man knows is that his guest resigned from a post of the highest possible secrecy. Refused to give his reasons for doing so, then promptly vanished. 'I was kidnapped!' 'Oh really. How dramatic.' Taking a harder line, the senior man intimates that his guest is a traitor, sent from behind the Iron Curtain to carry on the good work. 'No!' exclaims the other. 'No? Neit! Neit! What sort of imbeciles do you think we are?' Handed his drink, the subordinate asks the man what he wants him to do? 'Quite a lot of things,' the Colonel replies. 'But let's start at square one, shall we? First. Why did you resign?' 'It was a matter of conscience!' the man shoots back, as the chimes of Big Ben strike outside the window. 'Oh listen, Sonny Boy. Do you think you're safe in London?' Chime one. 'If they thought it worth kidnapping you, it's worth killing you.' Chime two. 'I doubt if you'll be alive 24 hours after leaving this building.' Chime three. 'Unless you get protection. Do you want it?' Chime Four. 'For the girl as well?' answers the man. The chimes continue. 'If you come across with the goodies, yes.' 'Political asylum *guaranteed* for the girl?' Big Ben continues to chime. 'Well, that depends.' 'It depends on *nothing*! It's guaranteed!' 'All right. As long as you stick to your side of the bargain.' The man being interrogated peers at his watch. 'Question one,' says the other. 'Why did you resign?' The man starts pacing the room. 'I resigned . . . because . . . for a very long time . . .' He pauses in mid-sentence, stops pacing the floor and crosses

Safe in Fotheringay's office, Number 6 and Nadia step out of their transit crate

to the window. 'Just a minute,' he says, mystified. 'Eight o'clock?' (Big Ben has just chimed eight.) 'That's right,' says the Colonel. 'The night is young – and there are many questions. First, why did you resign?' A quizzical look furrows the other man's brow. 'Big Ben has just struck 8. *My* watch says *8*?' 'So?' comes the reply. 'I was given this watch by a man in Poland. I particularly wanted it to check the time, to make sure that the trip *tallied* with a journey to London.' 'Which it presumably did?' says the elder, as the other removes his watch. 'Of course,' replies the man

'. . . Just a minute. Eight o'clock?'

being interrogated, moving towards the man before him. 'Would you like to explain to me how a man in Poland came to have a watch showing English time when there is one hour's time DIFFERENCE!?' he shouts, realisation dawning. 'Maybe he was slow,' stammers the Colonel, his jacket lapel crumpled in the man's fists. 'I bet he was,' growls the other, regaining his composure. Searching the office, tugging out electric cables as he goes, the man pulls the plug on the interrogator's designs. Throwing back the doors of a cupboard, he exposes the reel-to-reel tape recorder which the man has used to assimilate the sounds of London. Resigned to his fate, Number 6 leaves the defeated Villager behind and paces determindly down the corridor outside. Pushing open a set of white painted doors, he enters – the Village.

As Number 6 surveys the familiar surroundings, on the steps of the exhibition hall Number 2 thanks Fotheringay for his help: the latter being told to return to London quickly, before any embarrassing questions are asked. Joined by Nadia, Number 2 glances across to where Number 6 is pacing up and down. Turning to face them, with a Village salute and a 'Be seeing you,' the prisoner turns on his heels and walks back to his cottage.

In the control room, Number 2 dictates a further update on the man's file. 'You were right about him,' states Nadia, dressed now as a civilian, her expensive fur coat draped around her shoulders. 'I told you,' replies Number 2. 'Don't worry,' she calls back, climbing a staircase. 'It was a good idea and you did your best. I'll stress it in my report.'

AUTHOR'S NOTE: Two versions of this story are in existence. The one that played on television and the much-vaunted 'Alternative' version, located by *Six Of One* American co-ordinator Bruce Clark in a film vault in Toronto, Canada – a version that is believed to have been produced for Press screenings before *The Prisoner* was aired (although it did play on the show's first American outing). The alternative version (released on video in the USA, but not available in Great Britain contained several notable differences. The opening credits contained several scenes showing Number 6 attempting to escape from a Rover, and the closing credits saw the wheels of the penny farthing bicycle start turning, before changing into an image of the earth and the universe (see page 134). Other notable differences include a scene in which, having payed her first visit to the Green Dome, Nadia returns to her cottage after her 'long lunch' with Number 2 to find Number 6 outside his residence standing beside a tall wooden contraption, which is pointed skywards. Armed with a notebook and pencil, he is recording navigational observations and explains to the girl that his 'Triquetrum', is a device for plotting the location of the Village by studying the movements of the stars.

The alternative version also includes the Wilfred Josephs theme, and further incidental music by the composer – vestiges of which can be heard in *Arrival* (as Number 6 walks towards the helicopter and again after the helicopter lands and a Rover herds Number 6 back to the Village.

As transmitted, this episode has very little in the way of actual Portmeirion footage: the Village and its beach exteriors being filmed on a backlot at MGM Studios.

THE SCHIZOID MAN

Written by Terence Feely

Guest stars

Alison	**Jane Merrow**
Number 2	**Anton Rodgers**

with

The Butler	**Angelo Muscat**
Supervisor	**Earl Cameron**
Number 36	**Gay Cameron**
Doctor	**David Nettheim**
Nurse	**Pat Green**
1st Guardian	**Gerry Crampton**
2nd Guardian	**Dinny Powell**

Directed by Pat Jackson

NUMBER 6 is selecting cards from a pack placed on the table before him. Unlike a normal playing deck, the face of each card bears a geometric pattern. He is testing his guest Alison, who, displaying a close telepathic understanding with the Prisoner, is able to identify each card he selects – although she sits several feet away from her host. She thanks Number 6 for allowing her to practice her mind-reading act on him: no one else believed in her ability. 'They had no imagination,' he says, picking up a card marked with a broad red cross. 'You should concentrate, otherwise you won't be let into the Village festival.' Saying that she still has a month to prepare, Alison continues to identify each card he selects. An amateur photographer, she asks if she can take another picture of him with her Polaroid camera. Crossing over to her host, she accidentally knocks a soda-syphon onto his left hand, bruising the Prisoner's fingernail. 'Don't worry,' he says, as the girl asks if she can still take the picture, 'it will mend itself.' The girl has identified 17 cards out of the 25 he selected at random, a remarkable feat. 'It could mean that we're simpatico,' the girls suggests. 'It might,' he replies, adding up some numbers he has written in a note book, 'but there's more to it than that. Out of the last 4 runs you've got 73 out of 100.' The girls shows him the photograph she's taken. 'Like it?' Seeing his image slightly off-centre, he returns it with a smile. 'As you say. You need a little more practice.' Asking if they could try another, she requests that he adopts a certain pose. 'Put you hand to your face.' He does so, covering his profile. 'Yes, but not over your face . . . just to your mouth.' Number 6 teasingly places his finger to his lips. 'Yes, yes that's marvellous,' says Alison, releasing the camera's shutter. 'I'll keep this one for myself.' Would he like to try another run of the cards? 'No,' he replies, adding that it is late and she might reduce her average and get discouraged. 'Don't forget the cards,' he reminds her, as the girl takes her leave. Can they play again tomorrow? Telling the girl that they might, he bids her a cheery 'Be seeing you' and Alison departs. Elsewhere, the steel doors of the Control Room slide to a close behind the new Number 2. Descending the steps to the chamber's main observation area, he orders an operator to switch him to Number 6. Joined by a doctor, he stares into the darkness of the Prisoner's bedroom. 'Closer,' he commands, 'Infra-red.' Covered by a duvet, Number 6 is asleep. 'His breathing is shallow. His sleep is light,' the doctor observes. 'Let's deepen it for him shall we? . . . Pulsator . . . visual . . . oral,' orders Number 2. The patient sleeps on, oblivious to the pulsating lamp that slowly descends to a few feet above his head, or to the arrival of two white-coated medics. Injecting a serum into the Prisoner's arm, the men lift him from his bed, collect his wristwatch and calender from the living room, and carry the sleeping figure away. While he is still deep in slumber, a probe device is inserted into the skin above the patient's left wrist, and a further injection is administered into his right arm. Some time later, sitting up in his bed the patient receives two uninvited guests – the medics, who treat him to a series of therapy shocks with a long metal probe: the men insist that he should use his *left* hand to ward off the device. On Wednesday, 10 February, year unknown, a man bearing a remarkable likeness to Number 6 awakens in the patient's bed. Save for his black hair and moustache, he is the mirror image of the Prisoner. Stirring, he rubs the sleep from his eyes then, feeling the unfamiliar growth above his top lip, he surveys his changed surroundings. Peering at his reflection in a mirror, he staggers around the room, taking everything in at a glance. His wardrobe contains his own blazer, with one small but noticeable difference, his identification badge is now numbered '12'. Snatching the jacket from its hanger, he stares at the numerals in confused curiosity. A red telephone sitting on a table nearby purrs into life: it is Number 2. 'Good morning, Number 12. I hope you slept well after your flight. I'll expect you for breakfast in 15 minutes.' Leaving the residence denoted '12 – Private', he is greeted by one of the villagers, an Indian. 'Good morning Number 12,' the Asian man says, acknowledging the man's salute. A nurse pushing a patient in a wheelchair greets him in a similar manner. 'Why do you call me Number 12?' asks the man. 'Well, that's what you were called when I last saw you,' the woman replies continuing her journey. As the door to the Green Dome swings open to greet him, the mute Butler leads him into Number 2's quarters. 'My dear chap, delighted to see you,' greets the new Number 2. 'You're looking fine, you really are . . . I don't mind telling you, we had to pull every string in order to get you seconded back to us.' Breakfast is à la carte, or table d'hote. The guest lifts the lids of the dishes served on a table trolly in turn. Selecting three pancakes, he walks to the table and uncovers a hooded plate to reveal sliced lemon. 'Did you think I'd forgotten we used to call you Flapjack Charlie?' grins Number 2. 'Even in those days it was obvious that you were going to make a top field man. Here am I, stuck in Admin . . . you always did enjoy your food. Even before a job from the Black File.' 'Sorry I didn't shave . . . couldn't find a razor,' says the man denoted '12'. 'My dear chap, I'm so sorry . . .' begins the host. 'Must have been mislaid . . . strange apartment,' apologises the guest. '. . . And after all that flying,' says Number 2. 'You must feel a bit disorientated.' 'What's it all about?' questions the guest. 'Our prize prisoner. The one we call Number 6,' replies the superior. 'Toughest case I've ever handled. I could crack him, of course. But I can't use the normal techniques. He's too valuable. Mustn't damage him permanently say our Masters. That's why I need you.' 'Why do you need *me*? quips the man, a thought lodged somewhere in his brain telling him not to play the other's game. 'You bring two great gifts to bear. Firstly your ability as an agent . . .' 'Oh yes,' mocks the guest. 'Secondly?' '. . . You have a unique physical advantage,' concludes the other. 'Physical *advantage* of growing a *moustache* overNIGHT!' fires back the one numbered '12'. Amused by the man's words, Number 2 proceeds to give his guest details of his plan. 'No not quite. You took longer that time in Bucharest.' 'Bucharest?' 'You remember how Susan hated you without it? She told me she wouldn't kiss you till you grew it again.' 'Good for Susan,' snaps the guest. 'You know, you really do bear a remarkable resemblance . . . remarkable . . . Your job Number 12, is to impersonate him. To take his sense of reality away. Once he begins to doubt his own identity, he'll crack. What do you think of the idea?' Maintaining his reserve, the one denoted '12' replies 'I think it has fascinating possibilities, but you'll have an awful job convincing me that I am not *your* Number 6.' 'Excellent,' smiles Number 2, maintaining that the other is ever the professional. 'You've started living the part already eh. Oh, that reminds me . . .' He delves into his blazer pocket and places a badge numbered 6 on the man's left lapel. '. . . you're now officially Number 6.' Removing the button and returning the man's stare, the guest replies 'I shan't need *this* to remind me that I am *your* Number 6.' Unbowed, the superior throws the other a leather-bound file. 'You'll find all *his* background details in here.

'You want to watch that Number 12. Number 6 is right-handed'

Study it.' The guest catches the file with his left hand, leading the other to comment, 'You should watch that Number 12. Number 6 is right-handed.' A puzzled look crosses the guest's face as Number 2 tells him that they will only have to make a few small changes: the moustache, the hair. 'Oh don't worry. I'll get a couple of my girls to work you over a little . . . but they're very pretty.' The girls go to work, shaving off the moustache, dyeing and changing the man's hairstyle. Surveying the finished product, a delighted Number 2 remarks, 'You'd hardly know yourself, would you Number 12?'

Taken by Number 2 to his own residence, Number 6 (it *is* Number 6, *isn't* it?) points out that things have been changed: a magazine, an ornamental bust, they're not *his*. Showing disinterest, the superior tells him that the idea is that when *he* comes back, in a few short minutes, the new man will be in residence. Once the project has started, even Number 2 will not be able to tell the two men apart, in which event the imposter will need a password to identify himself: this will be Gemini. Aware that Number 6 is expected, Number 2 proposes that it would be better if the men met each other alone. Wishing 'his' man good luck, Number 2 leaves the cottage.

(Author's note: From this point onwards, life for Number 6 (and the author!) becomes somewhat confusing. With two identical Prisoners, the real and the fake, I have simplified matters by referring to the Prisoner as 'the Prisoner', and his double (The Schizoid Man) as 'White'.

As the resident is about to enter 'his' bedroom, the door behind him swings open and in walks a man identical to himself save for the fact that the newcomer's blazer is white, and trimmed with black piping. Catching sight of himself, the new arrival immediately begins to bait the other as to his true identity. 'What the devil . . . oh, very good, very good indeed. One of Number 2's little ideas I suppose. Where'd they get you? A people's copying service? . . . or are you one of those *double* agents we hear so much about these days?' 'Seeing that you've gone to so much trouble,' says the Prisoner, 'the least I can do is offer you a drink.' 'Scotch!' snaps back White. 'I take it I'm supposed to go all fuzzy round the edges and run off into the distance screaming: Who am I?' 'Probably,' replies the Prisoner flatly, asking the newcomer if he would like ice. But the Prisoner can not find his drinks cabinet, and White pours his own drink from a bottle placed on the *opposite* side of the room to where the resident normally keeps his drinks supply. 'Thank you,' mocks White, dropping two cubes of ice into his glass from *his* ice bucket. 'I think it spoils it myself.' '*I* always keep it in that thermos bucket over there . . .' continues the newcomer. 'Do you know I never realised I had a freckle on the right side of my nose . . . when they come to film my life story, you've got the part. Cigar?' he asks, indicating a tabacco box inlaid with ivory. Selecting a panatella with his left hand, the Prisoner places it between his lips. Reminding his twin that he will have to learn to smoke it right-handed, White offers him his lighter. Ignoring the offer and striking a match with his left hand, the Prisoner coughs as he inhales the smoke. 'And how to smoke *my* brand, without having a heart attack,' sneers the other, informing his double that there are some black Russian cigarettes in a box on the table. 'I never touch them myself . . .' 'It's not going to work you know!' exclaims the Prisoner. 'It certainly isn't . . . why don't you run away and play somewhere else.' 'I have a very strong sense of identity,' mocks the Prisoner. '*You* have?' laughs White. 'Oh yes, of course, I'm sorry, I was forgetting – you're supposed to be *me*. *You* are the goodie Number 6, and *I* am the baddie who is supposed to be proving you wrong. Is that it?' 'That's right. Except there's no *supposed* about it,' confirms the Prisoner. 'Tell you what, why don't we settle this like gentlemen?' suggests White. 'You're claiming to be a gentleman too . . .' comes the reply. 'Very good, very good indeed . . . that line is worthy of me. We're both claiming to be Number 6. Are we not?' says White. '*I* am Number 6, *you* are doing the claiming,' snaps the Prisoner. 'Well let's prove which one is correct,' White challenges. 'How?' 'Oh there are many ways . . . pistol shooting for instance. What is Number 6's average?' '90 per cent' says the Prisoner. 'Correct,' snaps White, 'Shall we go?'

In the recreation room, the two men test their shooting abilities on the firing range with electronic guns, with White commenting to the other that he does not wish to take an unfair advantage. 'Check into position . . . One,

'It's uncanny. Number 12 has caught the man's whole style'

two, three . . . Electronic gun you see, no bullets . . . can't kill anyone with them . . . Number 2 takes no chances . . . 3-second intervals, alright?' 'Whatever you say,' smirks the Prisoner. Noting that his opponent is gripping his pistol in his *left*(?) hand, White reminds the other that Number 6 is a right-handed shot. Bewildered, the Prisoner reverses his hold. Each man fires five shots – several of the Prisoner's going astray. Watching the contest from the Control Room, a delighted Number 2 comments that the way that Number 12 has caught the man's whole style is uncanny. 'In Haiti, we'd say that he has stolen his soul,' says his coloured Supervisor. The contest has proved nothing except, as White puts it, that the other should have put in more shooting practice before taking on the job of imposter. 'How's your fencing?' he asks. 'You should know, you've studied my file,' the Prisoner retorts. 'Turning the tables. Very neat. These foils have all a length,' mocks White, teasing his opponent with quotes from Shakespeare. Handing the Prisoner an épée, White engages his double in a fencing match. The Prisoner is beaten. Leaving the recreation hall, they go outside where, although he continues to claim to be Number 6, the Prisoner when challenged to a boxing match is unable to decide whether he is an orthodox or southpaw. He soon finds himself on the wrong end of his opponent's fist. A roar announces the approach of a Rover. 'Oh dear,' says White, staring at the man he has knocked to the ground, 'it looks as though we're in trouble with the headmaster.' The Rover hustles them forwards. 'It must be confusing for it – not knowing which one of us to bite,' he continues, leading his twin towards the Green Dome.

But a surprise awaits White. Entering Number 2's front door, he is hauled away and taken to be interrogated by Number 2. The Prisoner, meanwhile is greeted personally by the superior – a recognition that raises a smile – and is taken to the interrogation room as a guest. Under guard, White is placed before Number 2's latest thought-probing device. The man is invited to spill the beans, the machine vibrating with a hum as Number 2 asks his first question. 'Who are you?' 'Switch that idiot thing off, I'm getting cramp,' returns the Prisoner's twin. 'Who are you?' repeats Number 2. 'You know who I am. I am Number 6,' says White. 'Where did you come from?' demands Number 2. 'You know that too.' 'How did you get here?' '*You* know that better than I do. *I* was unconscious at the time, if you remember,' states White. 'What was your purpose in coming here?' 'I had *none*! I'll go away again if you like.' 'How did your people know that Number 6 was here?' 'What people?' 'How did they know enough about *him* to produce *you*?' 'I do not understand.' Number 2 signals to his colleague to increase the machine's strength. 'What were you doing in the recreation room?' 'Teaching that synthetic twin of mine how to shoot and fence,' says White. At a further signal from Number 2, an oval-shaped dot appears on White's forehead. 'For the last time. What do your people want with Number 6?' shouts the superior. '*I* am Number 6. I am Number *6* . . . Number 6! 6! 6! 6! . . .' The light grows in intensity and the man being interrogated collapses to the floor. 'Ugh,' says the Prisoner. 'Your boy is dedicated to his work.' 'I told you he was a tough nut Number 12,' replies Number 2. 'Er – 6, *6*' reminds the Prisoner, turning to face the Superior. 'Yes, you're quite right, of course. Careless of me. He might have heard,' smiles Number 2, as the one dressed in the white blazer is dragged before him. 'Do you still insist that you're Number 6?' he asks the Prisoner's twin. White remains silent. 'Your mind can lie, but your body can't. You'll see,' confirms Number 2, signalling for the guards to take the man into custody. The superior proposes to test the man's fingerprints against those of Number 6's. 'Yes, I know my own fingerprints,' quips the Prisoner. 'Let's start with the thumb nail shall we,' says Number 2, as the records as flashed onto a screen. 'That's mine,' says the Prisoner, as the print appears. Turning to the man constrained by the guards, Number 2 asks if he knows his fingerprints?' 'Yes,' says White, looking at the screen, 'that's mine.' 'So that if I say that on the contrary, it belongs to Number 6, one of us is lying?' says Number 2. 'Not at all,' returns White. 'As I am Number 6, we'd both be telling the truth.' 'Let's find out, shall we?' says Number 2. 'There, that's my thumbprint . . . now it's your turn.' The man being guarded is taken to the console and his thumbprint is flashed onto the screen. Viewed side by

'Simple. Foolproof'

side with the first print, they do not match. 'Simple, foolproof,' boasts Number 2 to the Prisoner. 'Too simple, too foolproof,' states White. 'Oh?' says Number 2. 'Very ingenious and scientific. The trouble with science is that it can be *perverted*' The Prisoner is inclined to agree. 'You agree?' says an astonished Number 2. Stating that he is inclined to believe in *human* instinct and agrees with his twin that he would rather be convinced by a human being than by a piece of machinery, the Prisoner rests his case. 'You have something in mind?' asks Number 2. Proposing a test that will conclusively prove which man is which, the Prisoner begs leave to telephone Number 24 – Alison, the girl with whom he did the card test. 'Yes,' answers the girl when the Prisoner phones her. 'I'm at Number 2's residence. Could you come over right away.' The girl was about to wash her hair, but as it's important, she's on her way. 'What do you hope to achieve?' asks Number 2. 'To prove that I am Number 6, and he is a fake,' states the Prisoner. 'That's what you wanted isn't it? That's what all this is about?' 'Yes,' confirms the superior. 'Good heavens, it can't be . . .' says Alison, appearing in the chamber, amazed to find two identical men waiting for her. 'Mother nature has been up to her tricks again,' quips the Prisoner. 'It's weird . . . Who is . . . Which one . . .?' 'I am the original. He is the economy pack,' confirms her card-playing friend. 'It's impossible,' says Alison. 'On the contrary . . .' quips the Prisoner. 'But I still don't understand which of you . . .' 'That is what you are here to settle . . . Number 2 says it's not possible.' 'I see,' says the girl. 'That's why you wanted me to bring the cards.' 'That's right,' confirms the Prisoner. 'I don't follow,' says a bemused Number 2. 'Number 6 and I have a mental link . . .' Alison confirms. 'So let's see which one of us has a mental link with her,' says the Prisoner. The girl agrees to the test. Selecting a card, the Prisoner concentrates on the picture on its face. The girl fails to identify it. He tries a second card, with the same result. Another, and another, but the girl is still unable to come up with the right answers. White goes next – and scores 5 out of 5! The Prisoner has lost! Forced to concede that the man in the white blazer is the real Number 6, Alison produces the photograph she took of him earlier. 'Isn't it awful, I took it last night, he's all arms and legs. Actually, there was a much simpler way to identify Number 6. He has mole on his left wrist.' 'Of course,' sneers White, slipping back his cuff. The Prisoner does the same – his wrist is spotless! 'Well if we've finished for the day, and you don't mind, I'll see the young lady home,' says White, leading Alison from the room. Number 2 is furious. 'What in heavens name made you do a stupid thing like that?' he asks the man left behind. 'Surely you must realise Number 6 and that girl have got a genuine rapport. Someone's going to have to pay dearly for this!' He signals to Number 118, the medic who took Number 6 from his bed earlier. 'Number 118, why was there no mole on Number 12's left wrist?' The man remains silent. 'I said why was there no mole? Don't you realise that you've jeopardised the whole operation . . . report to me first thing in the morning. First thing!'

Back in his room, the Prisoner contemplates his position, summoning his willpower to fight against the steadily-mounting evidence that he is someone else – a man simply masquerading as the man he believed himself to be. Watching the man writhe in nightmares, Number 2 tells Number 12 that it will not be long before he cracks. Rising from his bed, the Prisoner notices his bruised fingernail. The congealed blood has moved downwards, indicating several month's growth. Musing this over in his mind, he removes Alison's photograph from his pocket. The mark on his nail is clearly displayed. So too is the date on the calender behind him. A magnifying glass allows comparison of the fingernail then and now; the bruise is just beginning to form, the date on the calendar reads 10 February. Memories from the past begin to flood into his mind. Crossing to the mirror he recalls being drugged and placed into a bed, while someone operated on his left wrist – a wrist that no longer bears a mole! He recalls being given therapy treatment to change his right-handedness; the days spent indoors growing the beard that was trimmed to a moustache; a tape-machine ploughing the knowledge into his brain that he was Number 12: the flapjacks, the cigars . . . Picking up a box of cigarettes timidly with his left hand, he drops the container into his right palm. He selects a cigarette and shreds it. It appears to be normal. The cigar box comes next. Breaking open a panatella, he discovers the plastic filament which made the cigars unpalatable to the smoker. Crossing to the settee, he selects a second cigarette from the box on the table, left-handed. Is that right? Pausing, he peers beneath the table lamp, inspecting it for hidden microphones, but finds nothing. Raising it gently, he places it before the fire grate and reaches towards the cottage's gas appliance. Gripping the supply pipe, he cautiously reaches for the table lamp with his other hand. Upon contact, the appliance short-circuits, throwing the Prisoner to the floor. Gripping a table for support, he regains his feet, knocking a trinket box from the table as he does so. He catches it – an automatic response – with his *right* hand! He is now cured, ready to take on anyone – including Number 2!

It is night time and Number 2 is being treated to a massage by the mute Butler. 'Let's see how Number 6 is getting on, shall we,' he says, rising to switch on the monitor screen. Number 6 is not at home. Guards are alerted to the find the Prisoner. They do so as he traverses a street. He gives them the password, 'Gemini', which is wrong and a fight ensues. The men beaten, the Prisoner escapes from a Rover by pretending to race off in a buggy In the Control Room, the Supervisor informs a distraught Number 2 that Number 6 cannot be found. 'Send out a general alarm, Orange Alert,' orders the superior. The Prisoner, meanwhile, has crept back to his residence to confront his twin. Hearing the man enter, White is waiting for him in the bedroom with a nerve gas gun: 5-yard range, one squirt will paralyse, two squirts will kill. 'Couldn't sleep,' says the Prisoner to the man lying on his bed. 'Came here to . . . Who am I?' 'You know who you are, you're Number 12,' says White, believing his twin to be disorientated. 'Yes, I'm Number 12 . . .' the Prisoner begins, '. . .but sometimes in my dreams I'm . . . I'm somebody else.' 'Who?' mocks White, covering the other with his gas gun. 'I don't know . . . Sometimes in my dreams, I resign my job.' 'Why did you resign your job – in your dream?' asks White. 'Sometimes I'm here in my dreams, and then I come back,' sobs the Prisoner, feigning exhaustion. 'I want to know . . . Who am I? Why am I here?' Believing that his twin has reached the end of his tether, White offers to ring Number 2. He might be able to help. A mistake. His defences are down and the Prisoner makes full use of the opportunity. Leaping onto his double, he throws White to the floor. A no-holds-barred fight ensues, which culminates in White's defeat. 'The password,' threatens the Prisoner. 'I don't know what you're talking about,' denies the other. 'What is it?'

'Nerve gas. One squirt you're paralysed. Two squirts, you're dead'

says the victor, his fist raised in a threatening manner. 'What password?' 'What is IT!' exclaims the Prisoner. 'Schizoid . . . Schizoid Man . . .' 'Schizoid man . . . what's your name?' 'Curtis,' gasps White. Catching Number 6 off-guard, White makes a run for it. His second mistake. Racing outside, he is swallowed up by a Rover. Back in his residence, the Prisoner telephones Number 2. 'Password,' asks the superior, taking no chances. 'Curtis . . . Schizoid Man,' says Number 6, hastily correcting his mistake. 'Number 6 is dead. Rover got him.' 'WHAT!' exclaims Number 2. 'He's dead,' replies the Prisoner, savouring the taste of victory. 'Rover got him.' Furious at this news, Number 2 issues orders for Rover to be deactivated immediately, pending further instructions. Donning White's blazer, Curtis, the Prisoner visits the superior in the Green Dome. Still trying to discover why Rover killed the Prisoner, Number 2 tells the man he believes to be Curtis that he is to return immediately to report his failure. 'My failure,' mocks Number 6. 'You wanted him broken. I've broken him. I wasn't to know he'd go beserk.' 'Nor was I,' Number 2 confirms. 'You studied him. You should have known. It was your idea.' 'That's a strange thing to say,' retorts the superior. 'You know it wasn't.' 'Well, you certainly didn't resist . . .' 'Bearing in mind its origin, no I didn't! Nor did you.' 'Recriminations aren't going to help. It's a disgrace to us both, when do I leave?' He is due to depart in an hour's time, but *they* want to talk to Alison before he goes; they believe that she may have some insight into the Prisoner's motivations. Watching the man leave, a thought enters Number 2's head, but dismissing the idea he returns to his desk. At Alison's home, the girl states that she has nothing significant to report. 'I don't believe in such things myself,' Number 6 tells the girl, 'but you were supposed to be able to read each other's minds.' 'It doesn't work like that,' says the girl, sensing something different about the man. 'Oh. How does it work?' quips Number 6. 'In spasms . . . little things. Sudden coincidences which aren't really coincidences,' Alison replies, picking up a cigarette. 'Oh,' says he, turning to offer her a light. The girl stares at him. 'It's a had habit of mine, playing with lighters,' he mocks. 'I'll probably start a fire one day. Well if you've got nothing to tell me, I'll be on my way. Be seeing you.' He leaves to prepare for his journey home. Dressed in civilian clothes for the first time in many months, he takes Curtis' wallet out of his jacket. It contains a photograph of a pretty blonde girl – the dead man's wife, and is signed 'From your loving wife, Susan.' Joined by Number 2, the men climb aboard a Village taxi. During the short trip to the helicopter pad, the superior questions him about a proposition he put to Curtis when he arrived: has he thought about it further? 'Sorry, haven't had the time,' the Prisoner replies. 'But you must have some views . . .' probes Number 2. 'I'm afraid not.' '. . . Look old chap, we've been through many scrapes before, but we've never fallen out over them. The General's not going to behead you.' 'We won't know – until I've reported to the General, will we?' comes the terse reply. 'Report to the General . . . that's a new one.' 'I don't mean report to him personally . . . for Pete's sake you know what I mean,' throws back Number 6, aware that he's on dangerous ground. 'You are edgy,' replies Number 2. 'I've never known you quite so strung up.' 'You mean I'm not as I was,' replies Number 6. 'Yes . . . I remember Susan saying only a month ago, that you're genuinely quite unflappable. You have changed,' returns Number 2, a hint of suspicion in his voice. 'We *all* change. The job, it changes us.' 'Yes,' says Number 2 as they arrive outside the recreation hall where a helicopter waits to take 'Curtis' away from the Village. 'It's just a quick flip in the helicopter to the landing strip and the jet picks you up there. Excuse me . . .' Alison is waiting for them. 'I'm ashamed of what I did to Number 6 yesterday,' she tells the man. 'Why are you telling *me*?' he asks. 'Everyone has to tell someone.' 'It was your job,' he smiles. 'It was a betrayal,' she replies. 'Isn't everything we do *here* a *betrayal*.' he retorts. 'It's not often one gets a second chance,' quips Alison. 'There are *no* second chances,' he points out. 'There are sometimes. For the *lucky* ones. If *I* had a second chance, I want you to know that I wouldn't do it again.' She knows. But he realises that his secret is safe with her. 'Bon voyage,' bids Number 2, as Number 6 turns to board the helicopter. 'Thank you,' grins the Prisoner. 'Oh, one last thing,' says the superior. 'Yes?' 'You forgot the security regulations. Must be obeyed. The blindfold old chap.' 'Oh yes, of course,' sighs Number 6 with relief. 'You won't forget to give Susan my regards, will you?' asks Number 2, as the departing man boards the machine and slips the blindfold to his eyes. 'I won't. *Goodbye*' The helicopter blades begin to rotate and the machine climbs skywards, taking its passenger to freedom. High over the Village it soars until, unseen by the man in the blindfold, it lands back at its departure point outside the recreation hall. Unaware of what is going on, Number 6 is man-handled back to face a grinning Number 2. His blindfold is stripped away and a triumphant superior reminds him 'Susan died a year ago!' The man is still a PRISONER!

So that's how it's done. Patrick McGoohan faces up to himself – stunt double, Frank Maher

AUTHOR'S NOTE: This is the only story to refer to Rover by name.

The extensive split screen shots showing Number 6 and Curtis (The Schizoid Man) on screen together, was achieved by use of McGoohan's regular stunt double, Frank Maher.

IT'S YOUR FUNERAL

Written by Michael Cramoy

Guest Stars

New Number 2	**Derren Nesbitt**
Watchmaker's Daughter	**Annette Andre**
Number 100	**Mark Eden**

with

Retiring Number 2	**Andre Van Gyseghem**
Watchmaker	**Martin Miller**
Computer Attendant	**Wanda Ventham**
The Butler	**Angelo Muscat**
Number 2's Assistant	**Mark Burns**

and

Supervisor	**Peter Swanwick**
Artist	**Charles Lloyd Pack**
Number 36	**Grace Arnold**
Stall Holder	**Arthur White**
M.C. Councillor	**Michael Bilton**
Kosho Opponent	**Gerry Cramptom**

Directed by Robert Asher

WATCHED BY Number 2 and the Supervisor, a beautiful young girl enters the residence denoted '6 – Private'. Its occupant, apparently asleep, lies in his bed. But as the girl stretches out her hand to wake him, she finds herself flung onto the bed, the man's hand tightly clasping her wrist. 'What are you doing here?' he growls. 'I was just going to wake you up,' stammers the girl. 'You have. Who are you?' he yells, releasing the girl. 'I'm a number, just like you. Does it matter which?' she replies. 'How did you get in?' 'The door was open,' comes the answer. 'It always is, isn't it . . . to *them*!' the Prisoner snaps back, as he tightens the belt on the dressing gown he has donned. 'I'm not one of *them*,' the girl replies forcefully, rising from the bed. 'No? What do you want?' 'Help,' she throws back. 'Go to the Town Hall, the Citizens Council promises help and advice to everyone,' he retorts. '*Their* citizens council,' sobs the girl. 'As far as I'm concerned what's theirs is *yours*,' shouts Number 6, approaching the intruder. 'I am *not* one of *them*!' she fires back, her eyes beginning to well with tears. 'No. No one is,' he replies, suspicious that the girl may be a plant. 'Go back. Tell them that I was *not* interested . . . that I wouldn't even listen . . .' Then, acknowledging the fact that everyone in the Village is always under surveillance, he adds 'What's the point. They know already.' He peers around the room at the unseen surveillance cameras. 'I won't go for it, whatever *it* is . . . so you may as well stop trying,' he shouts, opening the door to see the intruder out. '*We* never stop, Number 6,' says Number 2, observing the man's outburst on the control room wall screen. With a glance at his wristwatch, he adds 'Now we'll see how accurately they've timed it.' Back in the Prisoner's cottage, the girl suddenly collapses to the flooor. 'She was given the drug yesterday,' Number 2 tells his Supervisor. 'One of the new super-strength moprobomates that we've developed. *She* doesn't know anything about it, of course.' 'Yesterday?' questions the Supervisor. 'Well the drug remains dormant until triggered by the nervous system.

and then it releases itself, to the desired quantities, to produce instant tranquility, or temporary oblivion,' the Superior replies. 'But why?' queries the bespectacled man. 'Well in anticipation of Number 6 throwing her out . . . which he was about to do.' 'And *will*, when she revives,' replies the Supervisor. 'Oh no no,' a grinning Number 2 replies. 'You see she has now become a lady in distress. He's going to be all good deeds and sympathy.' Then, noticing that the door to Number 6's residence is still ajar, he tells his assistant that he can't recall his procedure agenda authorising this. Told by the Supervisor that it was an after-thought – to make certain that once the girl had made up her mind to go and see Number 6, she'd have access, Number 2 points out the obvious. 'Doesn't she know how to knock on a door, then?' 'He doesn't always answer,' defends the Supervisor, realising his mistake. 'It seemed like a good idea . . .' 'It *wasn't*,' snaps Number 2, 'because now he is going to assume that we sent her. Now we don't want that – do we?' 'No!' the assistant admits. 'This plan,' continues the superior, 'is too important for little slapdash improvisations, you know. No matter how good the idea may seem at the moment.' 'Yes Number 2,' says the Supervisor as the other draws his attention to the fact that the girl in Number 6's room is coming round. 'Look at that,' giggles Number 2 pointing to his wristwatch, 'exactly the time the chemists anticipated.' Apologising for making a fool of herself, having accepted a glass of water from Number 6, the girl pleads exhaustion. 'No,' says the tenant, lifting the girl's eyelid, 'Drugs! Your pupils are contracted.' 'I don't take drugs,' she answers in alarm. 'Forced feeding then,' he suggests. 'Why should they?' she queries. 'You tell me,' he says, acknowledging that he is prepared to listen – as long as what she tells him does not become too obviously phoney. Convinced that she is wasting her time, the girl makes to leave. 'I'll find help somewhere else.' 'They told you to find it here, didn't they?' 'Believe what you like . . .' says the girl, 'I . . . it doesn't matter any more.' Then, pausing to gather her thoughts, she turns and acknowledges that it does matter. 'This concerns the welfare of everyone in the Village.' 'And welfare is our biggest consumer item. Yes,' quips Number 6. 'Joke about this if you can – assassination!' she exclaims. 'Are you trying to organise, or prevent one?' he throws back, uninterested. 'Prevent!' she acknowledges. 'They would have to take reprisals, everybody would suffer.' 'Alright,' he concedes. 'What can *I* do for you?' She replies by saying that she needs his help to prevent the assassination attempt. '*They've* heard. They are aware and *they* don't need anyone's help!' '*They* don't believe me,' cries the girl. 'No comment,' he says. 'So much caution, in a man like *you* it seems so wrong.' 'Many times bitten, forever shy. But *they* are not shy. *They* love to listen,' says the Prisoner. Informing him that he does not understand; her name, her number is on a list, she replies to his quipped 'Honours or Department' with just one word: 'Jamming'.

'I'm sorry I ever bothered you'

'Jamming?' he says. 'Oh, domestic science.' Informing him that he will learn all about jamming soon enough and that it is one of the most important ways of fighting back, his comment that he is prepared to learn all about it at that very moment leads the girl to remind him that he was formerly convinced that she was lying. 'I'm sorry I ever bothered you,' she says, walking towards the door. 'Call in anytime you like,' he calls after her. Disappointed that his first attempt has failed, Number 2, told by an unseen caller (whom we learn later is an elderly Number 2) that he must find a way of making Number 6 take an interest in the girl, the young Number 2 promises to do so. 'Yes, I realise that Sir, but what put us behind was the girl's hesitancy. As you know she took a long time making up her mind to see him. I had hoped to catch up, but Number 6 flatly refused to have anything to do with her . . . and that's caused another delay. Well, perhaps if we could replace him with someone more tractable, less suspicious . . . Yes, I realise that sir, the reason why we selected Number 6 . . . A matter of credibility, without which the plan might backfire. Indeed I will sir. As you say, I must find a way to make him interested.' Turning to the Supervisor, he calls for the day's Activities Prognosis on Number 6. 'As quickly as possible!' Within minutes the Control Room is a hive of activity. The Computer Attendant orders her colleagues to maintain a top priority interest on the Prisoner, and an audio-taped record is kept of the man's every move: 6.30 am subject exercises daily with a walk around the Village; daily the subject climbs to the bell tower – reason unknown . . . subject eccentric; certainly watching, waiting, constantly aggressive . . . it is possible the subject likes the view, 7.30 am physical workout using subject's home made apparatus . . . 8.15 am, the subject cooling off by skiing on the lake, 9 o'clock, coffee at cafe and buys some newspapers. 9.20 am, subject will proceed on foot to Old People's Home where he plays a game of chess with an elderly man – the game ending with an 11-move checkmate win, by subject . . . He then humours other eccentric resident, by sitting for portrait – or perhaps subject has an ulterior motive for doing so? As the Prisoner sits with the portrait painter, the computer attendant seals the report on his activities into an envelope addressed: 'Official. For the attention of the acting Number 2. Day's activities prognosis. No: 6.'

In the control room, the young Number 2 is holding a conversation with Number 100, one of his assistants, who, dressed as a villager, spies on the community. 'Then you're satisfied with your progress to date on Plan Division Q?' asks the young Number 2. 'My division will be operational exactly on time . . . you can quote me in your report,' confirms the other. 'Mmm mmm, well I shall. You're still confident of your cover? There's no sign of penetration?' 'No. They still think of me as just another prisoner. We're kindred spirits, comrades,' says Number 100, referring to the Prisoner. 'There'll be no trouble from him.' Number 6, meanwhile, converses with the man painting his portrait. 'You moved,' says the artist. 'Sorry . . .' 'What they do, these jammers,' continues the other, 'is talk. They talk about the plots they've been hatching.' 'Plots?' queries the poser. 'Well escapes mostly. But plans and developments for all kinds of mischief. They do it to confuse the observers. Still – please!' 'So sorry,' says the Prisoner, resuming his pose. 'The plots they talk about are always make-believe. Non-existent. But control can't know that until they've checked them out. Used to run themselves ragged investigating the schemes of jammers.' 'Used to?' 'They don't bother much anymore. Now they keep a list of all known jammers. Anything control picks up from these, they just let it ride,' the artist replies picking up the completed canvas. 'What do you think?' he adds, showing the subject his 'portrait' – a wild abstract of confusing daubs of paint. 'A perfect likeness,' confirms Number 6. Marching into the control room with the envelope she sealed earlier, the computer attendant stands before the young Number 2, who asks her to detail the prognosis' reliability. 'I'm afraid we don't know that,' replies the woman. 'Why not,' asks the superior. 'Twice we programmed our machines for percental appraisals of their own efficiencies. Each time they've refused to give back the requested information.' 'Refused? How?' challenges the young Number 2. 'Simply by not returning the data to us,' the attendant replies. Sipping his tea, an astonished Number 2 suggests that they'll be wanting their own trade union next. 'Well go ahead and read it to me.' Reading from the report, the woman looks at her wristwatch and begins 'It is now 10.19 exactly. According to the prognosis, the subject is now taking his daily stroll through the village. At approximately 10.20, he will go to the kiosk . . .' The young Number 2 stretches out on his lounger, anticipating a boring display of the assistant's thoroughness. He turns to the monitor screen where, as confirmed by the report, Number 6 is handing over his credits for a copy of the *Tally Ho* news-sheet. '. . . there he will buy a copy of the newspaper, a bar of soap, and a bag of sweets . . .' 'Oh no no . . . he *never* eats candy,' cries the superior. 'According to the prognosis he . . .' the girl begins. 'It doesn't matter about the prognosis, it's wrong – it doesn't work!' insists the young Number 2. Explaining that it will only take a moment to find out and told by the superior to continue, the girl and Number 2 turn their attention to the monitor screen. They watch as an old lady standing next to Number 6 pleads with the kiosk attendant. 'But I must have them,' she sobs. 'For the last time . . . your week's credit allowance is all used up,' states the attendant. 'Come back tomorrow.' 'But I can't go through an entire day without my sweets,' pleads the woman, her eyes welling with tears. 'Sorry,' says the trader, ignoring her and devoting his attention to Number 6. 'Yes sir?' 'Er, a bag of candy for the lady,' says Number 6. The onlookers watch these proceedings with rapt attention. 'My apologies. How did you know?' asks the young Number 2. 'An efficient prognosis progamming must include a quantum permutation of the cause and effect of all supplementary elements,' replies the computer attendant. 'In other words the computer calculated the old woman's behaviour would change the behaviour pattern of Number 6,' states the superior. Sighing, and aware that her position has been vindicated, the woman continues to record what Number 6 will be doing for the rest of the day. Hearing that the Prisoner will arrive at the gymnasium between 11.40 and 11.50 for his semi-weekly Kosho practice, the young Number 2 stops the woman in mid-sentence. He has heard enough. He's found what he was looking for. The girl is dismissed and the superior turns to Number 100. 'You know what I have in mind,' his colleague is told.

In the gymnasium, Number 6, dressed in a red cossack-style coat with his left wrist covered by a guantlet-type glove, his right encased in a white cotton mitten, and his head protected by a white helmet, stands challengingly before his similarly-attired opponent – although his opponent's helmet is black. Each man is balanced precariously on a trampoline. The trampolines are separated by a six-foot divide and erected over a huge water tank, the objective being to knock your opponent into the water below. Bowing to each other as the competition begins, the opponent leaps into the air, clears the divide and lands at the other's feet. But Number 6 is no longer there. He has sprung to the safety of the ledge behind him, his hands firmly grasping the handrail to prevent him falling backwards onto the spring mat. In the wink of an eye, the men have swapped places. Time and again they leap from the ledge, to escape each other's grasp. Landing together on the Prisoner's side of the trampoline, the opponent gains the advantage, pressing the Prisoner's body precariously close to the edge of the divide. A kick sends the man reeling backwards, but he quickly regains his feet and springs back into the attack.

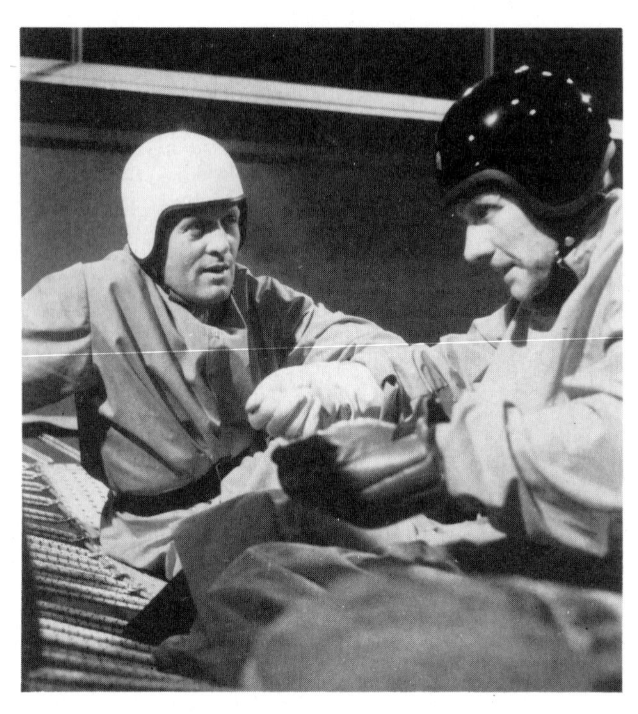

Patrick McGoohan and stuntman Gerry Crampton discuss the Kosho fight

Unseen by either man, the one numbered 100 has entered the gymnasium and found his way into the men's locker room. Locating the Prisoner's locker, he exchanges the man's wristwatch for an identical one and departs, unobserved. The Kosho battle rages on, each man somersaulting to escape the other's clutches. Again and again they leap into the air until, anticipating his opponent's next move, Number 6 leaps to the handrail a split second before the other and with a tug of the man's collar, sends him headlong into the water below. Triumphant, the Prisoner springs to the trampoline and then to the floor of the gymnasium, executing a perfect headlong flip as he does so. Bowing twice to his water-logged opponent, he retreats to the locker room to dress. Discovering that his wristwatch is broken, he takes the timepiece into the watchmaker's shop. 'It's stopped,' says Number 6, handing the device to the wizened old shopkeeper. Inspecting the wristwatch, the man asks him to wait and retreats into the rear of his shop. The Prisoner finds an odd-looking device the watchmaker had been working on when he entered, and lifts it from the man's workdesk. As a plunger is pressed on its uppermost side, an equally strange looking device left on the worktop clicks into motion, its tubular finger turning clockwise. Having made a small adjustment to the customer's timepiece, the watchmaker returns and hands the watch back to its owner, stating that it is working again. Clipping the Prisoner's credit card, the old man tells him that the device he has been playing with is simply a toy. As the customer exits, Number 100 appears from his hiding place at the rear of the shop. 'Well?' he enquires. Acknowledging that he has done the man's bidding, the watchmaker says that he cannot understand why the other asked him to expose their methods. 'All will be explained to you in time,' replies the spy. 'No, now! What can we gain by letting *them* know what we're up to? The enemy?' demands the watchmaker. 'We add to *their* confusion. That's what we stand to gain,' replies the other. 'You see, they don't believe anything we say. Or do. Or intend to do. That's why we are able to carry out our plan,' he ends, handing the device which the customer had been playing with back to the watchmaker. In the street outside, Number 6 bumps into the girl who passed out in his cottage. 'How did you find out?' she asks, acknowledging that she saw him enter the shop. 'Beg pardon?' says he, confused. 'I never mentioned the watchmaker to you. What did you want with him?' Indicating that his wristwatch had stopped and that he had taken it to the shop to be repaired, the man grins when the girl tells him that she is the shopkeeper's daughter. 'Ah, that explains why you're so concerned, doesn't it,' he mocks, his senses alert to a trap. 'And you?' she asks. 'The same total disinterest?' 'Not quite the same, no,' he confirms. 'What happened?' What's made you so interested?' she queries. 'Because I don't believe that a device to detonate explosives by radio is a toy – and neither does your father,' he replies. Number 2's assistant, meanwhile, watching this scene with his superior in the control room, acknowledges that Number 2's plan could work. 'It *is* working,' grins the young Number 2. 'But I'll take the bows later on.' 'Whatever you like to call it. Plan Division Q is still murder,' states the other. Sneering, the young Number 2 retaliates: 'You have *your* specific duties, stick to them and leave the rest to one double zero. 'You think Number 6 has fallen for it?' asks the other. 'No, no not yet,' replies the young Number 2 shaking his head. 'But he will . . . he *will*.' 'And after it's all over you'll be showered with official congratulations.' 'Yes,' nods the superior, 'well after he's been here to warn me that an assassination is being plotted . . . and that *I* am the intended victim!'

Sitting with the girl at a table in the cafe outside the Old People's Home, Number 6 asks the girl what she knows. Precious little appears to be the answer: she is aware that her father and another man – one she has never seen – intend to assassinate Number 2, but she has no knowledge as to when they intend to do it, nor how, nor where. In an attempt to make the girl's father see reason, they visit the watchmaker. But the old man flatly refuses to abandon his plan, even when told by Number 6 that the whole Village will suffer because of his foolishness. 'Maybe it's what they need to wake them up. To shake them out of their lethargy. To make them angry enough to fight,' he states. 'Assuming they survive the punishment,' an irate Number 6 points out. 'What's the use? You'll never understand,' replies the confused an angry watchmaker, retiring to his work room, as an equally frustrated Number 6 storms out of the shop. In the control room, a delighted Number 2 congratulates the one numbered 100 on a job well done. 'Since he cannot reason with the watchmaker,' confirms Number 100, 'he must now come here to warn you.' At that very second, that is exactly what the Prisoner is doing. Watched by the men on the monitor screen, Number 6 is tracked by the surveillance cameras to the Green Dome, from which Number 100 is leaving as the Prisoner enters. 'Ah, Number 6, my dear fellow, do come in,' greets the young Number 2 as the Prisoner enters. 'Shall I order you coffee, or would you prefer some tea?' 'You can forego the amenities,' quips the newcomer, 'this is not a social call.' 'To what then do I owe the pleasure of your company?' asks the superior. 'I'm here to deliver a warning.' 'A warning? What about?' asks the young Number 2. 'A plot to kill you.' 'To what?' asks the other, feigning surprise. 'To kill you ... *assassinate* you,' grunts Number 2. 'Mmm.' 'To ass-ass-in-ate YOU!!' 'I don't believe it,' mocks the superior. 'They should have told you. There are some unhappy people here,' confirms Number 6. 'Yes ...' replies the young Number 2, '... well I have seen the list of malcontents ... it might interest you to know that *you* happen to be top of the bill.' 'I'll do my best to live up to it,' quips the Prisoner, confessing that the only reason he is warning the man is to prevent the mass reprisal that would surely take place after the killing. A smug and confident Number 2 pooh-poos the man's words, informing him that he knows all about the jammers and the watchmaker. 'Yes well we expected something like this ... that they'd try to get through to us through a dupe. Hmm, so they chose *you* to lead us into believing their fantasy eh? Tell me, how did they sell you the idea Number 6? Did they show you the gun?' 'Oh they're not going to shoot you,' grins the Prisoner, 'they're going to *blow you up*!' 'Did they tell you how they were going to go about it. When? Where?' asks the young Number 2. 'Would you find out for me, because, well, a laugh would do me an awful lot of good!' Riled by the man's over-confidence, Number 6 marches from the room, turning while doing so to tell the other that he may find out himself, quite suddenly, in which case, he certainly will not be laughing. Alone, a delighted Number 2 is informed that both cameras and audio-tape have captured the conversation.

'Oh don't tell me. It's the little watchmaker that concerns you'

Meeting the watchmaker's daughter, Number 6 explains that he has no choice but to continue his attempts to defuse the situation. Number 2 believes him to be a communications medium and did not believe him. As they talk, the Village voice announces that the Citizens Council have officially proclaimed Thursday, the day after tomorrow, as Appreciation Day, a day when the Village community pays due honour to those brave and noble people who govern them so wisely. Everyone will be delighted to hear that the proceedings will be opened with an address by Number 2 himself, and concluded by the unveiling of the new appreciation monument. There will be speeches, thrills and excitement. 'Maybe *more* excitement than planned,' quips Number 6 to his partner. That night, in her father's shop, the girl and Number 6 find Number 2's Great Seal of Office, which he always wears at ceremonies. The pendant contains a slab of explosive which can be detonated by radio.

The following morning, Number 6 enters the control room with the intention of informing Number 2 about his discovery. The oval-shaped chair rises from the floor to greet him, but as it turns to face the newcomer, a new man is sitting in the seat – a man Number 6 has never seen before! 'Number 6 isn't it?' asks the figure. 'I've been expecting you.' 'I want to see Number 2,' informs the newcomer. '*I* am Number 2,' says the other with a grin. 'You've come to tell me that there's a plot against my life, haven't you?' Confused by this turn of events, the Prisoner begins to pace the room. 'You know my colleague is very concerned about these imminent death by violence projects that you've been reporting during my absence,' confirms the new Number 2, a man with silvery hair. 'Plots?' replies the Prisoner, coming to a halt in front of the stranger. 'I've reported one only.' 'Not so,' snaps the elderly Number 2, 'my every efficient colleague – or should I say my heir presumptive, has been collecting evidence, that every interim Number 2 who has served here while I've been on leave, has been cautioned by you, about some improbable conspiracy to murder him.' Number 6 stares at the man. 'Really,' he replies with obvious distrust. 'You obviously don't believe me. Well the psychiatrist warned me that that might be the case. Shall I show you proof?' With a wave of his hand, Number 6 bids him do so. Leaning forward in his chair to press a button on the control console before him with the tip of his rolled parasol, the superior leans back in his seat as the television monitor glows into life – to show Number 6 warning a succession of Number 2's – all bar the first (the young Number 2 seen earlier) people the Prisoner has never laid eyes on – that their lives are under threat of assassination. 'More?' asks the confident voice behind him. 'Why bother,' replies Number 6. 'So you're convinced?' asks the other switching off the device. 'I'm convinced that those excerpts are fakes!' retorts the other, aware that his earlier warning to the young Number 2 had been monitored and that the sequence which has just been paraded before him is a compilation of events which occured earlier, spliced together with additional material. 'You think they've been *doctored*. For what purpose? Why should we want to convince you that you're not well?' returns the man in the chair. 'Perhaps it is *you they* want to convince,' offers Number 6. 'Me? Tomorrow I hand over to my successor – I retire!' states the other. 'Perhaps they are trying to save a pension,' the Prisoner throws back, as he departs from the room, leaving the elderly Number 2 to consider his words.

Joining the girl, Number 6 shows little surprise when she

(You're going on with it?) 'I haven't much choice'

points out that Number 100, sitting at a table opposite them is her father's fellow conspirator. Hearing the Prisoner tell the girl that he has seen the man earlier, leaving the Green Dome – no doubt after plotting the assassination attempt with 'another', the retiring Number 2, strokes his chin, considering the truth of the man's words. Joined by his assistant, he orders the man to have the tapes made by the incoming Number 2 to be brought to him: he wishes to review them. 'At once,' says the junior. 'Subject?' 'Subject – warning of assassination plot. Persons Number 6 and my successor,' replies the elderly Number 2. The assistant falters, considering the request. 'Well get on with it,' urges the superior. 'It would be a waste of time. There is no recording of that description,' confirms the assistant. 'How strange,' states the elderly Number 2. 'You must have been misinformed,' tries the junior. 'Strange that although you have no duty functions with the Bureau of Visual Records, you can think instantly, and with total assurance, that the records I require are non-existent. Please explain,' orders the superior. 'Number ... Number 2. I'm not able to,' stammers the assistant. The fact that his junior will not explain is proof enough for the departing Number 2: the Prisoner has told him the truth, his successor means to kill him! His successor, meanwhile, telephones Number 1. 'Absolutely sir, just as it's been planned, it's going like clockwork ... oh thank you sir ... No no, there's no danger of that, Number 6 is no problem ... we have fully convinced him ... and you do have my word.' Sitting outside the Old People's Home, the girl pleads with the Prisoner to prevent the assassination, for her father's sake. 'For everybody's sake,' he reminds her.

The outgoing Number 2 receives a visitor – Number 6. Worried now, he informs the guest that he now realises that he was telling him the truth. 'I'm to be assassinated.' 'For assassinated substitute *executed*!' the Prisoner returns. 'Since it's arranged by my own people you mean?' stammers the elderly Number 2. 'You don't *mind*?' yells Number 6. 'Of course I mind. It's just that I thought it would never happen to me.' 'It never does,' mocks the Prisoner, 'to anybody. But it can be prevented.' Informing the visitor that prevention is only a postponement, the superior tells his guest some home truths. 'You've never understood us Number 6. We *never* fail. Anyway, why should you care what happens to me?' 'I don't,' replies Number 6, 'But innocent people will be blamed.' 'Yes, I know,' confirms the elder sympathetically, apologising that he is unable to do anything. 'The ceremony can take place *without* the seal,' offers Number 6. 'The seal *is* the ceremony,' replies the superior. 'It's hollowed out! It's packed with explosives ...' the other begins. 'And before I hand it over to my successor.' '... it will be detonated by radio,' says Number 6, confirming the elder's suspicions. 'I can think of better ways to die,' concedes Number 2. 'And better *causes* to die for !' snaps Number 6, leaving the man shivering in his chair. Elsewhere, the incoming Number 2 updates his report to Number 1: Plan Division Q is running according to schedule. It is set to succeed. It is working beautifully, *dead* on schedule in fact. (A joke?) 'No sir, no no, just the way you ordered it ... the people are already gathering, it will be very, er, very spectacular. Nothing can go wrong now, I'll stake my future on it.'

The holiday Thursday arrives. Exuberant, the villagers acknowledge the Master of Ceremonies with joyous applause. The retiring and the incoming Number 2s stand side-by-side on the Town Hall balcony, the former frowning as the Master of Ceremonies mouths words of joy, the latter contacting Number 100 via a transmitter secreted in the stem of his eye glasses. 'Can you hear me? Come in please ...' 'I can hear you,' confirms his confederate. 'Is everything alright?' 'Everything is alright. Stop worrying ... repeat, stop worrying,' replies Number 100, as Number 6 joins the crowd. Everyone appears happy, all save the watchmaker's daughter who, joining the Prisoner, admits that she is worried: her father did not come home last night. 'The shop?' asks Number 6. 'He's not there, he must be here somewhere,' she confirms. 'Not necessarily ...' he replies, confirming that the transmitter her father had made has a very wide range. 'He could be anywhere.' Scanning the crowd and catching sight of the watchmaker in the bell tower, he pushes his way through the crowd and races upwards, followed by the girl. Simultaneously, the mute Butler carries the Seal of Office to the Master of Ceremonies. Lifting the medallion from its red, velvet tray, the speaker places it snugly around the neck of the outgoing Number 2. His successor stands to one side, his carefully-laid plan only seconds away from fruition. Arriving at the bell tower at the very second the watchmaker lifts the radio-controlled detonator to his chest, Number 6 wrestles with the man for control of the device. Below them, the outgoing Number 2 makes his farewell speech, aware that at any moment his retirement will end too early. The young Number 2, meanwhile, worried that the explosion is overdue, signals to his confederate to find out what is wrong. Having snatched the radio detonator from the watchmaker's hands, Number 6 hastily descends the clock tower. 'Farewell my friends,' says the departing Number 2, anticipating that his words will send him to heaven. But the explosion he expects fails to occur. At that very moment, Numbers 6 and 100 are fighting each other to regain possession of the detonator trigger, which has been knocked from the Prisoner's hand by his opponent. As the men fight, a confused but nonetheless relieved ex-Number 2 is only too glad when the Master of Ceremonies lifts the seal of office from his shoulders and crosses the balcony to place the medallion around the neck of his successor. A look of terror and bemusement fills his eyes as, via the transmitter in his glasses, he hears Number 6 ordering his defeated opponent to confess his involvement in the affair. At the foot of the bell tower, the one numbered 100 throws the Prisoner backwards, but the struggle soon ends when Number 100 is punched into submission. Back on the balcony, the achievement sculpture is unveiled and the new Number 2 looks on with anger as Number 6 hands over the detonator trigger to the out-going Number 2. 'Take it,' he says. 'What for?' begs the other. 'It's your passport. No one will question its authority. The helicopter's waiting.' 'But they'll get me eventually,' stammers the elder. 'Fly now, pay later,' jousts the Prisoner. 'They'll find me, wherever I am,' confirms the other. 'As long as it's not here. Take it and go,' Number 6 advises, returning the new Number 2's icy stare. Watched helplessly by his successor, the retired Number 2 leaves. As the villain of the piece attempts to raise the medallion over his head, Number 6 springs forwards to pin his arms to his sides. 'And so the great day is nearly over . . .' mocks the Prisoner. '. . . Came off rather well I thought. Better than planned. And now you can look forward to your own retirement and I'm sure they'll arrange something equally suitable for you, when the day comes.' Seething, the new Number 2 is unable to do anything as, patting the man on the shoulder, the Prisoner quips 'Be seeing you . . . Won't I?' and strides from the balcony.

'Went off rather well I thought. Better than planned'

A Change of Mind

Written by Roger Parkes

Guest stars

Number 86	**Angela Browne**
Number 2	**John Sharpe**

with

The Butler	**Angelo Muscat**
Doctor	**George Pravda**
Number 42	**Kathleen Breck**
Supervisor	**Peter Swanwick**
Lobo Man	**Thomas Heathcote**
Committee Chairman	**Bartlett Mullins**

and

Number 93	**Michael Miller**
1st Member of Social Group	**Joseph Cuby**
2nd Member of Social Group	**Michael Chow**
Number 48	**June Ellis**
1st Woodland Man	**John Hamblin**
2nd Woodland Man	**Michael Billington**

Directed by: Joseph Serf (alias Patrick McGoohan)

WORKING OUT ON his home made high-bar gymnasium apparatus in the woods, Number 6 finishes his exercise with a rope swing and a few well-placed blows to his punch-bag. He instantly becomes aware that his fitness routine is being monitored by two thugs. 'Training for the big break?' asks the first man, entering the clearing. 'Why not use the Village gymnasium?' probes the second, joining his accomplice. 'Perhaps I prefer privacy,' quips the athlete, his senses alert for trouble. His reply provokes a fight. Using his home-made equipment to good advantage, the Prisoner

Nunber 6 lays out the opposition

soundly thrashes the men. Racing away, the taller of the two thugs swears to have Number 6 brought before the committee. Later that day, while waiting in the council chamber ante-room for their cases to be heard, Number 6 joins other miscreants and listens as a tape recording piped in from the chamber below informs those gathered that: The council chamber has considered Number 93's case, but already there are signs of disharmony in his behaviour: he appears to be a reasonable man, but there is plenty of evidence showing his unwillingness to work for the community. There are several cases waiting to be dealt with: Number 6 is seriously in need of help, and they want to do something for Number 42, who appears to be in a permanent state of depression: she is always in tears. It is Number 93's clear duty to prove that he is once again a suitable member of society. The only way he can achieve this and regain the respect of his fellows is to publicly acknowledge his shortcomings. He must go to the rostrum and confess. They will tell him what to say. In the space of a second, Number 93 enters through the door leading to the chamber below. He mounts the rostrum at the rear of the ante-room and, repeating verbatim what a voice on the public-address system tells him, the man tells the gathering that he is in turn: inadequate, disharmonious, and truly grateful, believe me . . . believe me . . . The authoritative voice over the public-address system, continues to echo the word until, sobbing now, Number 93 leaves the rostrum and marches from the chamber to the hearty applause of those gathered in the room. 'Number 6 enter,' pipes the voice. Entering the council chamber, a vast circular auditorium containing a semicircle of tables behind which sit the committee members, the Prisoner descends the elongated ramp to the arena below. As the mute Butler wheels away a control console which records the court's proceedings, Number 6 sidles through the opening. To applause from his companions, the Committee Chairman, a bespectacled man, dressed in a striped vest and top hat, opens the proceedings. 'I take it you have completed the written questionnaire of confession?' he asks. 'Of course,' mocks the Prisoner, tearing the document he carries into shreds. 'Naturally!' 'Please do not be hostile to the committee. We are here to help you,' says a bodyless voice, as the accused sits scornfully in the chair provided for him, scattering the torn pieces of the questionaire to the floor. 'I take it you've checked my file . . . regarding hostility?' he quips with an air of indifference. 'Your files are no concern of ours,' drones the voice. 'Any information about *you* is with Number 2.' 'Really,' replies the accused, twiddling his thumbs as the chair he occupies begins to rise and rotate. 'It is the duty of this committee to deal with complaints,' says the chairman. 'Complaints!' snaps Number 6, rotating rapidly in his chair. 'Well done, I have several.' The voice from the console drones on. 'You realise a serious charge has been levelled at you, particularly regarding your attitude towards your fellow citizens . . . we deplore your spirit of disharmony.' 'That's a *common* complaint around here, isn't it,' grins Number 6, as the chairman counsels him to be discreet. 'You do appreciate that everything you say is being recorded . . .' challenges the voice. '. . . and may be used as evidence against me . . .' mocks the Prisoner. 'This is a strictly impartial committee . . .' says the voice, interrupted by the chairman who informs Number 6 that he has not been called before them to defend himself. '. . . All we ask,' continues the voice, 'is for your complete confession.' Advising the accused to cooperate, the bespectacled man informs the others that it is time they all had a tea break: the accused man's group and medical records will be considered in full at the resumed hearing of the committee. Applauding Number 6, the committee leaves the chamber and the accused man does likewise. As the doors leading to the chamber slide shut behind them, the Butler reappears to push away a section of the circular tables to allow the Prisoner to exit. Passing through the ante-room above, Number 6 pauses for a moment at the confessional rostrum where, hearing a re-run of Number 93's confession, he salutes his fellow miscreants and marches from the room, applauding as he goes. While returning to his cottage, the Villagers show their hostility by avoiding him and refusing to acknowledge his salute. The *Tally Ho* newspaper magically carries the hot-off-the-press headline: 'The Committee Hearing Continues: Number 93 confesses disharmony and Number 6 awaits further investigation'! Entering his cottage, the ostracised man crumples up the newspaper and flings it into the hearth. Number 2 waits for him. 'There is a saying, the slowest mule is nearest to the whip,' greets the elder. Countering with one of his

A jovial, but devious Number 2

own – he who digs a pit will one day lie in it, the Prisoner presumes that his guest is above investigation? '*Nobody* is above investigation,' retorts the other, adding that failure to cooperate makes one an outcast. 'What? No more taxis. No more credit?' quips Number 6. 'Believe me, it could be only a beginning,' suggests Number 2, placing a biscuit to his lips. 'You should know,' the Prisoner replies, preparing to brew himself a drink. 'I hope that you do not think that *I* am a member of the committee?' questions the superior. 'Oh no, of course no – never.' 'I assure you,' smiles

Number 2, 'no matter what significance you may hold for me, to the Village and its committee, you are merely a citizen Number 6, who has to be tolerated – and if necessary shaped to fit.' 'Public Enemy Number 6,' mocks the Prisoner. 'If you insist. But public enemies cannot be tolerated *indefinitely*. Be careful. Do not defy this committee. If the hearings go against you, *I* am powerless to help,' sneers Number 2. The other is about to reply, when a beautiful blonde girl enters the cottage. Greeted by the Superior as Number 86, it appears that she has had valuable experience of the committee. 'As a member?' asks the Prisoner. 'I suffered the shame of being posted. Disharmonious,' the girl replies. 'How terrible for you,' grins Number 6. 'The hearings were fair and just. *I* was at fault,' she replies turning to Number 2. 'Oh but this is irrelevant. With your permission sir, Number 6 has a busy schedule. First the social group, then the medical.' 'Of course,' replies the elder, placing another biscuit into his mouth. 'Do carry on.' 'No time for tea?'quips the Prisoner playfully. 'No. Only your future,' confirms Number 2. Stating that the man's attitute towards the committee is both frivolous and dangerous, the girl informs him that the hearings are televised. That is why his behaviour is so important. 'You stand before the entire community. The social group is your one hope. Fortunately I, too, have been attached to the Group.' 'Most fortunate, yes,' quips Number 6, pouring the girl a cup of tea. 'Oh please, you must try to cooperate . . .' He confirms that he will. '. . . Join in with the Group's spirit.' 'Naturally.' 'Only they can help you with the committee.' 'Naturally.' Frustrated now, the girl looks at her wristwatch. Indicating that they are already overdue, she ignores the man's offer of tea, and bundles him through the door. Watching this with his Supervisor on his monitor screen, Number 2 remarks 'Females! If that woman makes one mistake we could lose Number 6. D'you hear that. Lose him!'

Determined to show her pupil community life, Number 86 leads the Prisoner into the Village to where, gathered in a group, a bunch of citizens are discussing ways of curing Number 42 of her depression. Stating that there can be no mitigation, they all have a social obligation to stand together, the senior member of the group shouts down a second member who, though not contesting the validity of her claim nevertheless feels that . . . 'No exceptions,' says the senior. 'All right, so you say you're a poet. You were composing when you failed to hear Number 10's greeting.' 'Neglect of a social principle,' cries another. 'Poetry has social value,' pipes up the Prisoner. 'He's trying to divide us,' claims the senior member. 'His intentions are obvious,' says Number 86. 'To stop us from helping this unfortunate girl.' 'You're trying to undermine my rehabilitation, disrupt my social progress . . .' claims the girl. 'Strange talk for a poet,' says Number 6. 'Rebel. Disharmonious. Rebel' cry the group. 'Reactionary!' Scornful of the group's attempts to reinstate Number 42 into society, the Prisoner breaks up the debate, elbows his way past the group and heads for the woods – ignoring Number 86 as he goes. But he does not get far. Three white-coated medical men wait for him, and he is driven to the hospital for his medical. 'First rate, Number 6,' says a doctor unstrapping a blood pressure sleeve from the patient's arm. 'Life here suits you.' 'Finished?' throws back Number 6, rolling his sleeve to his wrist. 'Just your patelia reflexes,' replies the medical man, tapping the Prisoner's knees in turn. 'Excellent. Fit for any contingency.' 'Anything specific in mind?' asks the patient donning his blazer. 'How suspicious you are of us all,' grins the doctor, bidding the patient a cheery 'Be seeing you'. Outside in the corridor, the Prisoner's attention is drawn to a door marked 'Aversion Therapy.' Peering through its observation glass, he sees a drugged man strapped to a chair. Before him sits a television screen on which are projected images of a Rover which appears to be bouncing towards him, an image that is intercut with shots of Number 2's face and the word 'unmutual'. Time and again the word flashes onto the screen as the fraught man attempts to break his bonds. Concerned by what he sees, Number 6 attempts to enter the room. The door is locked. Behind him in the corridor, another patient calls for him to be calm. 'Are you his keeper?' the Prisoner challenges, crossing to the man's side. 'So excited all of you. Rushing and shouting,' the patient replies, his glassy stare showing that he is not quite at peace with his surroundings. 'Have *you* been in there?' 'Not in *there*,' replies the patient, staring at the therapy room door. 'That's odd.' 'Not odd, please . . .' stammers the deranged man, stroking a scar on his forehead, '. . . *different* maybe.' 'Different?' The patient gives a weak smile. 'I'm one of the lucky ones . . . the happy ones . . . I was . . .' 'Yes?' 'I was unmutual,' replies the 'cured' man.

In a darkened council chamber, the Chairman submits his report to an apparently unconcerned Number 6. Submitted by the social group, the report leaves the Chairman no choice but to classify the accused as unmutual! He is warned that if any further complaint is lodged against him, it will be necessary to propose him for the treatment known as Instant Social Conversion. As the sentence is passed, the chair upon which the Prisoner sits grinds to a halt, the chamber is flooded with light and Number 6 finds himself staring into the face of the Butler. The committee have vanished! Number 6 and the po-faced servant are alone. Rising from his seat, the Prisoner storms out of the room. Outside he passes a poster bearing the legend 'Your Community Needs You', its image of Number 2 mocking his progress. The streets outside are void of life, not a citizen to be seen. The *Tally Ho* newspaper headline carries a report of the committee's declaration, and the Village Voice rings out over the public address system: 'Your attention please, here is an important announcement. Number 6 has been declared Unmutual until further notice. Any unsocial incident involving Number 6 should be reported immediately to the appeals sub committee. Thank you for your attention.' Arriving at the cottage denoted '6 – Private', he lifts the telephone receiver. The line is dead. Within seconds of his arrival, a group of female villagers arrive at his door, led by Number 42. They represent the appeals sub committee and wish to help him. He refuses their help and they leave, a spokeswoman advising her colleagues that their offer is premature. Monitoring all this from the control room, Number 2 grins and tells his Supervisor that they will shortly be able to see how the loner withstands real loneliness – although he hopes, for the Prisoner's sake, that it will not take too long for the man to reach his senses. They continue to monitor the subject's progress as he walks alone through the woods, his eyes staring skywards as a flock of geese fly overhead, taking an avenue of escape that is beyond his reach.

The following morning finds Number 6 ordering coffee at a table in the cafe. His request is ignored. The other customers rise as one from their seats and walk to the sidewalk, their presence there forcing him to return to his cottage. Inside he is greeted by the female sub committee who tell him it is no longer a game. Number 42 informs him that they are socially conscious citizens and are provoked by the loathsome presence of an unmutual. 'They are sheep!' he throws back, leading the spokeswoman to declare that if he insists on rejecting their offer of help, so be it, there remains but one course open to them. The door to the cottage swings open and the women leave, at which point his telephone purrs into life. It is Number 2. 'I warned you. The community will not tolerate you indefinitely,' confirms the superior. 'You need a scapegoat ... Citizens unite to denounce this menace in our presence,' challenges Number 6. 'A scapegoat. Is that what you think it is? Allow me to reassure you that after conversion, you won't care what it is ... you just won't *care*,' states the elder. 'Oh yes,' jests Number 6, 'The ordeal of social conversion.' 'You'll soon have lasting peace of mind and adjustment to the social system here,' explains Number 2. 'Drugs?' 'Would *drugs* be lasting?' asks the other, suggesting that the only available treatment for one such as Number 6 is the isolation of the Prisoner's aggressive, frontal lobes of the brain! The line goes dead. The tenant's in-house speaker-system carries a message to all staff psychologists and psychiatrists, stating that those wishing to study the conversion of Number 6 on the hospital's closed-circuit television should report immediately to the hospital common room! Retreating outside, the Prisoner finds himself confronted by hoards of angry citizens. Led by the social sub committee's spokeswoman and Number 42, they begin to attack him with their umbrellas. Thrown to the ground, Number 6 finds himself man-handled into the hospital's theatre. Through a dazed stupor, he sees an injection administered into his arm by a doctor, and feels himself being wheeled into an operating theatre on a stretcher. Secured to a table, he struggles as an ultrasonic device is lowered over his head, and muff-like attachments are placed over his ears. Outside in the common room, the Chairman and his committee take their seats in front of the closed-circuit television, its cameras focused on Number 86 who, dressed in an operating smock, is describing the step-by-step conversion process. They are using standard equipment. The unit suspended over the patient's head contains a quartz crystal, which is activated by a variable electro-magnetic field, governed by two high-voltage condensers. The crystal emits ultrasonic sound waves, which are then bounced off a parabolic reflector. The focal point of the reflector can be seen by the use of light waves. Number 86 demonstrates the molecular turbulence by burning a hole in a block of white-coloured material. Throughout the demonstration, unable to move a limb, the Prisoner blinks his eyes, alarmed by what may lie ahead. As the girl continues to describe the operating procedure, the committee members shuffle in their seats, craning their heads forward to obtain a better view. The prime concern, states Number 86, is to locate the link point of the frontal lobes. To achieve this, the machine will be changed to a low voltage rating and the surgeons will feel the focal point. A circular white dot appears on the patient's forehead, a few centimeters above his right eyebrow. Controlling the light, the girl moves the beam four centimeters to the right, then point two-three-zero centimeters down and the position is held, the ultrasonic beam focussed now on the exact link point they require.

'The crystal is activated by a variable electro-magnetic field'

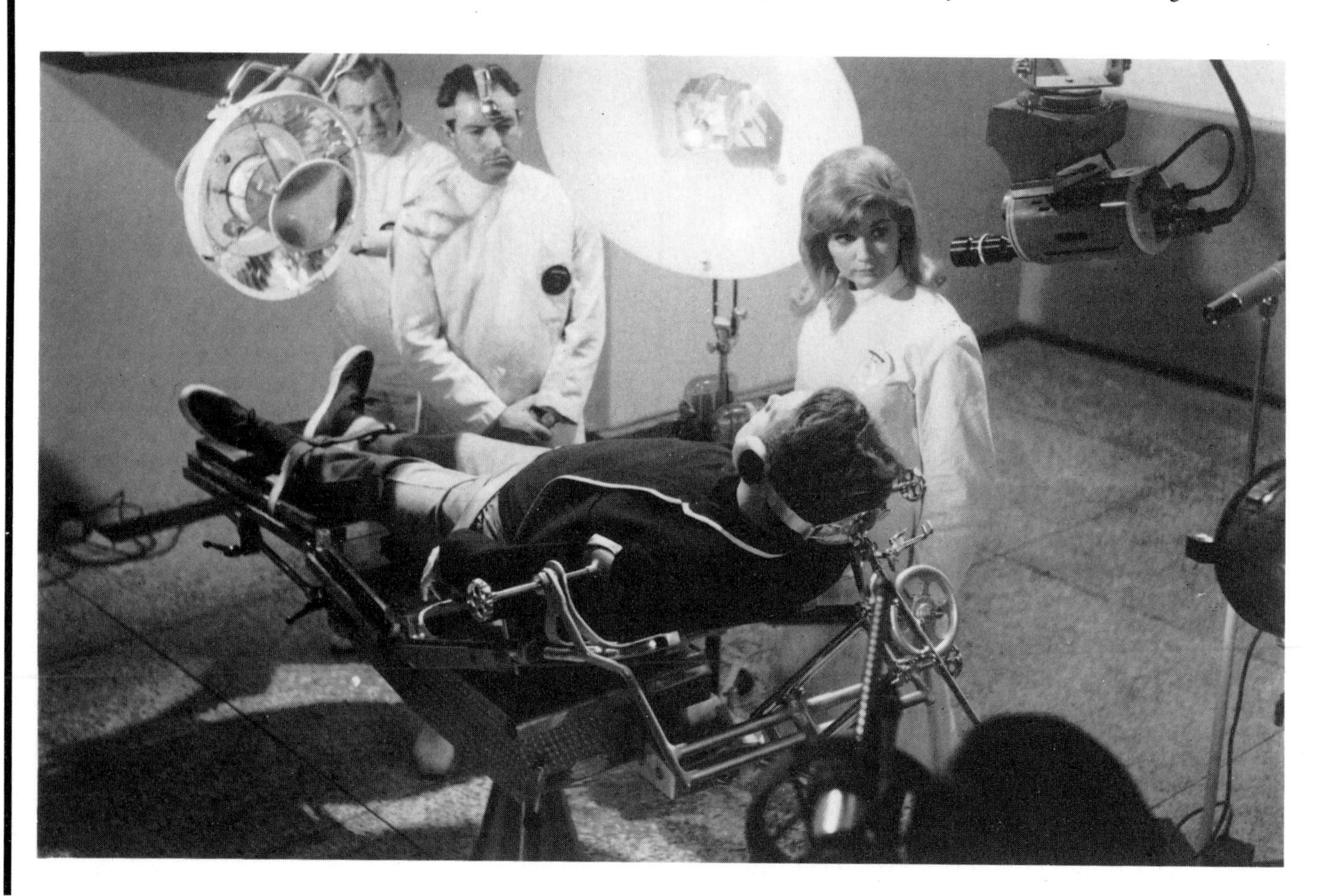

Moving close to the patient's head, the girl applies a lanolin barrier to the spot she has selected: this will minimise external cell breakdown and subsequent scar tissue. The patient is then injected with a relaxant to preclude muscular reaction. The patient is now ready, the voltage being stepped up until the ultrasonic bombardment causes permanent dislocation. The machine purrs into a higher frequency, and the patient's lips contract into a grotesque grin.

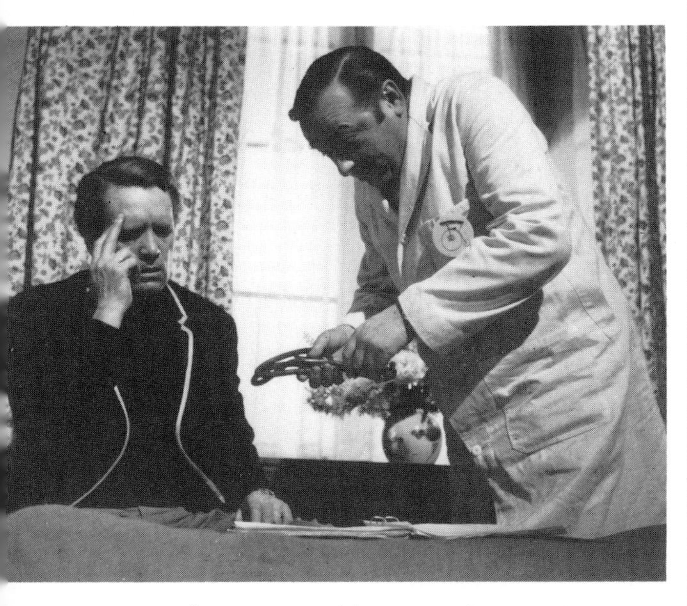

'If I were you I'd keep it on for a couple of days'

Number 6 wakes up in a hospital bed. 'You went to sleep Number 6. Just at the most interesting point you went to sleep,' a doctor relates. Warned against any physical exertion, the patient grins as he discovers the plaster above his right eyebrow – a dressing he is advised to keep in place for a couple of days – to remind himself to take things easy. From the far side of the hospital ward, Number 86 promises the doctor that she will take good care of him. Together they leave, he stopping for a moment to catch up on the progress of the patient being subjected to the aversion treatment, she beckoning him outside. A group of villagers race forward to greet them, delighted that the 'loner' is cured. Throughout their drive back to his cottage, citizens line the streets, each acknowledging their joy at his return to the community. Indoors they are greeted by Number 2, who welcomes the lamb back to the fold and suggests that the girl makes Number 6 a soothing cup of tea – a celebration drink. Saying that he will see them later, he leaves as Number 86 leads her charge to a couch: he looks tired after his ordeal and she wishes him to relax. With lowered eyelids, the Prisoner spots the girl slip a pill into his tea cup. Handed this, he avoids sipping its contents by pretending to need a blanket. 'Cold,' he suggests, in a childlike whimper. 'Cold?' says the girl. 'Rug . . . bedroom . . . rug.' 'Rug?' 'Rug! Wardrobe.' Disturbed by his request, Number 86 crosses into the bedroom. Alone, he pours the contents of his cup into a nearby flower vase. Returning with a blanket, she covers the man and removes the empty cup from his hand. Believing that the drug has taken effect, she strokes his brow. 'Rest well,' she remarks heading for the door. 'Be seeing you,' he quips to the retreating figure. The door has barely closed behind her, when Number 2 snaps his fingers in front of the sleeping man's eyes. 'It's time for our talk Number 6,' says the elder. 'Our talk?' the Prisoner replies, his eyes flickering open.'Oh yes, now that all your aggressive anxieties have been expunged – let us say forever, I know that you'll feel free to speak.' 'Feel free to speak,' repeats the other. 'Yes, particularly about that little incident which has been causing you such absurd distress,' coaxes Number 2. Through half-closed eyes, his lips drawn back in a grimace of drug-induced stupor, the Prisoner mutters some unintelligible comments. The elder continues, 'The trivia . . . the trivia of your *res-ig-nation* . . .' The Prisoner stirs. '. . . Yes . . . you resigned. But why? . . . why prematurely . . . Why-did-you-resign?' 'It's difficult,' stammers Number 6, indicating that he needs time to think. 'Oh time, that was it was it?' urges Number 2. 'No, it wasn't *time*,' says the other. 'You couldn't stand your job . . . you needed time to think.' 'No! No!' 'I'm asking you, not telling you,' hisses Number 2, anxious to calm the one being interrogated. 'Please don't be angry,' smiles the other weakly. 'I'm not angry my dear friend. That is just the way things seem to be to you . . .' whispers the superior. '. . . Because your new world is so quiet by contrast . . .' 'Is it?' '. . . for you agitation is a thing of the past. Lay back and rest, lay back and rest,' smiles Number 2, rising and heading for the door. 'We can have our little chat later on . . . when you've had time to collect your thoughts.' Alone now, the Prisoner rises from his couch and walks into the bathroom. Standing in front of a mirror, he peels off the plaster, gently rubs the scar with his fingertips and replaces the dressing. Joined in the Control Room by Number 2, the girl denoted Number 86 watches the Prisoner's actions with interest. 'Strange. Very strange,' she comments. 'What is?' asks the superior. 'Already he suspects.' 'The scar at any rate is genuine. He'll learn nothing from that,' observes Number 2. 'No, but he suspects already. I gave him 8 grains of Mytol,' confirms the girl, explaining that the drug should preclude all such reactions. 'He's still very confused,' the elder points out, observing Number 6 slam down his fist on the kitchen divider. 'He's shocked, as I anticipated,' says Number 86. 'Well he's seen what he *thought* was the operation. He should be convinced . . .' Commenting that there is really no reason for Number 6 to suspect that the operation never really took place, the girl is astounded when Number 2 orders her to go back to the man's cottage and repeat the dose. 'Now? But 16 grains of Mytol is quite impossible!' Drawing her attention to the man being observed, who is now racing around his kitchen pounding the units with his fist, Number 2 points out that the patient is already beginning to show aggression and suspicion; they cannot afford a relapse. 'Yes, but this drug . . .' 'The man is as strong as a bull. You simply *must* step up the injection!' exclaims the other.

To the accompaniment of the Prisoner's nervous finger-tapping, a tattoo played out on a table top, the girl brews Number 6 a cup of tea – drugged of course. 'You still have some impatience, impulsiveness,' she says placing the drink before him. 'Do you like my dress?' 'More feminine than slacks,' he replies. 'One thing though, he adds rising to carry the cup and saucer to the kitchen sink, I cannot stand girls who don't know how to make a decent cup of tea.' Emptying the teapot, he then demonstrates the correct procedure: warm the pot, one scoop of tea for himself, one for his guest, one for the pot – and an extra one for luck. Add boiling water, allow the pot to stand for a moment and . . . He turns back to the girl, asking her to pour the milk. While she is doing so, he collects a second cup and saucer, instantly aware that the girl has dropped a pill into his own – a cup he exchanges for hers while the girl's back is turned. 'All charming and domestic,' Number 2 tells the Supervisor and his mute servant, suggesting to the latter that he, too, would enjoy some tea. 'Excellent my dear,' he continues as the couple being observed lift their tea cups to their lips. 'Just leave him . . . leave him to *me*.' By now, the girl has fallen victim to her own drug. Observing this on his television monitor screen, an angry Number 2 leaps to his feet. 'Stupid woman!' he cries, crossing to the console to relay a message to the girl that she is to report to him immediately. 'Stupid woman,' he repeats to the Supervisor, 'she'll ruin everything!' 'Be seeing you,' calls Number 6 as the girl leaves his cottage. Aware that Number 6 is about to take his daily stroll, the elder's attitude mellows. 'Why not. Let him go out, feel free. He'll sift it out if he has doubts. A little outside contact will soon reassure him.' Outside, the Prisoner meets the man with the scarred forehead who he spoke to earlier – the unmutual who was 'saved' by social conversion. Asked by Number 6 if he feels different, the man breaks into laughter. 'You should know,' he says, indicating the sticking-plaster on the Prisoner's forehead. 'I should?' queries a bemused Number 6. 'Who better? See you soon,' grins the imbecile, laughing as he walks away.

At his woodland gym, Number 6 wrestles with his changed personality. The exercise apparatus looks familiar but he appears to lack the know-how to put them to their intended use. The sound of a twig snapping underfoot heralds the return of the thugs he met earlier. 'Back here again,' says the first man. 'But not so sure of himself now,' quips the other. 'Not so much punch in him this time,' grins the first man. 'We have some unfinished business,' confirms his companion, baiting the man. The taller of the two calls Number 6 a social convert, while the other sends the Prisoner reeling backwards by swinging his home-made punchbag into his face. Suddenly, both thugs begin to throw punches to the Prisoner's jaw. 'Remember?' grins the tall one, sending his fist into the bemused man's face. The jolt to his senses does the trick. Springing upwards to the high-bar, Number 6 reverts to his acrobatic self. Casting the men aside in a flurry of flying feet and well-timed punches the contest is over within minutes and the thugs are nursing their bruised egos.

Returning to the Village, the Prisoner meets Number 86. Still drugged, she is picking flowers to take to Number 2. 'Having a funeral?' quips Number 6. 'I have to report . . .' grins the girl. 'On plant life?' '. . . To Number 2. I want to make him happy.' 'The ecstasy of illusion,' mocks the Prisoner. 'I'm higher . . .' she begins. 'Are you?' he teases. '. . . Higher than Number 2.' 'Are you?' She insists that she has to report. 'Go on then, report,' he says. In the Control Room, her superior orders the Supervisor to put out a general call for the girl. Hearing the order over the Village loudspeaker system, Number 6 hits on an idea. With the girl under the influence of drugs meant for him, he hypnotises her into accepting that he is her superior. At his command, she then makes a full report on his social conversion. Told by the girl that the ultrasonic device was just a prop, and that the tranquilisers he was given were fakes and the illusion is being maintained by keeping the patient heavily tranquilised, he gives the girl her final instructions. 'Listen carefully, this is what I want you to do. When the Village clock strikes four . . .'

Number 2 receives a welcome guest. It is Number 6 who, confessing that he feels much happier, wishes to have a little chat. 'Why yes,' grins Number 2. 'Clearer in your mind now?' 'Oh much clearer, and happier. I want you to know that . . . such peace of mind,' teases Number 6. 'Well of course, only to be expected,' confirms the other. 'And I resisted, to think that I resisted for so long . . .' 'Understandable. A man of your training, but now you er . . . ' invites Number 2. 'Yes, everything's clear cut now. Quite simple,' says Number 6, telling the other what he wishes to hear. 'Quite so. No more problems eh . . . and now at last we can have our little chat.' 'Yes I hope so. But . . .' 'But?' challenges the elder. Number 6 asks if he can tell everyone how grateful he is for his treatment: such a confession might inspire others to speak out also. Pleased with himself and seeing victory within his reach, Number 2 issues a radio announcement that, following his successful conversion, Number 6 has expressed his touching desire to address the community in person. All those that are not otherwise occupied, should report immediately to the Village square. Turning to his guest, he tells Number 6 a proverb. 'He who ploughs a straight furrow needs owe for nothing.'

The Villagers arrive in droves, all applauding loudly as Number 6 begins his speech from the Town Hall balcony. 'Citizens,' begins the 'cured' man, 'you're cheering me, but that is a mistake. It is Number 2 you should applaud.' The superior can hardly restrain his excitement. 'Until he brought about my social conversion . . .' continues Number 6, '. . . and believe me, it was *him* and not your committee, until then I was a rebel – an unmutual.

senselessly resisting this, our fine community.' An ecstatic Number 2 leads the applause. 'To borrow one of Number 2's sayings,' the speaker continues, 'the butcher with the sharpest knife has the warmest heart.' A murmer of discontent runs through the crowd. Smiling in the elder's direction, Number 6 carries on. 'Some of *you* have resisted in the past – have withheld *knowledge* that was important to Number 2. Now, thanks to social conversion, I want to tell you all something, and I trust that my example will inspire you all to tell ... to tell ...' Stopping in mid-sentence as the Village clock strikes four, the speaker glances at Number 2 and smiles as Number 86 steps forward to declare that Number 2 is unmutual. 'Social conversion for Number 2,' she yells, as Number 6 takes up her cause. 'Number 86 has a confession that Number 2 is unmutual – an unmutual who desires to deceive you all!' he shouts. The elder can hardly believe his ears, as, led by Number 86, the crowd takes up the chant and the 'convert' standing beside him accuses him of being a tool of those who wish to possess their minds. A look of failure crossing his face, the elder races from the balcony, the Prisoner's words that the community should reject the superior's false world echoing in his ears as, attempting to fight his way through the angry villagers, he finds himself jostled and pushed. Chanting for his blood, the crowd race after the fleeing figure, leaving behind the Butler who, following alone, raises his black and white striped parasol aloft to block out the sun's rays.

'There's something I have to show you. Very important – Number 2's orders'

A. B. AND C

Written by Anthony Skene

Guest stars

Engadine	**Katherine Kath**
Number 14	**Sheila Allen**
Number 2	**Colin Gordon**
'A'	**Peter Bowles**

with

The Butler	**Angelo Muscat**
Blonde Lady	**Georgina Cookson**
'B'	**Annette Carel**
Flower Girl	**Lucille Soong**

and

Maid at Party	**Bettine Le Beau**
Thug	**Terry Yorke**
Thug	**Peter Brayham**
Henchman	**Bill Cummings**

Directed by Pat Jackson

HIS HANDS clasped tightly behind his back, Number 2 paces backwards and forwards across the vast expanse of his Green Dome control room. Without warning, the large red cordless telephone dominating his control console purrs into life, its high-pitched hum bringing a look of concern to the elder's face. Crossing to the instrument, he tentatively lifts the receiver to his ear. 'Number 2 here. Yes sir. I am doing my best. He's very difficult. I know it's important sir ...' Sighing, he swallows, determined that the unseen caller should be made aware of the difficulties. 'He's no ordinary person sir, but if I had a free hand ...' Pausing in mid-sentence, he listens to the other's opinion. '... I know sir yes, I'm not indispensable.' Lowering the receiver, his head drops in abject despair. Pouring himself a glass of milk, he ponders the caller's words. Then, with resolve, he lifts a second telephone and asks to be connected with Number 14. 'Number 14? The experiment must come forward!' he snaps. A woman's voice is heard to reply that that is not possible, she will require at least a week's preparation. 'I haven't got a week!' barks Number 2, as the voice informs him that she has not even finished testing it on animals, let alone people. 'Then now's your chance,' snaps Number 2 impatiently. 'When?' asks the voice. 'Tonight!'

As darkness falls over the Village, lightning accompanied by rolls of thunder and a deluge of rain heralds the arrival of two men in oilskins to a laboratory corridor. A third figure wrapped in a black plastic shroud, lies unconscious on the stretcher-trolley which the men wheel into the building. As the metal door they entered through glides to a close behind them, a woman dressed in a white surgical smock orders them to stop. 'Don't bring that wet in here, take your macs and boots off,' she yells. Having done so, the men wheel the man on the trolley down a ramp and into a chamber – a laboratory occupied by Numbers 2 and 14, the woman who called to them. Having unwrapped the body, the two men lift the intended victim onto an examination couch. The patient is Number 6. Their work done, the men leave. Number 2 reminds Number 14 that, for her own sake, her brainchild had better work; if the

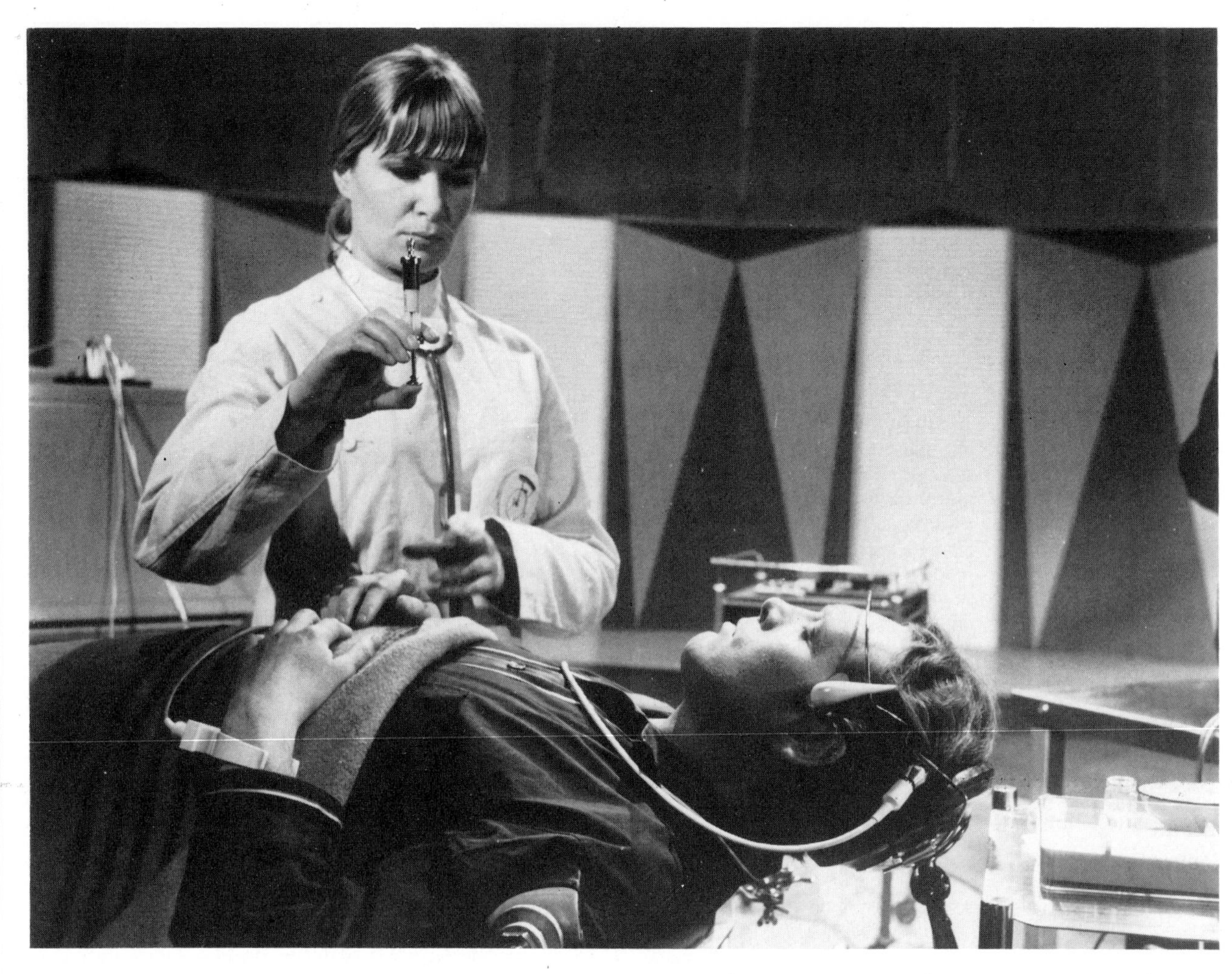

Number 14 prepares to administer injection number one

patient is damaged she will be held responsible. He looks on as the girl, an attractive blonde, attaches plastic bracelets to the patient's wrists and electrodes to his head. 'You know I haven't had the time to prove the drug,' she throws back. 'Just get it *right*, or I'll see that it's proved on you,' threatens Number 2, as the girl attaches wires leading from the electrodes on the patient's head to a monitor machine, which immediately begins to display the drugged man's brain patterns. 'What's all that about?' questions Number 2 staring at the monitor screen. 'Energy from his brain,' answers Number 14. 'Thoughts, like sound waves converted into electrical impulses and finally . . .' crossing to a tuning console, she tweaks a control, '. . . into pictures.' 'Extraordinary,' comments Number 2 as the patient's sub-conscious thoughts are converted into pictures and a television screen displays images of the one known as Number 6 handing in his resignation. 'How very single-minded,' comments Number 2, witnessing the event for the first time as the dreamer conjures up the sequence time and again. 'He's not conventional,' says Number 14. 'I sometimes think he's not human,' states the other. 'It's an anguish pattern,' sighs the girl, crossing to select an hypodermic syringe from a plastic container containing three injection cartridges marked 1, 2 and 3 respectively. Each is filled with a pinky-brown liquid. 'So this is your wonder drug,' the elder remarks. 'Yes,' she confirms, dabbing the tip of the syringe she has selected with a wad of cotton wool. 'Three doses . . . and that's the absolute limit.' 'Why?' the superior demands. 'Three is dangerous enough. Four would kill him.' Crossing to Number 6, she swabs the patient's right wrist and prepares to administer the injection. Subconsiously, Number 6 raises his eyelids, but with a gentle stroke of her hand she closes his lids. Injected with the drug, the patient slips further into drowsiness. 'His mind is now yours,' the girl instructs. 'What do you want from it?' 'Why he resigned,' replies Number 2. 'I believe he was going to sell out. I want to know what he had to sell and to whom he was going to sell it. We've researched and computed his whole life and it boils down to three people . . . A, B, and C.' Crossing to three red-coloured box files perched on top of a filing cabinet, each of which bears the label 'a', 'b', or 'c', he taps each one in turn, as he informs his junior that the patient must meet each one of them. This way they will learn what *would* have happened had they not got to him first. 'Where do you want them to meet?' asks Number 14. 'Paris,' replies the superior. 'They all had one thing in common. They all attended Madame Engadine's celebrated parties. Here's some film of the most recent.' He hands the girl a film cassette. Placing the film spool into its slot on the master console, Number 14 presses a button. Almost instantly the television monitor displays film of the garden of a luxurious French chateau. People in evening dress enter and exit from the house. 'Ah, nothing like a good party,' smiles the girl. 'I'm sure he'll welcome the change of environment.' Frowning at this remark and anxious for the experiment to proceed, Number 2 orders the junior to begin. 'Go on, feed it into him.' As bidden, Number 14 crosses to the console and trails a long electric lead feeding from the film cassette holder to the recumbent figure on the operating couch. Contacts are snapped tightly around the patient's wrists and a jack-plug attached to the lead is slotted into a device on the Prisoner's head. As she turns to rejoin her superior, Number 6 utters a single cry. Swinging back in alarm, the woman checks his heartbeat with a stethoscope. 'Is he all right?' calls a concerned Number 2. 'So far,' she answers, staring at the patient, as she turns a knob on the console a half-circle. The moment of truth has arrived.

Mentally transported to Paris, Number 6, now dressed in a tuxedo and black bow-tie, meets his hostess Engadine, a middle-aged, vivacious lady. 'You look tired darling,' greets the woman. 'Things are bad?' 'No, not now,' replies Number 6, explaining that he has started his holiday. 'The *English* holiday,' she jokes, 'Big boots and fishing sticks.' 'Not quite like that. Somewhere different. Somewhere quiet, where I can think,' he replies. Engadine laughs. 'There is no quiet anywhere.' She apologises that she has to mingle. However, before doing so, she cannot resist reminding her guest that he 'belongs' to her. 'Be horrible to other women,' she teases as, blowing him a kiss, she departs to rejoin her guests. 'Of course, yes,' smiles Number 6. 'I think it's time we introduced "A"', Number 2 decides, opening the box file labelled 'a', which contains a photograph of a suave-looking man with a moustache. Beneath a clip lies another can of film which, handed to Number 14, is attached to its relevant slot on her equipment. 'His face looks vaguely familiar,' she comments as the man's face fills the monitor screen. 'What's his real name?' 'I'm surprised you don't remember him. He made world news a few years ago,' confirms Number 2. With the flick of a switch, they watch as the man denoted 'A' sidles over to Number 6. 'I'm surprised,' greets Number 6. 'Not unpleasantly I trust,' says the newcomer, handing his fellow guest a glass of champagne. 'I knew you came to these parties . . .' begins Number 6. 'And wondered why we'd never met?' answers 'A', suggesting that Engadine has tactfully kept them apart. 'Until tonight,' grins Number 6. 'Perhaps tonight is

'I hope you're happy with your new life'

special,' suggests 'A'. 'I feel it is special too,' smiles the other. 'To us,' returns 'A', raising his glass. 'As we are, or as we were?' quips Number 6. 'Oh I remember him,' recalls Number 14 watching the scene. 'He defected about 6 years ago.' 'It's been a long time,' the defector confirms, continuing his conversation with Number 6. 'Not long enough!' quips the other. 'We used to be friends.' 'Once,' comes the short reply, 'but that's in the past.' 'Then let's think of the future,' tries 'A'. 'We're still the same people.' 'Working for different sides,' snaps Number 6, acknowledging a greeting from a fellow guest with a nod. 'Sides don't matter, only success.' 'In that case, we should still have a great deal in common,' counters the other. 'We do the same jobs.' 'For different reasons,' reminds Number 6. 'I see you still overrate absolute truth,' condemns 'A'. 'Whatever way you look at it, we both want to conquer the world. I hope you're happy with your new life?' 'New life?' enquires the other, leaning forward to catch the other man's words. 'Well news of old friends travels quickly.' 'In a few hours.' 'To you and to me, news is like air. We breathe it deeply, draw it from far and wide.' 'If it's interesting,' smiles Number 6. 'What are you going to do with your freedom?' quizzes the other. 'Go fishing,' replies Number 6. 'Perhaps you're fishing now? What's your price?' 'What am I selling?' grins Number 6. 'I'm anxious to find out,' whispers 'A', broaching the subject of a deal being struck. 'Madame's wine is always excellent,' mocks the other ignoring the remark. 'If you haven't got a price, you must have a reason,' prompts the other. He receives no reply. Tiring of the game, Number 6 moves away. 'They're not always the same thing. Excuse me.' 'He's going!' exclaims a deflated Number 2 from his laboratory observation point. 'And we haven't found out if he . . . He must not *go*!' 'He's only doing what he *would* have done. I can only create the situation,' explains Number 14 watching the screen as Number 6 is handed his topcoat by a footman. 'Get him *back!*' demands Number 2. 'It's his *dream*,' the girl replies helplessly. 'It must take its course.' Back at the party, it comes as no surprise to Number 6 that, as the footman swings back the door to allow him to leave, 'A' is waiting for him, also dressed in his topcoat. 'You never could take a hint,' he tells his determined ex-colleague. 'I don't want a hint. I want *you*,' mocks "A".' With a snap of his fingers, the defector signals for his colleague, the previously benign footman, who grabs the Prisoner's arms and Number 6 is led away. 'I'm saving myself money,' quips the kidnapper as Number 6 is shoved into the back seat of his car, between 'A' and his henchman. Driven away at speed, the vehicle soars down the Champs-Elysées, cutting its way through the traffic like a knife. 'Paris hasn't changed much, has it . . .' comments Number 6. 'Where are they going?' asks a concerned and puzzled Number 2. 'I don't know,' replies Number 14, 'but it's what would have happened. That's what you wanted.' After a long journey, the vehicle arrives at a deserted country chateau and the hostage is ushered out of the car at gunpoint. 'Well you're in my country now,' grins 'A'. Feigning levity and saying that he enjoys travel, Number 6 plants a solid right hook to the kidnapper's jaw. A fist fight ensues, Number 6 emerging victorious. Squaring his bow-tie, the hostage departs the scene with a cheerful 'Be seeing you'.

The outcome is a disappointment for Number 2; the Prisoner's actions indicating that he would never have sold out to subject 'A'. Anxious to continue, he demands that the patient be given a second dose, but Number 14 says the risk is too great to give him a second injection immediately: at least 24 hours must elapse. 'Why?' demands the impatient elder. 'It's a very dangerous drug,' reminds Number 14. 'He must have time to re-adjust.' Looking nervously at the large red telephone sitting ominously on his control console, the superior sighs in anticipation of what the future may hold.

It is morning. Sitting on the foot of his bed, a still dazed Number 6 stands up, stretches his spine and dons his bathrobe. The front door magically opens of its own accord and his attention is drawn to two women talking on the terrace outside his residence. One, a pretty Oriental, is handing the other a bouquet of carnations she has selected from her flower cart. Accepting the flowers, the purchaser turns and gives the onlooker a brief glance. Recognition is hazy until, focusing his eyes on the woman's badge numbered '14', Number 6 instinctively glances at his right wrist. It bears a small but distinct puncture mark, the skin around it showing signs of bruising. Somewhere, in the back of his confused mind, the girl's face seems familiar . . .

Later that day, dressed now in his Village uniform of blazer and flannels, the Prisoner seats himself at a canopied table outside the Old People's Home. The table is already occupied – by Number 14, who is reading the latest edition of the *Tally Ho* newspaper. 'My handbook on social etiquette doesn't deal with this,' he confides, seating himself opposite the girl. 'How does one talk to someone that one has met in a dream?' Folding her newspaper, the girl gives him a quizzical stare. 'Look er, Number . . .?' The man is not wearing a badge. 'Six,' he offers, eyebrows raised. 'Six. I'm usually a social animal, but not now. Another time?' She attempts to continue reading the newspaper. 'Last week, Number 14 was an old lady in a wheelchair,' he continues. 'You're new here, and you're one of *them*!' 'Your nonsense bores me,' she returns, folding her newspaper a second time and preparing to leave. 'Oh, my mistake!' he throws back as the girl gathers up the bunch of carnations she purchased earlier. 'Don't worry, we all make mistakes . . . sometimes we have to,' replies the girl leaving the table. Seated in his oval chair inside the Green Dome, Number 2 receives a visitor – Number 6, escorted into the chamber by the mute manservant. 'Come in my dear fellow,' calls the superior from behind his control console, 'Come in and sit down.' 'I'm not tired. I slept well,' throws back the newcomer, descending the ramp with his arms clasped tightly behind his back. (Good, We don't seem to have seen a lot of each other) 'I haven't seen very much of *you*,' quips Number 6, staring quizzically at the bespectacled man. (I don't spend *all* my time spying) 'Don't you. Your predecessors did,' replies the other. A grin, and a statement that *he* has other things to do, Number 2 raises the subject of the Prisoner's resignation. 'Now all this nonsense about why you resigned. If people can't chuck up a job, things have come to a pretty mess. Do sit down.' 'I'm still not tired,' confirms Number 6. 'In that case, perhaps you'd pour me out some milk . . . *I* didn't have a very good night.' The newcomer does as requested handing Number 2 his glass of milk in such a way that he cannot fail to catch sight of the puncture mark on the Prisoner's wrist. The superior attempts to ignore the injection scar by extolling the virtues of milk. 'Milk is the perfect food. It creates good temper . . . would you like some?' 'My temper's fine,' snaps the other. 'Anyone who had nothing to hide would ask where I got it,' he plies, raising his wrist before the elder. 'Where did you get it Number 6?' 'In my sleep.' 'Oh you must have been restless. Perhaps you need a check up.' 'I have a favourite doctor,' mocks the Prisoner. 'Really.' 'Number 14,' grins the other. Having delivered his trump card, Number 6 turns and walks out of the chamber. Lowering his glass, Number 2 raises his body from his seat and begins to pace the room, deep in thought. Behind him, sitting ominously on the control console, the large red telephone bleeps into life. Walking hesitantly to the instrument, the bespectacled man answers the summons. 'Sir,' he sighs. 'Yes sir, within two days. You have my word.' He swallows deeply. 'Yes sir, I realise my future's at stake. Two days. I guarantee.'

Night, and an elderly maid brings Number 6 his evening drink. Laying it on the unit by the side of the Prisoner's bed, she bids Number 6 goodnight and leaves. Dressed in pyjamas and dressing gown, the Prisoner sits on the edge of his bed, raises the cup to his lips and drinks deeply. One mouthful achieves the desired effect and he stumbles to the carpet in an unconscious heap, the cup and saucer clattering to the floor beside him. Within seconds he is back on the operating couch and the hypodermic numbered '2' returns him to his dream and Engadine's party in Paris. Seated on a balcony overlooking the garden, he is approached by the hostess. 'Where have you been darling?' she asks, enquiring what has happened to her other handsome guest, the 'old friend' he was talking to. 'Oh he's gone,' he replies. 'Just like that,' she asks with a wave of her hand. 'Yes.' 'How very rude, without saying goodbye. Anyway, I never did like that man . . . it doesn't matter.' Called away by a footman to greet new arrivals, she says that she will see him later and re-enters her home. Observing this in the company of Number 14, Number 2 snaps shut another file. 'Time for "B",' he suggests handing the girl another film cassette, which she snaps into place on her machine. The face that materialises on the television monitor is that of an attractive dark-haired woman. 'She even looks like a spy,' comments Number 14. 'A very good one. From a long line of spies,' confirms the elder as he joins Number 14 before the monitor screen where the subject being observed is seated at a table. 'He's full of the party spirit, isn't he,' quips Number 2, staring at the man sitting alone. 'Where *is* she?' 'I don't know,' replies his assistant. 'She should be there,' insists the elder with concern. 'I think he's resisting,' states Number 14 crossing to the patient who, covered by a red blanket, is lying immediately below the monitor screen. 'It may take longer for the drug to work this time,' she comments checking the patient's pulse. As her superior joins her, the man on the screen rises from his chair. 'I imagine she's coming,' grins Number 2, catching sight of a girl's head flitting through the folliage which blocks her face from sight. It is only a maid going about her business. 'No, no that's certainly not "B",' corrects Number 2. 'I expect she's there somewhere,' comments the woman beside him, holding the patient's wrist tightly in her hands. 'I very much hope so,' says the superior with a shrug of his shoulders. They watch as the maid reaches the man on the balcony and Engadine walks out to meet her. 'Ah Lucette, I was looking for you. What have you been up to?' 'Nothing madame,' replies the maid, 'I was helping Louis to collect the glasses.' Spotting the envelope the girl carries in her hand, Engadine asks what it is. 'A note madame. A lady she gave it to me.' Believing it to be meant for her, the hostess reaches out her hand. 'No madame, it's for the man. 'Thank you Lucette,' says her mistress, handing the note to her guest with the comment that it is in a woman's handwriting. 'I am jealous. What does she want?' asks Engadine as Number 6 slices open the envelope. 'I dare not tell you,' he quips, happy to play the game as he shoves the note under the hostess' nose.'Oh,' she says reading the letter, 'to meet her in the arbour? My guest, at my party, in the arbour?' 'She's an old friend,' replies Number 6. 'There's no name,' the woman points out. 'Old friends don't need names,' he says, as feigning indignation and joking that for her the party is over, ended because her escort has been 'stolen' by another woman. Engadine rejoins her guests, pausing momentarily to tell her guest to enjoy himself. Walking into the garden, Number 6 enters a maze of neatly-trimmed bushes. The letter writer is nowhere to be seen until, led by the familiar pop of a champagne cork being drawn from a magnum, he finds 'B' seated at a solitary white table in a clearing. 'I'd recognise that signal anywhere,' he calls, crossing to the beautiful woman as she fills a second glass with champagne. 'Let's get distressed together,' she responds. 'There you are,' boasts Number 14 as she and Number 2 watch the man approach the mysterious newcomer. 'You are still the most intriguing spy I have ever met,' grins Number 6. 'It's taken a lot of thought and experience,' confirms 'B'. 'The last I remember you were hiking across the mountains to Switzerland,' he teases, pointing his finger. 'I got sore feet,' grins the girl. 'You should have stayed,' he says, joining the woman and accepting the glass she offers. 'I have no friends there.' 'Your enemy is a very bad loser. He was here earlier. Does he know you're back?' 'His chums are all over the place,' she confides, glancing over her shoulder. 'He and I had a little ride together. I left him in a most unforgiving mood. He may return.' Apparently unconcerned, 'B' remarks that being killed is an occupational hazard. 'Like a sitting duck,' he suggests. 'Don't worry. Tonight's a party,' she smiles dismissing his challenge. Taking her by the hand, he leads her from the table. 'You used to be a very good dancer,' he acknowledges, placing his arm around her waist. 'I still am.' 'Are you?' They begin to glide around the clearing, picking up the tempo of the music that filters through the trees from the chateau. 'Where are you going for your holiday?' she asks. He laughs. 'So you've heard. I don't know yet.' 'A long one?' she queries, gliding away from his arms. 'Oh a very long one.' 'Why?' 'I need time to think,' he says. She glides back into his arms. 'I can't bear to think. I can't bear to be alone. That's why I like parties. I drown myself in chatter.' 'Tonight,' he says, 'there is no need for that. Just dance.'

'He's far too relaxed,' complains an impatient Number 2, staring at the patient as the man on the operating couch grunts. 'He may be there, but he's not here,' confirms Number 14 peering at her scanning machine. 'With this kind of resistance he'll burn up the drug in no time,' she predicts, telling her superior that they have not got long. 'Then you'd better do something about it,' demands Number 2. Pondering the elder's words, Number 14 paces the floor. 'The only way to manipulate his dreams is to get into them,' she states, toying with her stethoscope. The superior is intrigued. 'Is that possible?' 'I was wondering . . .' she begins. 'What?' '. . . If we can put words into her mouth?' 'How?' The assistant patrols the floor. 'We've fed him the pictures. Why can't we feed him with sound.' 'But the voice? Would he hear yours or hers?' questions the elder. 'That's the danger. If he hears *my* voice and recognises it, the shock would wake him, he'd see everything and we'll have failed.' 'We *must* make the most of this chance, or we'll never know if it was "B"', insists Number 2. His assistant throws up her arms in exasperation. 'It's the worst time to try anything. Look at the state he's in,' she urges, pointing at the patient. 'Where's your scientific enthusiasm?' challenges the superior. Resigned to the fact that she has but one course left open to her, the assistant crosses to her console, connects a microphone handset to the machine and pauses, awaiting instructions. 'What shall I say?,' she asks the bespectacled man. 'Anything, try it. Go on!' Above them on the screen the couple are still dancing. 'Shall we have some more?' says Number 14, attempting to put words into the mouth of the man's dancing partner. 'Shall we have some more?' repeats the woman in the man's arms. 'More?' says he. 'Champagne,' whispers Number 14. 'Champagne,' echoes 'B'. Aware now that the audio link works, Number 2 urges his assistant to get to the point. 'You said we haven't long.' 'I wonder if they will kill me?' says 'B', repeating Number 14's words. 'I thought you didn't care,' replies her partner pausing in mid step. 'I do.' 'I'll help you. You know that,' confirms Number 6 as the woman returns to her seat at the table. 'They are here to kill me,' replies 'B' nervously. 'They want me to make a deal with you. They want to know why you resigned.' Her words, manipulated by the girl in the laboratory, appear to shock Number 6. 'Go on!' urges Number 2. 'If you'd just talk about it they'd let me off the hook,' says Number 14. 'If you'd just talk about it they'd let me off the hook,' repeats 'B'. 'Are you shocked?' 'I'm surprised,' hisses Number 6. 'I can't believe it's you.' 'I'm in such a mess. I need something to swap. Will you meet them? They're here now,' says 'B' nervously, her voice reaching a higher register. 'Are *you* asking this?' 'Don't hate me. We all make mistakes. Sometimes we have to,' pleads 'B', inserting the final nail into her coffin. The man has heard this before. 'Have you the feeling that you're being manipulated?' he asks calmly. 'Manipulated?' 'Who are you?' yells Number 6, lunging at the woman, his anger a shock to her senses. 'They're here . . .' she stammers. He turns to see a man dressed in an evening suit observing them from the trees. She implores him to tell them. 'If you don't, they'll kill me!' she exclaims. 'You're not who you pretend to be. Excuse me,' yells Number 6 striding away. The one watching them is joined by a second man. His exit blocked, the Prisoner engages them in a fight, attacking the tuxedo-attired thugs with venom. No match for his expertise, the men soon wind up at his feet. Staring at the woman at the table, Number 6 sees a third assailant holding the barrel of a gun at the girl's right temple. 'Tell him! He'll kill me!' she screams. 'I don't believe in you,' the Prisoner confirms. 'He'll kill me!' pleads 'B'. 'How long

Number 6 dispenses with one of A's thugs

has your husband been dead?' the man calls back. 'B' shakes her head, unable to comprehend the man's question. From his observation point, a concerned Number 2 hurriedly gives his assistant the reply. 'Four years,' states Number 14. 'Four years,' 'B' replies. 'How old is your son now?' This startles Number 2, who, leafing through the woman's file, is unable to come up with the right answer. Number 6 tries again. 'What is your son's name? That's an easier question.' The woman at the table pleads with him to help. 'Son? Husband yes. There's no son . . .' says a panicked Number 2. 'Help me please,' screams 'B'. 'Thought you couldn't answer,' mocks Number 6, turning on his heel and walking from the clearing. 'Come back, don't leave me, come back. I can explain everything. Please,' screams 'B' to the man's back. In the laboratory, a mortified Number 2 raises his arm to cast aside the woman's file but, seeing the large red telephone sitting on top of his console, he resignedly shrugs his shoulders.

Morning in the Village, and Number 6 slips from beneath the duvet on his bed. Easing himself to the edge of the divan, he blinks, a thought nagging his brain. Slipping up the sleeve of his pyjamas, he finds another puncture mark alongside the first one on his wrist. He ponders this, his mind recalling earlier events and the conversation he had with Number 14. Dressing swiftly, he races over the woman's residence, arriving there as the girl leaves. Hidden behind some foliage, he follows her from a safe distance and watches her enter a steel door set into the side of a rock face. Racing after her, he attempts to prise open the barrier but it refuses to open. Undeterred, he climbs up the rock face to search for another entry point. Meanwhile, in the laboratory below, Number 14 goes about her business unaware that the subject of her careful preparations, having discovered an air vent, is climbing down the laboratory's air duct. By the time that Number 14 has completed her task, Number 6 has edged his way down the chimney to floor level and is at that very moment watching the girl leave the operation room through a mesh-covered grill. As Number 14 vacates the corridor, the Prisoner kicks out the mesh and gently lowers himself into the deserted passageway, replacing the air vent cover behind him. The doors to the laboratory slide open to greet him and he enters the chamber where, hours before, he was the unwilling victim of Number 2's latest endeavour to break him – although, at this stage of course, Number 6 cannot know this. However, he soon realises what has been going on: the pictures of Engadine's party flashed onto the monitor screen giving him a clue to the doubts which have been nagging his brain. Finding the box files marked 'a', 'b', and 'c', he throws back their covers, noting the faces of boxes 'a' and 'b' – file 'c' containing nothing but papers. Carefully replacing them, he switches off the television monitor and prepares to leave. It is now that he sees the last remaining hypodermic, numbered '3'. He holds it to his wrist and makes the obvious deduction. Spotting a carafe of drinking water nearby, he removes the handkerchief from his breast pocket and siphons off two-thirds of the hypodermic's pinky-brown contents into the handkerchief's white absorbent cotton. Making up the deficiency by siphoning in an equivalent volume of the drinking water, he carefully replaces the syringe into its plastic container, returns the water carafe to its former position and swiftly departs from the chamber.

In the Green Dome, the mute Butler serves Number 2 his early-morning jug of milk. Dressed in pyjamas and silk dressing gown, his bespectacled superior is far from being his usual confident self. Worry lines etch his forehead and he is nursing a headache. 'I couldn't sleep,' he confides to the silent figure, the strain of the last few days obviously beginning to tell. Rising from his chair, he thumps down a button on the control console and crosses to gaze at the exterior scene of his giant television screen. 'What's that Number 6 doing?' he says aloud. 'He's always walking. Irritating man. Don't you ever get tired?' he shouts as the figure on the screen turns to the surveillance camera, performs a mock salute and bids the observer 'Be seeing you.' 'No! I'll be seeing *you*!', returns the man in the dressing gown. That evening, Number 6 exits from his bathroom to find the usual hot night-cap waiting for him in its cup and saucer. Forewarned this time, he calmly pours the contents of the cup into his kitchen sink. Selecting a clean glass from the sink unit's top, he turns on the tap fills the glass to its brim and gulps down a mouthful. Nevertheless, the previous night's events are repeated. Crossing to his bedroom, he staggers, the glass slips from his grasp and he topples to the floor.

He is once again recumbent on the operating couch. Having administered the contents of her syringe marked '3', Number 14 raises the patient's wrist, confirms that his pulse-rate is normal and turns to Number 2 who is pacing the floor behind her. Confirming that they can go ahead, she flicks on her machine and the experiment enters its third stage. But something is wrong. The monitor screen lights up as usual, but the picture is distorted. 'What? . . . What's gone wrong?' demands a concerned Number 2 as the picture on the screen waves drunkenly before them. 'The strain's too much for him. I'm going to stop it,' yells the girl, racing to the patient's side. 'No!' shouts her superior, grabbing her arm. 'It's our last chance. It's now or never.' 'It's on your own head,' reminds Number 14. 'I'll worry about *them* later,' groans Number 2 staring at the on-screen events. Dressed immaculately in an evening suit, Number 6 walks behind a lovely brunette. 'Haven't they killed you yet?' he quips behind the girl's back. The girl turns, he fails to recognise her. 'Sorry, must have been thinking of someone else,' he apologises, rejoining the other guests. Spotting him out of the corner of her eye, Engadine walks towards him. 'It's so wild darling. It will end in tears,' she warns. 'All the best parties do,' he returns. 'Oh you're so . . .' Engadine's reply is lost in laughter as she rejoins her guests. '. . . Not terrible,' Number 6 calls back. 'It's dreamy. This is a DREAMY PARTY!' The guests turn. The man appears to have had one glass too many. Raising his fingertips to his temples, Number 6 cups his head in his hands. Staggering, he sways across the room towards an ornate mirror suspended on a wall. He stares. His reflection appears lopsided. He attempts to ease the glass back into its perpendicular position. The strain of doing so wrinkles his brow as, back in the laboratory, a concerned Number 14 tells her superior that they have to hurry. 'Get me 'C's picture.' Her colleague reaches behind him, snatching up the papers from the file denoted 'c'. 'There isn't one,' he confesses, picking up the typewritten pages. 'This is all we have on him.' He reads from the file. 'Known to be French. Known to have attended Engadine's parties, probably disguised. Known to have been in contact with Number 6.' The girl looks perplexed. 'How do you expect me to bring them together if there's no picture?' she asks. 'It's a process of elimination!' snaps the superior. '"C" is the only one left. He'll find him.' 'Well he'll have to hurry,' confirms Number 14. Miraculously, the picture behind them returns to normal. 'Champagne,' says Engadine to Number 6. 'We all need champagne.' She attracts the attention of a pretty blonde woman, wearing a low-cut evening gown. 'Watch him for me will you darling. He's the last man in the world.' 'I like sane men. Are you in business?' asks the girl approaching the man. 'I was.' 'You're too young to retire.' 'Age is relative,' he replies. 'Meaning you're *free*?' 'Possibly,' he ponders. '*I* know of something and the pay is very good.' I'm free!' he grins. Removing her left earring, she hands it to him with a smile. 'Number 6. I'm sure it's your lucky number.' Taking the earring to the roulette table, he lays the glittering bauble squarely on the square numbered 6. Closing the betting, the croupier spins the wheel. Giving the gambler a knowing smile, the blonde girl walks away. 'Six, noir!' announces the croupier, lifting the trinket and placing an overlarge key in its place. Tapping the key in time with the party music, Number 6 walks across the room. Unannounced, a hand stretches out before him – a hand holding an identical key. 'It can't be,' gasps an astonished Number 2. *She* can't be 'C'.' The hand belongs to Engadine. 'It takes you a long time to sell yourself darling,' smiles the hostess. 'It took a lot of thought,' the Prisoner replies. 'Come on,' grins the woman, waving the key before her and beckoning her guest to follow. 'She's fooled us for years. But not any longer!' hisses Number 2. 'We're bringing her to the Village?' asks Number 14, as the elder races to position himself before the monitor screen. 'Yes!' he snaps, staring at the woman on the screen.

Leaving the partygoers behind, Engadine escorts the man into the ground of her home. 'You are sure? No change of mind?' she probes. 'No change of mind,' he confirms. 'And no doubts?' 'Not any more.' 'It's a one-way journey. You have the fare?' 'Yes' he sighs, drawing a sheaf of papers from his pocket, 'these papers from London.' 'If you want to go back you can. Back to the party. Back to your life. But once through this door, you can never return,' the woman confirms. In reply, he proffers his key. She does the same and both are inserted into the heavy wooden door before them. 'This is what I've been waiting for,' whispers

'No. It's our last chance. It's now or never'

Number 2, his face pressed to the wall screen, his index finger pointing towards Number 14, who is holding the patient's wrist as the figure on the operating couch stirs restlessly, his eyelids flickering as a concerned Number 14 strokes his perspiring brow. Suddenly, the picture starts to rotate, spinning faster and faster until, with a final grunt, the patient's head flops to one side and the television screen goes blank. 'It's gone dead. What's happened?' shouts an exasperated Number 2. 'He's collapsed!' exclaims the assistant. The patient is fed oxygen. 'That's it,' states Number 14 staring at the helpless Number 6.'We've pushed him as far as we dare!' 'No! I must have the dream back, screams her superior over her shoulder. 'You know who 'C' is,' says Number 14, anxious to stop the experiment. 'Yes! But I still don't know what he was selling.' The girl turns. 'And if it kills him?' she warns. 'I shall have to take that risk, replies the superior biting his lip. 'I'll try a heart stimulent,' sighs Number 14, resigned to the fact that she must follow orders. The injection is given, and the tuxedo-suited man and Engadine reappear on the screen, she at the wheel of his open-topped sports car, motoring at speed down the Champs-Elysees. 'Where are you taking me?' asks the passenger. 'To the summit, to hand over your papers,' the driver replies, her hair flowing in the wind. 'Not to *you*?' 'Even *I* work for someone,' she confides with a grin. 'Someone else . . .?' hisses Number 2, unable to believe what he hears. 'Who?' asks the passenger. 'I've never seen him,' Engadine confesses. '*No one* has ever seen him.' 'I thought you'd boiled it down to three,' comments Number 14. 'I *had*,' confirms the superior, staring at the television screen, a smile of anticipation widening his lips. 'I didn't know about this one. It's great!' 'You'll have to call him "D"', concludes Number 14 her eyes twinkling at this unexpected departure from the script. The car draws up at a large country estate akin to a mediaeval castle, minus its moat. 'We're here,' says the driver, switching off the engine. 'Are we?' grins the passenger unable to believe his eyes. 'Oh yes he likes impressive offices,' smiles Engadine, nodding her head and wishing her passenger good luck. 'Aren't you coming?' he asks. 'I must go back. I can't leave the party for long, people will talk.' Number 6 climbs out of the car. 'How will I know him?' he turns to ask. '*He* will know you.' Crossing the courtyard as Engadine reverses away, the man approaches the huge wooden doors that bar his way. Unlocked, they glide open at the touch of his fingertips. Passing through, he receives a surprise. The doors lead not into a room but a dimly-lit cul-de-sac: the exterior of the building being but a facade. A voice greets him from the darkness. 'I am *glad* that you could come.' 'Where are you?' yells Number 6. 'It doesn't matter.' 'I want to see you!' the visitor affirms, staring around him. 'I've been dying to see you.' 'It won't make any *difference*.' People who *hide* are *afraid*!' exclaims the intruder, casting a glance over his shoulder, his own voice resounding from the darkness. In the distance, he hears the sound of a bell, not too dissimilar from that of the Village tower bell. As he makes his way forward, another figure appears at the end of the passage. In the laboratory, Number 2 leans forward in anticipation. Stopping within a few feet of his host – a man shrouded in black, his face concealed behind a black face mask – Number 6 acknowledges that he did not know that the other existed. 'It is often the case with really important people. Anonymity is always the best disguise,' mocks the stranger. 'You are afraid,' asserts Number 6, reaching into his pocket for the papers from London. 'This is very important to me.' he turns the papers over in his hand. 'It is only a commodity,' suggests the masked man. 'No! It's my future,' says the other. 'You belong to me now. You were told, there is no return.' Leaning forward, transfixed by the events unfolding before him, Number 2 stares avidly at the screen. 'Not until I know who *you* are. I've never liked *secrets*,' says the man with the papers defiantly. 'Nor have I!' exclaims Number 2, racing up the steps towards the television screen. 'I want to see him!' No one will ever see me,' the shrouded figure insists. '*I* will. I want to know who I'm selling out to. We must *all* know,' challenges Number 6. '*All*? Aren't you alone?' questions the faceless one. 'No . . . but *you* are,' confirms the other, replacing the papers in his inside jacket pocket. 'Violence will do you no good,' warns the hooded man, as the intruder steps forward. 'It relieves the feelings,' grins the antagonist, raising his hands to strip off the other's mask. It's wearer grabs the assailant's wrists. 'Does it matter?' he asks staring into the other man's face. 'It does to *them*. We mustn't disappoint them . . . the people who are *watching*.' The masked man's grip is broken and the hood is ripped from his face, the assailant turning the figure around so that only the back of his head is seen by the onlookers. Number 2 gasps as the man in the street studies the exposed face. 'I *knew* of course. Now show *them*!' shouts Number 6. Grabbing the man's shoulder, the assailant spins the unmasked man around to face the observers. Number 2 gasps, his head slumped back in amazement. Number 14 throws up her hands to stifle a scream. The revealed face is that of Number 2; the superior is staring at himself! 'You see,' shouts Number 6, as the limp Number 2 hobbles down the laboratory steps, his shoulders slumped, his knees sapped of strength. Behind him the man on the screen approaches the foreground. The heavy wooden doors swing closed in his face. Undeterred, he eases them open to bring into focus – the Village! He knew all the time. He was playing with you,' Number 14 confirms to her dejected superior. The man on the screen, dressed now in his Village blazer, has passed through the dooors and entered the Village, turning as he does so to give the shrunken Number 2 a knowing smile. 'Your drug failed,' croaks a weary Number 2, his shoulders bowed in an admission of defeat. But the girl is not prepared to accept his accusation. 'No! *He* succeeded,' she chides. But Number 6 has not yet ended the game. As they watch, he is climbing the rock face and, carrying the papers from London, he enters the corridor outside the laboratory. Viewing the screen, the observers watch in amazement as the doors behind them slide open and Number 6 enters the laboratory.

But this cannot be taking place: Number 2 and 14 are now viewing *themselves* standing over a sleeping Number 6, who, on the television screen at least, has now entered the room – but he is not behind them! Are they going mad? As one they turn to look at the metal doors behind them: they are still closed. Returning their eyes to the screen, they stare in bemusement as Number 6 enters the laboratory to confirm to the man on the screen – the *other* Number 2 – that he owes him an apology. 'I forgot to give you this,' says Number 6, handing the superior the white envelope he carries with him. 'A bargain is a bargain.' 'Open it you fool open it!' exclaims Number 2 to his image. 'I must see what's in it!' The man on the screen does so, removing some papers from the envelope. They are travel brochures! 'He *was* going on holiday,' confirms Number 14. 'I wasn't selling out,' says Number 6 from the screen. 'That wasn't the reason I resigned.' Totally dejected, an ashen-faced Number 2 stares at the screen as the man in the piped blazer reclines on the operation couch, his body twinned with that of the patient sleeping peacefully behind the onlookers. His 'dream' completed, the screen fades to black. One second later, the man reappears to act out his original resignation scene and the beaten Number 2 lowers his head in defeated silence as Number 14 removes the electrodes from the sleeping patient's head.

Preparing to leave, Number 2's attention is drawn to the ominous red telephone, its bleeping a portent of the horror in store. He rests his weary body against the control console behind him, his brain unable to blot out his failure – a failure that will cost him dear.

AUTHOR'S NOTE:

Originally known as *Play in Three Acts*, before final editing the episode became *1, 2 and 3* and finally *A, B and C*.

Actor Colin Gordon's first appearance as Number 2. He would reprise the part in *The General*.

THE GENERAL

Written by Joshua Adam

Guest stars

Number 2	**Colin Gordon**
Number 12	**John Castle**
Professor	**Peter Howell**

with

The Butler	**Angelo Muscat**
The Announcer	**Al Mancini**
Professor's Wife	**Betty McDowall**
Supervisor	**Peter Swanwick**
Doctor	**Conrad Phillips**
Man in Buggy	**Michael Miller**

and

Waiter	**Keith Pyott**
Man at Cafe and First Top Hat	**Ian Fleming**
Mechanic	**Norman Mitchell**
Projection Operator	**Peter Bourne**
1st Corridor Guard	**George Leech**
2nd Corridor Guard	**Jackie Cooper**

Directed by Peter Graham Scott

SEATED AT A table of the cafe, Number 6 watches a helicopter soar high over the Village. A young man is staring at him from a neighbouring table. Their eyes meet and the second man turns away as a proclamation is piped over the Village public address system. 'Attention. This is an announcement from the General's department. Will all students taking the Three Part History Course, please return to their dwellings immediately. The Professor will be lecturing in approximately 30 minutes. I will repeat that. This is an . . .'. The message is repeated, and the inmates sitting on either side of the Prisoner cease their conversations, rise as one and depart. Although he has no intention of leaving, Number 6's request for a second cup of coffee is refused by the elderly waiter who arrives with a tray to clear away the vacated tea and coffee cups. 'Sorry sir, we're closed. You did hear the announcement sir, about the Professor?' 'I'm not one of his students,' the Prisoner states. Sweeping the speaker's cup and saucer from the table, the waiter, adamant that the cafe will remain closed, asks the customer to settle his account. 'One coffee sir. Two credit units if you please.' The other hands him his credit card. 'You're never too old to learn sir,' reflects the waiter, handing the customer back his duly clipped credit slip. 'Who told you that? The Professor?' queries Number 6. 'No sir, the General.' 'The General?' probes the customer. 'Best of luck with your exams sir,' returns the old man, lifting his tray and leaving the solitary figure behind. The announcement drones on. Rising from his seat, Number 6 crosses to view a poster attached to the wall of an archway. It bears a photograph of a man he has never seen before and the message: 'Our Aim. One hundred per cent entry, one hundred per cent pass. Speed Learn, a 3-year course in 3 minutes. It can be done. Trust me.' Pondering its meaning, the Prisoner's thoughts are disturbed by a voice behind him. It is the young man who was staring at him a few minutes earlier. 'You don't believe it. A university degree in 3 minutes,' says the newcomer. 'It's improbable,' Number 6 replies. 'But not impossible?' 'Nothing's impossible in this place,' returns the other. 'You should enrol Number 6. You'll find the Professor most interesting.' 'Really?' 'He has an extraordinary range of knowledge,' adds the other. 'The only subject I'm interested in is getting away from this place,' comments Number 6. 'Exactly,' says the newcomer forcibly, gaining the other's attention. 'Who are you?' the man smiles. 'A cog in the machine.' 'And the General?' asks the Prisoner. Their conversation is interrupted by the helicopter flying low overhead and the sound of a siren as a buggy towing a trailer swoops down a nearby lane. People are racing across the broad expanse of the beach onto which the buggy now races at speed. 'Who are they after?' asks Number 6 turning back to the newcomer. 'The Professor I think,' says the other. 'Why?' 'You know Professors. Absent minded. Best of luck with your exams,' returns the other, making his exit. From the Control Room, the Supervisor sends out an Orange Alert. 'All units. All Posts. Orange Alert,' comes the message as, pursued by several villagers, a figure races across the beach. Following at a distance, the Prisoner treads on something buried in the sand and his attention is attracted by a voice coming from the sand beneath his feet. Kneeling, he uncovers a portable tape-recorder. Turning up its volume control, he listens to its urgent message: 'Ladies and gentlemen, fellow villagers, students . . . This is the Professor speaking, this is the Professor speaking. I have an urgent message for you . . .' Hearing the sound of approaching sirens, he climbs to his feet, walks several paces then, switching off the machine, he drops the tape machine in a short tuft of grass. A buggy races up to him, its shrill-sounding siren settling to a hum as he surreptitiously buries the tape-recorder with his foot. Leaping from the buggy, two men approach him. 'Are you a student?' asks the bearded one. 'Who isn't. Are you prefects?' jokes Number 6. 'What are you doing here?' the man wishes to know. 'Playing truant?' quips the one being questioned. In the distance, the crowd who have been pursuing the man across the beach finally overtake him and pounce on their quarry – the Professor. Stumbling to the sand he is manhandled back to the Village. The bearded thug meanwhile offers to give Number 6 a lift in his buggy. 'Where to?' 'Home. Hundred per cent entry. Hundred per cent pass,' boasts the man. 'You know what the General said.' 'Who's the General?,' the Prisoner interjects. 'C'mon,' says the other walking to his buggy. 'You don't want to start the term with a black mark.' 'Alright . . .' concedes Number 6, climbing into the vehicle, '. . . let's go.'

Dropped at his cottage, the Prisoner enters to find his television set switched on. From it emits a torrent of propaganda proclaiming the significance of their friend the Professor's discovery. '. . . a significance far beyond the confines of this community,' says the announcer on the screen. 'To quote the Professor's own words, Speed Learn is nothing less than a revolution in educational techniques . . .' Entering his kitchen, the announcer's words resounding in his ears, Number 6 helps himself to a glass of tomato juice from his refrigerator, before returning to his lounge and easing himself into a chair in front of the television set. '. . . And now,' continues the announcer, 'someone who needs no introduction . . .' A short pause, and an attractive middle-aged woman appears on the screen. It is the Professor's wife who brings her husband's apologies for detaining the viewers for a few moments. As they know, the huge success of his course has placed an added strain upon her husband, who, even as she speaks, is completing his notes for the second lecture and should be with them shortly. Meanwhile, poor substitute though she is, she will bring them up to date on their programme. 'The extra Curricular Seminar for Post Graduate and Advanced students will be held next week . . .' At that moment, the announcer sitting next to her receives a telephone call. Offering his apology to the woman, he lifts the receiver then, having been given a message, he turns back to the Professor's wife and informs her that her husband is now ready to complete the lecture. 'We now take you over to the Professor in his study. Best of luck with the exams . . .' concludes the man on the screen. Panning to another room, the cameras turn their lenses onto the subject of the broadcast. Seated behind his desk, the Professor makes an apology for the delay and tells the viewers that he would like to say a brief word about his teaching method. Sipping his tomato juice, Number 6 settles back in his chair, his attention devoted to the Professor's words. 'Speed Learn . . .' begins the elderly man, '. . . is quite simply the most important, the most far-reaching, most beneficient development in mass education since the beginning of time. A marriage of science and mass communication which results in the abolition of years of tedious and wasteful schooling. A 3-year course indelibly impressed on the mind in 3 minutes. Impossible? That's what I said until I was introduced to the General. And then I realised that not only was it possible but that Education was ready for a giant leap forward from the dark Ages into the twentieth and twenty-first centuries. Ladies and Gentlemen, I have been a teacher for 30 years. Speed Learn has made me as obsolete as the Dodo. And we are going to prove it . . .!' A fanfare of trumpets reintroduces the television announcer who tells viewers that the subject of tonight's lecture is Europe since Napoleon. A hard, complicated 6 months study. 'Ladies and gentlemen, sit back and relax. Watch the screen. We are going to cover it in 15 seconds flat!' The television picture changes to black and white, and the Professor's face is projected onto the screen, the camera focussing on the man's intense stare, zooms in on the subject's left eye and enters the cornea, which appears to change to an intense blue dot, the centre of which burns with a piercing white orb. Accompanied by weird electronic music, the image expands and contracts, the blue-coloured spot pulsating in time with the accompaniment. Even the Prisoner cannot avert his gaze from the uncanny effect. His eyes focussed intently on the television screen, the glass he holds slips from his hand, its contents spilling onto the carpet. Fifteen seconds later, a fanfare of trumpets brings the Speed Learn course to an end. Blinking his eyes in bemusement, Number 6 shakes his head and kneels to mop up the tomato juice from the carpet. '. . . 15 seconds flat,' proclaims the televison announcer, advising those students who want supplementary information to address their queries to 'The General, Speed Learn, the Town Hall.'

'Mopping up operations Number 6?' says a voice behind him, as the Prisoner places his empty glass on a table beside him. The speaker is Number 2, who, entering with a man carrying a Geiger counter, shows little concern when the man crosses to the occupant and scans the Prisoner's body with the device. 'Have you lost something?' quips the tenant. 'Not me, the Professor,' returns the superior with a grin. 'Oh.' 'I believe you took a stroll on the beach?' 'What beach?' queries Number 6 sarcastically, as he mounts the steps leading to his kitchen. 'Poor old Professor,' says the Number 2 ignoring the man's insolence, and following the tenant up the steps, 'losing his recorder with all his notes in it. *You* didn't see it of course?' 'Would it be something about that big?' enquires Number 6, indicating a size with his hands. 'The Professor is rather worried about it,' snaps Number 2, dismissing the tenant's attempts to goad him. 'Why doesn't your man look in the wardrobe,' proposes the Prisoner as the man with the Geiger counter runs his locating device around the walls of the cottage. At a nod from the superior the man does so, sliding back the doors of the unit to reveal nothing but the tenant's clothing. 'Very amusing,' growls

Number 2. 'Tell me. Are you as keen as ever to leave us . . .?' 'Any more questions?' replies Number 6, tiring of the intrusion. '. . . I was thinking that a compromise could be arranged – in exchange for the recorder,' tries the superior, his face a mask of determination. 'I wonder who has it?' mocks the Prisoner with a grin. The superior and the man with the locating device turn to leave. 'Enjoy the lecture?' asks Number 2, turning back to his inhospitable host. 'What lecture?' asks the tenant. 'It's a great experiment

Number 6. You can learn a lot,' sneers the superior. 'History is not my subject.' 'Isn't it? When was the treaty of Adrianople?' Without thinking, Number 6 gives the correct answer. 'September 1829.' What happened in 1830?' asks Number 2. 'Greek independence was assured and guaranteed.' 'By whom?' barks the superior. 'Russia, France and Britain.' 'Who was Bismark's ally against the Danish Prince Christian of Glucksburg?' Suddenly, Number 6 finds himself giving all the right answers to the questions fired at him by Number 2 – questions that yesterday, *before* the Speed Learn telecast, he would have been hard-pressed, if not totally unable to answer! 'Very good,' grins the superior. '10 out of 10. Don't

'Tell me. Are you as keen as ever to leave us?'

underestimate yourself Number 6 . . .' he grins as he turns to leave '. . . and don't underestimate *me*!' Satisfied that he gained the upper hand, the superior leaves. Shocked and bewildered by his knowledgeable performance, Number 6 races over to his telephone. 'Can I help you?' asks the operator. 'When was the Treaty of Adrianople? What happened in 1830 . . .?' asks the bemused caller, laying down the receiver as the voice rattles off the replies that he himself had barely seconds earlier recited to Number 2. 'Curfew time . . . 15 minutes,' calls a voice from the loudspeaker across the room. 'Curfew time 15 minutes.' Pacing backwards and forwards, deep in thought, Number 6 halts in mid-step. Staring at his front door, he departs in haste into the blackness beyond. Back on the beach, he searches in vain for the Professor's tape machine. Hearing the sound of a twig being snapped underfoot behind him, he rises and with a sudden movement, pulls the man he met earlier from behind a bush. 'Anything I can do for you?' he growls, his hands clasped firmly on the man's collar. 'You want to get out of this don't you?' asks the other. 'So?' whispers the Prisoner through clenched teeth. The other is about to reach into his jacket pocket, but Number 6 grabs his wrist. Easing the missing tape recorder from his pocket, the intruder raises it to his assailant's face. 'Here's your passport. Number 2 offered you a deal didn't he? Don't you trust him?' asks the man, handing the tape machine to the Prisoner. 'People don't trust Number 2 . . . I don't trust you and I don't trust your tame Professor,' hisses Number 6. 'Who do you trust Number 6?' asks the man we now learn is Number 12. 'I trust *me*!' 'Join the club,' grins Number 12, turning to leave. He stops a few feet away. 'Oh, what was the Treaty of Adrianople?' 'September 1829,' snaps Number 6 without thinking. 'Wrong,' says Number 12. 'I said *what*, not when. You need some special coaching.' Satisfield with the outcome, the man leaves the bemused Number 6 staring at the tape recorder which, flicked into motion by its holder's finger, sounds out the warning: 'This is the Professor speaking. I have an urgent message for you. You are being tricked. Speed Learn is an abomination. It is slavery. If you wish to be free, there is only one way. Destroy the General. Learn this and learn it well. The General must be DESTROYED.'

It is morning. In the Green Dome, the mute manservant wheels in Number 2's breakfast trolley and finds his superior talking to Number 1 on the telephone. Handing Number 2 a glass of milk, the Butler wheels away the trolley as the bespectacled man assures his superior that everything is going well. 'I assure you there is no problem sir. We're getting a 100 per cent co-operation from everyone. I'm anticipating a truly exciting result . . . who sir? Oh the Professor . . . just a mild aberration, I assure you. A couple of days rest and adjustment and he'll be doing everything we need . . . yes yes I will keep in touch sir, closest touch . . . thank you sir.' Laying down the receiver, he mutters under his breath. 'Probably the most important human experiment we've ever had to conduct and it's treated like a military exercise.' At that moment, Number 12 enters the chamber through the sliding steel doors. 'Anything on the Professor yet?' asks Number 2. 'He is responding sir. The doctor will be in to see you personally.' 'Get over there and tell them to hurry things up,' snaps the superior. The man makes to leave. 'No,' calls Number 2 changing his mind, 'No I'll do it myself,' he calls, sipping milk from his glass. 'Yes sir,' replies Number 12, turning back to face the superior. 'Frankly sir, I think we're going the wrong way about it with him.' He begins to descend the ramp, his hands clasped firmly behind his back, his tongue flicking over his dry lips. Number 2 stares at the newcomer. 'You mean about the Professor?' 'We indulge his idiocies far too much. He's a crank and should be treated as such.' Number 2 can scarcely believe the man's nerve. '*You* think so,' he purrs. 'I know he's the corner stone of Speed Learn sir but . . .' the younger man begins. 'Yes?' quips the superior inclining his head. '. . . I can't help feeling he's a trouble maker.

And he attracts trouble-makers.' 'How long have you been with us Number 12?' asks the bespectacled man, his tone placing the other on guard. 'Me sir? Quite a long time sir,' the junior confirms. 'But obviously not long enough!' snaps Number 2, indicating that juniors should be seen and not heard. 'Yes sir. Sorry sir,' whispers the other lowering his eyes. 'Number 12,' calls the superior as the junior turns to leave. 'Your opinions about the Professor should be carefully guarded.' Duly reprimanded, Number 12 makes a hasty retreat.

Entering the master Control Room at a brisk pace, Number 2 calls upon the Supervisor to put up Section 32, sound and vision. At the assistant's command, the Village cameras focus on the Professor's study, where the subject being viewed is busily typing at his desk. A doctor and a nurse enter without warning and, despite the typist's protestations, the Professor is lifted bodily from his chair and taken away for some mild therapy treatment after which, he is told, he will be able to work twice as fast. The doctor, however, remains in the study and removes the sheet of paper from the man's typewriter. Together with further papers taken off the Professor's desk, these are placed into a machine and are instantly converted into a long strip of negative film. 'Track the Professor?' asks the Supervisor. 'No, the Seminar,' orders Number 2. The scene on the monitor screen changes to an exterior view of the grounds outside the Old People's Home. Numerous villagers are seated in rows, each busily sketching away on their drawing boards. In the foreground sits Number 6, his pencil putting the finishing touches to a sketch he has drawn of a woman's head. 'It's Number 6!' exclaims the supervisor in astonishment. 'Really. How very odd,' states Number 2 peering at the monitor screen, as the subject of his attention raises his hand to attract the attention of a middle-aged woman. It is the Professor's wife. 'Can I help you?' she asks, crossing towards to the Prisoner's chair. 'I don't know. Can you?' he asks. 'Finding things a bit strange?' she says, reclining her head. 'That is the trouble. I can't find anything at all,' quips the man in the piped blazer. 'Well what exactly are you looking for?' 'What are we *all* looking for?' he challenges. 'Well, let's see,' replies the woman turning to a solitary figure sitting alone on the veranda tearing pages from a book. 'What do you think he's doing?' 'Tearing up a book!' exclaims Number 6 twisting his pencil in his fingers. 'He's creating a fresh concept,' says the woman. 'Construction arises out of the ashes of destruction.' She turns, indicating a woman standing on her head. 'She's developing a new perspective.' 'Really!' grins the Prisoner, indicating a man dozing nearby. 'And him?' 'He's asleep. One learns only when the mind wants to. Not at set times.' 'Is that what your husband believes?' he probes. 'It's self-evident, surely? What's your subject?' 'What's *yours*?' he retaliates. 'Mine? Modern art.' 'Really,' he replies, tearing the sketch he has been working on from his pad and handing it to the woman with a flourish. 'What do you think of this?' He has pictured her in a military uniform. The woman is not pleased. 'Not altogether flattering. So art's your subject too?' Informing her that he has a preference for military history, *Generals* and that kind of thing, the woman replies that he is wasting his time. 'What a pity,' he says, telling her that he understood that her husband was quite an authority on the subject. 'He may be,' snaps the woman, tearing the sktech in half, 'But I'm not!' 'Creation out of destruction?' he taunts. Giving him an icy stare, the woman rejoins the seminar. Rising from his chair, he flings his torn sketch onto his chair and strolls into the garden.

'Number 6 out of vision,' calls a Control Room operator. 'Scan,' orders Number 2. By now, the Prisoner has made his way to the Professor's house and gained entrance to the man's unlit study. Switching on the lights, he finds the room filled with sculptures of people's heads, each sitting on top of a pedestal, each covered with a white sheet. Venturing to the window, he peers out onto the veranda and observes nothing except two of the artists innocently going about their seminar lesson. Unseen by the man, the Professor's wife has entered the room and is standing behind him. 'This is a private room,' she calls, attracting the attention of the man at the window. 'Interesting view,' he throws back. 'Who are you? A spy?' 'How long have you been in this place?' he asks, staring around the room. Stating that she does not have to answer his questions, the woman asks him to leave. Pacing the floor, he points out that the house is most elegant. 'Books, paintings and a very beautiful garden.' 'The Professor and I have certain privileges,' she retaliates, snatching from him a book he has picked up from the desk. 'As prisoners? Or as warders?' Pointing out that they came here voluntarily, have everything they need and are perfectly happy, the woman loses her temper when, uncovering one of the sculptures, he intimates that as her husband is the teacher, she must be the artist. 'For the last time,' she demands, 'I'm asking you to leave.' 'Subjects from life?' he queries, uncovering further clay busts and ignoring her request. '*Rough* exercises,' she snaps. 'Very good,' he acknowledges, snatching the sheet from each sculpture in turn. 'You really have a considerable talent.' 'What are you looking for?' 'I would have thought that with all these privileges we might find at least one study of er . . .' He stops in front of another bust. Ripping off its cover, he stares at a bust of – himself. '. . . the General!' His lips widen to a grin. Turning swiftly, he tears away the cover of the next bust to reveal . . . 'It's really not a bad likeness, is it?' confirms Number 2, as he arrives in the room and stares at the bust of himself. 'Are you playing truant?' 'Doing a little homework,' quips Number 6. 'I didn't ask him here. I found him . . .' begins the woman nervously. 'You don't have to explain, my dear. Number 6 and I are old friends,' the superior interjects allaying the woman's fears. 'I can recommend him as a thoroughly zealous student . . . with a tendency to overdo it.' 'How's the Professor? Cooperating?' asks Number 6, selecting a heavy walking stick from the umbrella stand before him, and noticing for the first time a white-coated doctor and nurse in the adjoining room. 'I've given him some sedation,' confirms the Doctor, through the open door. 'Has *he* been overdoing it too?' quips Number 6, rejoining the Number 2 and the woman. 'Probably a bit excited,' the superior tells the Professor's wife. 'You know your husband my dear. This Speed Learn. He's as enthusiastic as a child.' 'And now he's sleeping like a babe,' the Prisoner whispers. 'He's not to be disturbed,' confirms the doctor. 'I wouldn't dream of it,' mocks Number 6, who, followed by the woman, slips past the doctor into the adjacent room where the Professor, supposedly ill, lies in his bed. 'Get out,' cries the woman as Number 6 raises his walking stick over the sleeping man's head. 'Stop him!' she calls to the doctor. Too late. With a determined stroke, the Prisoner brings his club crashing down on the head of the figure before him. The woman screams. The 'face' of the recumbent figure shatters as an eggshell. It is only a carefully-modelled clay bust. 'You should take better care of him Ma'am . . . he gone to pieces,' quips Number 6, handing the woman a fragment of her husband's 'head'.

'You are an odd fellow . . .' sighs Number 2 as the Prisoner struts past him. '. . . You have the wrong end of the stick.' 'I haven't,' grins Number 6, throwing the weapon of destruction into the doctor's arms, 'the doctor has.' 'Just a minute . . .' snaps Number 2, pacing after the man. '. . . the offer I made to you about the Professor's notes. It's cancelled!' 'Is it?' mocks Number 6. 'He's changed his mind. He doesn't need them now,' confirms the sarcastic superior. 'That's extraordinary, neither do I,' teases the Prisoner. Taking the tape recorder from his pocket, he throws it to Number 2. 'Best of luck with your exams. Why don't you open the blinds and let in some daylight . . . You've got nothing to hide – have you,' he mocks, spinning on his heel and leaving the room. 'I'd better warn control,' says the doctor joining Number 2. 'Don't warn *anyone*,' the superior snaps back. 'But he'll . . .' '*You* do your job, *I'll* do mine,' growls Number 2 then, crossing to the Professor's wife he remarks that the man has made quite a mess of her masterpiece. 'What does he want?' she asks, as the superior takes the fragment of clay from her hand. 'What some of us want, ultimately . . . to escape,' replies Number 2. 'He persists about the General,' she says. 'I shouldn't worry too much about him my dear. I have an obsession about him myself,' confirms Number 2 staring intently at the clay bust of the man who has left.

The streets of the Village are thronged with people in festive mood, their costumes appropriate to their attendance at the Mardi Gras. Radio and television reporters weave their way through the jostling crowd seeking interviews from the excited villagers as they fall over themselves to proclaim the joys of Speed Learn. Watched by a solemn Number 12, the television announcer walks over to Number 6 and plies him with questions about historical events. Without realising that he is doing so, the Prisoner rattles out the correct answers. 'Well done. Coming along nicely Number 6,' congratulates the television man. 'Yes,' replies Number 6. Viewing this, a saddened Number 12 walks away from the festivities, as does the Prisoner. He returns to his cottage to find the place in darkness and flicks on the lights. Seconds after he has done so, the room is plunged into darkness again and his telephone purrs into life. 'Please stay where you are Number 6. Do not move. The fault on the electrical circuit will be attended to forthwith. Electrics and Administration are on their way. You will find a candle for such an emergency in the upper kitchen cabinet second right . . .' Within a mili-second, a mechanic arrives, followed by Number 12, who, claiming to be from administration, shines his torch into the room and asks what has gone wrong. 'This sir,' calls the mechanic gazing beneath a lampshade. 'A deliberate short circuit across the contacts.' 'Sabotage. That's punishable,' says Number 12 entering the room. Having informed the administrator that they will require a replacement, the mechanic goes outside to his buggy to contact control and asks them to switch on the temporary reserve. Left alone in the dark interior, its resident asks the other if the power failure is his doing. 'Some. Listen carefully,' whispers Number 12. 'We have about 15 seconds. The Professor's real lecture . . . the one you heard on the tape recorder . . . Would you like it to go out?' 'I might,' returns the Prisoner cautiously.. The other hands him a pen-like device. 'Take it. In the ink cylinder. Micro. Be careful.' 'How?' asks Number 6. 'With these,' bids the other, handing him two circular white plastic chips. 'Passes.' 'When?' asks the Prisoner, twisting the chips in his fingers. 'Tomorrow.' 'Where?' Suddenly the room is bathed in brightness as the lights are switched

'I'll fix it. I'll fix it Number 6 . . .'

back on and the mechanic returns. 'I'll fix it,' states Number 12 resuming his authoritative tone. 'I'll fix it Number 6, so that you become aware that deliberate destruction of official property is a most serious offence. I must recommend the full penalty.' 'Which is?' enquires the Prisoner, stroking the pen he has been handed with his index finger. 'It could be imprisonment. It could be a fine,' snaps Number 12 as the mechanic leaves the cottage. 'I'll take the fine,' quips the man being being chastised. 'Yes. I thought you might. Report to my office in Administration tomorrow morning,' barks Number 12, aware now that the surveillance cameras are now recording their every word and movement. 'Yes . . . sir,' says Number 6.

The doctor lifts the Professor's eyelid. Sedated, the Speed Learn teacher lies in his bed, a nurse and his wife looking on. 'How is he, doctor?' asks the latter. 'Fine. Beautiful response,' replies the doctor. 'Will he be able to complete the lecture?' 'Able . . . and willing,' the doctor confirms, entering the patient's pulse rate on a medical chart.

A buggy races through the Village and two men dressed in black, each wearing a top hat, enter the Council Room. 'Your business please?' asks a voice from a red-coloured monitor box installed immediately inside the steel entrance door. 'Board member. Lecture approval session. Education,' answers the first man, staring at the device through his dark sunglasses. 'Proceed to pass . . . pass,' confirms the voice. Delving deep into his pocket, the man produces a special pass chip, identical to the ones given to the Prisoner by Number 12. When placed into a slot on the machine, an elongated finger emerges from the monitor, snatches the chip and the man and his colleague are allowed to enter the Council Chamber ante room where, waiting to greet them, is a similarly attired Number 2. 'You have them?' seeks the superior. Handing the briefcase he is carrying to Number 2, the newcomer confirms that he has and they have been processed. 'Excellent,' grins Number 2 handing another man a sheaf of papers. 'Summon the Board.' Taking receipt of the second man's briefcase, the superior removes its contents and lays them on the unit before him. Carefully sliding an inner sleeve from what appears to be a cigar case, he gently eases a long metal rod from the inner container. 'Micro reduction report satisfactory?' he queries, holding the object before his eyes. 'Oh first class sir,' confirms the first top-hatted man. 'Good,' grins Number 2 placing his fingertip on a button positioned on the unit's top. 'Number 2 calling the General's office. The lectures have arrived. Full security alert.' 'Everything all right sir?' enquires the first top-hatted man, clutching the top of the unit. 'I don't know about the General, but I think I can say in advance that the experiment is going to be a 100 per cent . . .' returns Number 2, removing a second object, a glass circuit tube from the sleeve, '. . . success.' In the corridor outside, several other top-hatted board members arrive and follow the routine set by top hat one earlier, each acknowledging their business before being allowed to pass into the ante-room. Among them is Number 6, his identity masked by the long black dress coat, his eyes unseen behind his dark glasses. Inside, Number 2 carries the lecture devices past two uniformed guards. 'Number 2, for Sublimator,' he snaps, entering a room denoted 'Projection Room.' Having handed the objects to the projection operator, the superior answers the junior's question whether the material has been cleared by the board. He tells the operator to prepare to transmit: clearance to do so will be forthcoming. Racing hurriedly down a corridor and placing a white-coloured chip into a second monitor box, the superior proceeds as directed, to the board room – unknowingly passing Number 6 who stands in the corridor, his face hidden behind a copy of the *Tally Ho* newspaper. '90 seconds to session time,' announces a voice over the corridor's loud speaker. Having watched Number 2 depart, the Prisoner places the paper he had been reading into his briefcase, and throws the document case in the direction of the control console on the wall. An electronic force field flips it back at him and he is forced to resort to following the departed Number 2's routine of placing his white pass chip into the monitor's mouth. After a few seconds of indecision, the monitor allows him to pass into a long corridor. As he cautiously walks along the corridor in the board room proper, Number 12 is addressing the education ministers. In return for their confidence in the General, he proposes to give them a breakdown of the entire operation – in confidence of course. Rising to his feet as the gathering applauds him, Number 12 opens his account. 'Speed Learn is the outcome of the general's prolific knowledge. Its basis is the students confidence in the tried and trusted Professor, and the Professor's confidence in Science . . .' Outside in the corridor, Number 6 weaves towards his objective, but finds the corridor patrolled by two guards. Snapping his fingers, he attracts one of the uniformed men's attention and within a second the man lies unconscious at his feet, his senses reeling from the knockout punch to his chin. Dragging the man into a room, Number 6 treats the second guard to the same fate. Then, having stretched the man out alongside his companion, he cautiously walks down the corridor and enters the projection room. It is five minutes to projection time when Number 6 dispenses with the projectionist and reports that the projection room is clear. He ignores the trickle of blood that runs down his wrist from a wound he received when the projectionist stabbed him during their fight. In the Board Room, Number 12 is ending his report as Number 6 removes the thin metal rod from the Sublimitor transmitter and replaces it with an identical one secreted in the pen handed to him by the man who is addressing the assembly. '. . . Thus the miniaturised course can be projected through the Sublimator at a speed thousands of times faster than the eye can record,' continues Number 12. 'It is imposed directly onto the cortex of the brain and is, with occasional boosts, virtually indelible. Tonight's lecture for instance . . .' His words are cut short by an interruption from Number 2, who says to the board that so much is theory, now for the practice. At the push of a button from Number 12, a wall screen in front of the assembly flickers into life and the men are given a visual rundown of the various departments that will be involved in the lesson. 'Final clearance please,' says a voice over the public address system. 'Sound studio, General's studio, Lecture studio . . . Cameras? Projection . . .?' However, when the surveillance camera zooms in on the man in the projection room, Number 2 spots the trickle of blood running down the man's hand and, recognising Number 6, a confused Number 2 has the projectionist replaced – unkindly – by having Number 6 clubbed on the head. The transmission begins as scheduled, and once again the Speed Learn process is broadcast throughout the Village, ending with the television announcer wishing its unknowing participants 'sweet dreams'.

'Projection! Will you clear please'

Seated in the centre of the circular row of boardroom tables, his head slumped onto his chest, Number 6 is being interrogated by Number 12. 'Who were they Number 6? Who let you in? What are their names? There's an organisation, isn't there? Dissidents. Who is the head man?' 'Santa Claus,' the Prisoner fires back. 'Who's the head of the organisation? You'd be wise to tell us,' replies Number 12. '*He* won't tell you anything. He's a trained conspirator . . . a very hard man!' pipes up Number 2 from his chair directly in front of the man being interrogated. 'This reactionary drivel that you were on the point of sending out to our conscientious students,' he continues, picking up a report from the table. 'The freedom to learn. The liberty to make mistakes . . . old fashioned slogans. You are an odd fellow Number 6. Full of surprises.' As he speaks, he receives a telephone call. It is the Professor's wife, wishing to know if the lecture was a success. Indeed it was. Number 2 is delighted. Can she see her husband? 'Of course. As soon as he has completed the first phase of the next instalment. He's performing so well, it seems a pity to disturb him now,' confirms the superior. 'How long? Oh who can tell?' But not too long my dear . . . he needs you.' 'You'll let me know?' asks the woman. 'Naturally,' replies Number 2, replacing the receiver. 'Lovely woman,' he confirms to Numbers 6 and 12. 'Warm. Sympathetic . . . she'd talk him into anything, to keep him alive.' 'The Professor?' whispers Number 6. 'Indeed. Such is the course of true love,' grins back Number 2. 'Do you need him?' 'They're both necessary. The one for the other. Even essential,' states the superior, springing to his feet. 'Now! To the matter in hand. I'm sure that a man of your calibre will appreciate that rebels must be kept under the closest possible surveillance with a view to their extinction if the rebellion is absolute.' 'The professor?' 'No, no, not the Professor. He's no problem. He has an adoring wife and an even more attentive doctor. No no, he's a lovely fellow. People love him. They'll take anything from him. It is the image you see, that is important. The kindly image,' confirms Number 2, raising a telephone to his ear and placing a call to the General's office. Staring at Number 12, the superior tells him that though they will not get an answer from Number 6, the General will know – he can answer anything . . . given the basic facts. A knowing glance passes between numbers 6 and 12, each considering their respective fates. 'Yes,' says Number 2, into the receiver's mouthpiece. 'Yes, it all went splendidly. Delighted, absolutely delighted. Er, just a slight problem for you. Mind if we come round? Thank you, right away.' Donning his top hat, he confirms that the General awaits them: they will soon know what's what? Escorted by Numbers 2, 12 and two guards, the Prisoner finds himself frogmarched without ceremony, through a maze of corridors to the General's office. Inside, the Professor sits unmoved at his desk, his fingers caressing the keys of his typewriter. 'Plato, Aristotle, Voltaire, Rousseau . . . and the rest, they're all here,' states Number 2, indicating the well-stocked book shelves immediately behind the typist. 'All available to the General. There is no question, no question from advanced mathematics to molecular structure, from philosophy to crop-spraying that the General cannot answer.' Behind him, the Professor rises from his chair and inserts the paper he has been working on into the jaws of a machine. In an instant this is converted to a strip of celluloid microfilm, which slides from beneath the roller of a complex printing module. 'This is how it works,' whispers Number 2, 'allow me to introduce you to the General.' A curtain behind the Professor slides back to reveal a long ante-room: the General, a huge computer with flashing lights and revolving tape spools, spanning the wall to wall division at the top of an approach ramp. 'All the Professor's own work,' boasts Number 2, joining the machine's creator. 'He gave birth to it and loves it with a passionate love . . . but probably hates it even more.' At a nod from Number 2, the Professor carries the strip of microfilm up the ramp and hands it to a blonde female assistant who is attending the machine. Number 2 meanwhile, continues his description. 'That mass of circuits, my dear fellow, is as revolutionary as nuclear fission. No more wastage in schools. No more tedious learning by rote . . . A brilliantly devised course, delivered by a leading teacher, subliminally learned and checked and corrected by an infallible authority . . . and what have we got?' 'A row of *cabbages*,' mocks Number 6, moving forward to seek a better view of the General. 'Indeed,' nods Number 2, '*knowledgeable* cabbages.' 'What sort of knowledge?' 'For the time being past history will have to do. But shortly we shall be making our own,' boasts the superior. 'Napoleon could have used it,' mocks Number 6. Ignoring the remark, Number 2 calls to the Professor and asks him to take down a problem for the General, an illustration of its infallibility. Inserting a fresh piece of paper into his typewriter, the teacher awaits the superior's command. 'Point one: a traitor in the Village,' begins Number 2. 'Point two: Security pass discs were issued to Number 6. Point three: Access to these is through . . .' He crosses over to stare at Number 12, '. . . through where?' 'Administration sir,' falters the accused. 'Exactly!' exclaims Number 2, turning back to the typist. 'Put that down. Also that Number 12 is an official in Administration. *Now* ask the General . . .!' '. . . A question that can't be answered,' interjects Number 6. 'What's that?' retorts the superior. 'There is a question that the General *cannot* answer,' the Prisoner insists. 'Impossible!' exclaims Number 2. 'Allow me to ask it.' 'No!' 'Are you afraid,' challenges the other. A pause. Then the superior gives his consent. 'Excuse me Professor,' says Number 6, crossing to the desk. Replacing the paper the teacher was working on with a blank sheet, the Prisoner types out four letters. Leaning forward in an attempt to read what the other has typed, Number 2's attempt to do so is thwarted as, with a flourish, Number 6 slides the paper from beneath the machine's platen. Then, asking the Professor's permission to proceed, he inserts the paper into the micro-processing printer. Handed the duly received microfilm, Number 2 gives it to the Professor and tells him to place it into the computer. Having done so, the teacher turns several knobs and adjusts the computer's memory circuits. To the consternation of both the Professor and Number 2, the machine goes into overload: the needle on its safety dial hovering dangerously close to the red danger level. Smoke issues from the General's ventilation grids and the Professor himself is soon enshrouded in dense smoke as the computer short circuits and blows a fuse. 'Switch it off . . .!' screams Number 2, '. . . Switch it off!' Racing up the ramp to detach the Professor from the machine, Number 2 falters in his tracks as Number 12 overtakes him and drags the Professor free from the General's hold: both men screaming as, electrocuted, they fall helplessly back down the ramp. Having successfully beaten off his two guards, Number 6 calmly joins Number 2 on the ramp as the latter, removing the burn-out strip of microfilm from the molten wreckage that was once the General, turns to ask. 'What was your question?' 'It's insoluble . . . for man or machine,' returns the Prisoner. 'What was it?' demands Number 2, his face a mask of defeat. 'W.H.Y. Question mark.' 'Why?' sighs the superior. 'Why,' gloats Number 6 'Why?' returns the other, through trembling lips. 'Why?' shrugs the Prisoner, staring at the blackened and scorched remains of the microfilm the superior holds in his hands.

AUTHOR'S NOTE:

The second episode to feature Colin Gordon as the milk drinking (but hard-as-nails) Number 2.

Joshua Adam is the pen-name of Lewis Greifer.

This episode contains the first view of the metal corridors which lie beneath the Village.

The basic interior set that was used as Number 2's Green Dome 'office', also doubled as the Council Chamber, the Control Room, the Labour Exchange and the laboratory in *A. B. and C.*

HAMMER INTO ANVIL

Written by Roger Woddis

Guest star

Number 2	**Patrick Cargill**

with

Band Master	**Victor Maddern**
Number 14	**Basil Hoskins**
Psychiatric Director	**Norman Scace**
New Supervisor	**Derek Aylward**

and

The Butler	**Angelo Muscat**
Number 73	**Hilary Dwyer**
Control Room Operator	**Arthur Gross**
Supervisor	**Peter Swanwick**
Shop Assistant	**Victor Woolf**
Laboratory Technician	**Michael Segal**
Shop Kiosk Girl	**Margo Andrew**
Female Code Expert	**Susan Sheers**
1st Guardian	**Jackie Cooper**
2nd Guardian	**Fred Haggerty**
3rd Guardian	**Eddie Powell**
4th Guardian	**George Leach**

Directed by Pat Jackson

WHY DID you slash your wrists, 73?' The attractive girl in the hospital bed attempts to hide her bandaged wrists beneath the sheets that cover her shapely figure. 'Aren't you happy here?' The girl rocks her head from side to side. 'You're not being very cooperative my dear.' 'There's nothing I can tell you,' she replies, choking back a tear. 'Come now,' the voice continues, 'you must know where your husband is.' 'He's still over there,' sighs the girl. 'Where?' 'Oh somewhere there. He had some work to finish.' 'Was he devoted to you?' He *is* devoted to me,' challenges the patient, her face showing signs of nervousness as the interrogator walks into view. It is the new Number 2. 'Oh, so you don't mind about him and the woman Maryka?' 'That's a lie!' exclaims the girl, shuffling her body beneath the sheets. 'Stop protecting your husband's memory, 73. He went to her hotel several times . . . then there was the villa, of course . . .' the patient clenches her teeth, her eyes welling forth tears as the man unzips an inner pocket of his blazer. Removing a photograph, he sighs. '. . . Let me show you just how loyal your dear husband is to you . . .' he sneers looking at the photograph. '. . . They look quite at home – together. Would you like to know the date, place . . . look.' He lays the picture on the bed, the evidence a challenge to the girl's resolve as she refuses to look at the photograph. 'I've wasted enough time,' insists Number 2, thumping down the girl's file in threatening manner. He turns to approach the patient's bed. Walking through the grounds of the hospital and hearing the girl's hysterical screams coming through an open window, Number 6 races into the building and bursts into the girl's room at the very second that the screaming patient breaks free of her captors and throws herself through the window. Ignoring Number 2 and his companions, the Prisoner crosses to the window and gazes down at the girl's broken body several stories below, her red dressing gown resembling a dried spot of blood on blotting paper. 'You shouldn't have interfered Number 6. You'll pay for this,' threatens Number 2. 'No . . . *you* will,' returns the Prisoner earnestly.

Back in his cottage, Number 6 receives a telephone call. It is Number 2, who wants him at the Green Dome immediately. 'We've got nothing to talk about,' replies the Prisoner, slamming down his receiver. But like it or not, Number 6 will obey the superior's instructions. Taking his daily stroll through the Village, his activity is terminated by force when three thugs appear before him to force home Number 2's request. Although he gives a good account of himself, the odds prove too strong and the Prisoner is carried, struggling, to a buggy. Seconds later he is dumped before Number 2. 'You defied my instructions to come here. We have things to discuss,'

'You defied my instructions to come here' (Scene unseen in tx version)

greets the elder. 'About the girl you murdered?' 'Oh never mind about the girl,' dismisses Number 2, 'I want to talk about you.' 'You're wasting your time. Many have tried.' 'Amateurs!' the other fires back. 'You're a professional . . . a professional sadist.' With a flick of his wrist, Number 2 unsheathes a rapier from his umbrella. Approaching to within an inch of the Prisoner's chair, he places its blade directly over the bridge of the seated man's nose. 'Light blue . . . fearless . . . or are you? Each man has his breaking point you know. And you are no exception.' The tip of the rapier is lifted to the Prisoner's forehead. 'Ah you react . . . are you afraid of *me*? What is going on up there?' mocks the sadist. 'Disgust . . . ' Strengthening his resolve, the superior stands erect and slaps Number 6 heavily across the face. 'You think you're strong. Mmm, we'll see. Du musst Amboss oder Hammer sein.' 'You must be *anvil* or *hammer*.' quips the Prisoner. 'I see you know your Goethe,' acknowledges Number 2. 'And you see me as the *anvil*?' 'Precisely,' confirms the superior. 'I am going to hammer you!' The red telephone sitting on top of the control console bleeps into life. A call from Number 1. 'Number 2. Yes sir. Yes sir, everything is under control. No sir, no problems. Assistance? No no sir, I can manage. Yes sir, of course. Be seeing you.' 'You were saying? . . . Something about a hammer,' taunts Number 6, aware that the other does not have things entirely his own way. 'Get out!' exclaims Number 2. 'Thank you very much,' returns the other, climbing to his feet. 'I'll break *you* Number 6.' Pausing to look back, the one about to leave hisses a knowing affirmative. Alone, Number 2 picks up the telephone. 'Get me the Supervisor . . . Supervisor? Number 2. Alert all posts. Special surveillance on Number 6. Report any unusual activity to me personally.'

Meanwhile, the subject of his report calls at the General Store. 'Good morning sir,' greets the shop assistant. '*Tally Ho*. That will be two units sir.' Pocketing his clipped credit slip, Number 6 turns his attention to a rack of classical record albums on display by the counter. 'These new records. I like to hear L'Arlesienne.' 'Ah yes sir. The Davier recording. Beautiful. There's no one to touch him on Bizet. It takes a Frenchman . . .' 'I'd like to hear them *all*.' The assistant can hardly believe his ears. 'I beg your pardon sir?' 'How many copies have you got?' asks the customer. 'Six'. 'May I have them?' 'If you insist sir, but they're all the same.' 'I doubt it,' grins Number 6. 'Yes sir,' replies the assistant, reaching behind him to gather up the required albums. 'Thank you, thank you very much,' grins the customer carrying the records to a listening booth. Selecting the first album, he places it onto the record deck provided, listens to several bars of music while viewing his wristwatch then, returning the record to its dust sleeve does exactly the same to the second record. The third album is given a longer hearing, and the listener makes notes on his *Tally Ho* newspaper. Apparently satisfied, the customer collects up the albums and returns them to the bemused shop assistant. 'Well sir?' asks the man. 'I'm afraid not. Not a very satisfactory recording,' replies Number 6. 'Really sir,' replies the assistant, 'I thought it was first class.' 'It's a matter of taste,' observes the customer, 'nevertheless, thank you very much. Be seeing you.' 'Be seeing you sir,' calls the assistant as the customer leaves. While replacing each of the records back into its sleeve, he notices that the customer has left behind his newspaper. The assistant peers at the words the man had written. Seeing that Number 6 has circled the word 'Security' on the bye-line of a feature and denoted the word with a question mark, the assistant urgently telephones Number 2. The Prisoner, meanwhile, having hidden himself behind a stone pillar outside the store, is on hand to witness the shop assistant leave his premises and race with the newspaper to the Green Dome. His plan is working.

Having played the L'Arlesienne recordings, Number 2 is as confused as the shop assistant. 'I don't understand. They sound identical.' 'Yes sir,' confirms the man from the stores. 'And you say that he was timing them?' 'Yes sir,' replies the one in the apron. 'There was one in particular.' 'I don't suppose you know which one?' enquires Number 2, comparing the album sleeves. 'I, er, have no idea sir. He kept looking at his watch and then he wrote something down on a piece of paper.' 'Did he now,' muses the superior, laying the records down on a table. 'The sleeves are all the same. There's no variation in tempo. What was Number 6 listening for? What makes one of these records different?' 'I've no idea sir,' replies the shop assistant. Then, producing the copy of the *Tally Ho* newspaper the customer had left behind, he adds, 'Oh and that's not all sir. He left his *Tally Ho* behind.' 'And?' sneers a confused Number 2. 'Well look at the front page sir.' The superior does so, glancing at the circled word. 'All right, you can go,' he says, dismissing the shop assistant. 'Yes sir.' 'And take these with you,' calls Number 2 indicating the record albums. The assistant moves to gather the items together. 'Ah, leave the paper . . .' orders Number 2, sliding the *Tally Ho* from the top of the pile as the shop assistant clutches the albums to his chest and departs from the chamber. Pacing the floor, his eyes scanning the by-line with its additional scrawl, the superior muses over what the Prisoner is up to. He crosses to the control console behind him and, with the flick of a switch his quarry is brought into view as he crosses the floor of his cottage and sits at his writing bureau. After scribbling a few words on a writing pad, he tears off the sheet, folds it carefully in two and places the note into his inside jacket pocket. Scanning the top sheet of the writing pad, he tears this off also before, folding it neatly, he strolls out of the cottage.

Number 2 watches with interest as the Prisoner scribbles a few words on his note pad

Within seconds, Number 14 (an agent of Number 2) enters the vacated residence, tears the top sheet off the writing pad and takes it to his superior at the Green Dome – unaware that Number 6 has been observing his every movement. Having inspected the notepaper by hand, Number 2 places the sheet into a projection enlarger, dismisses Number 14 and stares at the blown-up impressions left on the paper by the writer's pen. 'To XQ4. Ref your query via Bizet record. Number 2's instability confirmed. Detailed report follows. D6.' he reads, unable to believe his eyes. 'Number 6 . . . a plant?' Meanwhile, in the residence denoted '6-Private', the Prisoner glances at his wristwatch, lays down the book he has been reading while lounging on his bed, rises and slides a white folder from beneath the mattress. Surveilled by Number 2, he leaves his cottage under the cover of darkness. 'Come on,' says Number 2, handing

Number 14 a walkie-talkie, 'we'll follow him.' Together they set out on foot after the Prisoner, who has now crossed through the Village and is heading for the beach. Having followed their quarry for a short distance, the pursuers separate, Number 2 remaining behind in the darkness while his companion continues to follow the Prisoner alone. The men keep in contact via their communication devices. 'Where is he now?' demands Number 2. 'He's going down towards the beach sir,' replies the pursuer, keeping Number 6 in sight as he tiptoes down the steps leading to the broad expanse of sand. 'Keep on his tail. I'll follow you down,' comes the reply. 'Which way is he heading?' Confirming that Number 6 is going around the sea wall towards the swimming pool, Number 14 is told to keep after him, but to be careful. Then, after a short space of time. 'What's he doing?' 'He's going towards the Stone Boat,' replies Number 14. 'Keep out of sight and go on reporting,' comes the order. Seeing Number 6 reach his permanently-moored objective, the pursuer picks up his commentary. 'He's going aboard . . . He's going into the cabin. Now he's come out . . . he's heading back.' 'Let him go. I'll join you at the Stone Boat,' comes the reply. Having made his way up from the beach, Number 6 pauses for a moment to stare back at the sands. Then with a knowing grin, he returns to his cottage.

Numbers 2 and 14 enter the Stone Boat. 'You're sure he didn't have it with him when he left?' asks the superior. 'Yes quite sure sir,' confirms his companion, crouching to enter the vessel's cabin. Bending over a bunk, Number 2 easily finds what they are looking for – the white folder left there by their quarry. Carrying the folder back to the Green Dome, the superior once again dismisses the underling. 'But I thought . . .' 'Don't!' snaps Number 2. 'Just obey orders.' 'Yes sir,' returns the junior leaving the chamber. Alone now, the superior tears open his prize. It contains nothing but sheets of blank paper. A look of puzzlement crosses his face as he shuffles through the white sheets, his eyes searching for any hidden writing. Selecting a telephone from his console, he asks for the laboratory and orders a technician to join him. 'I want these tested immediately,' growls Number 2 as the laboratory technician enters the chamber. 'For what sir?' asks the newcomer taking receipt of the papers. 'Anything . . . words, figures, whatever is written on them!' exclaims the superior. The man stares at the papers again. 'There seems . . .' he begins. 'Don't argue with me!' snaps Number 2. 'I'm telling you there *is* . . . a message of some kind. Try everything. X-rays, infra-red . . . what are you staring at?' 'Nothing sir,' replies the confused technician. 'Then get on with it!' barks Number 2. With a stare of disbelief, the laboratory man leaves. Having had the papers tested, he turns to his assistant for confirmation. 'Well?' 'This one's negative too,' replies his junior, handing his companion a blank sheet of paper. 'Of course. I didn't expect anything else,' confirms the senior technician. 'Shall we put them through again?' asks the other. 'What's the point. We've tried everything,' confirms the senior. 'He isn't going to like this,' he tells his companion with a shrug of his shoulders. Waiting anxiously back in the Green Dome, a concerned Number 2 is astounded when the technician reports that the papers are blank. 'I'm sorry sir, but there's nothing.' 'Nothing! Nothing at all?' quizzes the frustrated Number 2. The other confirms that the papers are blank. 'They CAN'T be!' exclaims the superior, snatching the papers from the lab man's hands. 'Why should he hide blank sheets of paper in the Stone Boat?' He ponders for a moment before, looking curiously at the other he adds, 'Or are *you* hiding something?' 'What do you mean sir?' 'I *mean* was there a message here and you're not telling me?' growls the superior, turning to face the man. 'Why should I do that sir?' pleads the accused. 'Perhaps you're in with *him*!' shouts Number 2. 'In with whom?' 'Six . . . Number *6*!' returns an aggressive Number 2. The technician looks back in confusion. 'Oh, you don't know what I'm talking about. Get out!' concludes Number 2, ordering the man from the room. Relieved that the torment is over, the technician races back to his laboratory.

'Increased Vigilance Call From New Number 2' reads the headline of the *Tally Ho* paper which lies with its companions on the newspaper vendor's kiosk. 'Good morning,' greets the Prisoner to the pretty young girl behind the counter. 'Good morning sir, can I help you?' 'Yes. I'd like to place a private advert in the personal column of the next issue please.' 'Certainly sir. What is it?' asks the girl, sliding her advertising pad and pencil across the counter. 'I have it written down,' smiles Number 6, reaching into his inside pocket and handing the girl a slip of paper. 'There you are.' The girl reads the first three words aloud, struggling to get the pronunciation correct. 'Hay mas mal. . . .' she falters. 'Hay mas aml en el aldea que se suena,' corrects Number 6, confirming the message. 'Nine words. That will be three units please sir.' 'Good.' 'Spanish isn't it?' asks the girl while clipping the customer's credit card. 'That's right. Cervantes – Don Quixote,' he confirms. 'Oh yes,' replies the girl acknowledging her ignorance. 'Sort of personal joke between myself and a certain friend.' 'I see,' she replies. 'That word Aldea. Doesn't it mean village?' 'Yes!' he confirms with a grin. Pocketing his clipped credit card, he walks over to a telephone kiosk. 'Hospital . . . Yeah . . . Hospital? Psychiatrics, Head of the Department.' 'Director of Psychiatrics,' replies a voice. 'Ah yes Doctor, what's the verdict on our friend?' 'Friend. Friend, who is this?' quizzes the doctor. 'Your report . . . on *Number 2*,' urges the caller. 'Number 2? What are you talking about? Who . . . who is this speaking?' asks the somewhat bemused doctor. 'I understand. You'd rather not talk on the telephone. You're probably very wise. Never mind. I'll be seeing you later on . . .' grins Number 6 replacing the receiver.

'. . . I understand. You'd rather not talk on the telephone. You're probably very wise. Never mind. I'll be seeing you later on . . .' repeats the words from the tape machine which Number 2 now switches off, its ominous message sending a shiver down the spine of the doctor who now stands before his superior. 'Perhaps you'd explain,' says Number 2. 'I can't. I'm as much in the dark as you are,' pleads the psychiatrist. 'Are you?' mocks the superior, placing his hands on the tape machine. 'You don't know who it was who telephoned you?' 'No,' confirms the other. 'It was Number 6, and the oscilloscope will prove it,' warns Number 2, inserting the jack-plugged end of a cable that leads from the tape machine into an oscilloscope monitor. 'Voices are like fingerprints,' explains Number 2, tweaking a control on the monitor. 'No two are the same. Even if the voice is disguised, the pattern doesn't change. I'll now show you the voice pattern of your caller . . .' He reverses the tape recording and the doctor is treated to a visual display of the caller's voice pattern. Replaying the word 'you', after comparison with the voice of Number 6, the superior confirms that they match. 'It *was* Number 6 who telephoned you. Do you still plead innocent?' 'I tell you I haven't the faintest idea . . .' 'You aren't preparing a report on my . . . my mental health?' quizzes Number 2. 'Of course not,' grins the psychiatrist. 'And Number 6 *didn't* see you later . . .?' 'No!' '. . . Then why did he ring you?' barks the superior forcibly. The doctor goes on the defensive. 'I told you. I don't know!' 'You're a psychiatrist aren't you . . .' affirms Number 2, crossing to the doctor. '. . . Would you say that Number 6 was mad?' 'Not according to our records.' 'Then he had a *reason* for telephoning you, didn't he. What was IT?' growls the superior. 'Why don't you ask him?' 'Would you like to sit in this chair?' Number 2 snaps back, angry at the other man's sarcasm. 'I was merely suggesting . . .' 'DON'T TELL ME WHAT TO DO!!' bawls the superior. 'You can go.' 'Thank you,' sighs the doctor, turning to exit through the metal doors.

Approaching the bandstand, Number 6 pauses to whisper a few words into the bandmaster's ear, then continues his stroll, glancing momentarily at the green-coloured dome of Number 2's residence.

'A request you say?' 'Yes sir. That's all,' confirms the musician, relating that Number 6 asked him to play the Farandole from the L'Arlesienne Suite. 'What *else*?' asks the suspicious superior. 'I don't understand sir,' replies the bandmaster shaking his head. 'What else did he *say*?' urges Number 2. 'Nothing sir.' 'Nothing,' repeats the superior, linking his hands behind his back and pacing before the musician. 'Number 6 just asked you to play a tune . . . and then walked away.' 'Did he sir? I didn't notice,' replies the man being questioned. 'Does that make sense to you?' 'No sir.' 'No, it doesn't does it,' confirms Number 2. 'I'll ask you once again . . . Did Number 6 say anything else . . . about *me* for example?' 'About you sir?' 'Well, did he?' 'No sir,' says the other, his eyebrows raised. 'Perhaps you've forgotten. Try and remember!' 'He didn't sir,' confirms the bandmaster after a moment of thought. 'You're lying aren't you?!' screams Number 2, turning to face the man. Closing the gap between them, the superior glares into the musician's face. 'There's something going on!' 'I don't know what you mean sir,' stammers the bandleader. '*I don't know what you mean sir*. I'm as much in the dark as you are . . .' mocks Number 2. '. . . You're all lying! It's a plot! Going behind my back. Who do they think they're dealing with? Pygmies! Oh get out, get OUT!'

In the Village graveyard, Number 6 stares at a bouquet of daffodils which someone has placed on the deceased Number 73's tombstone. He leans forwards to peer at the headstone of the adjacent grave, one denoted by the numerals 113. Returning to the Village, he acknowledges a salute from a passing inmate as he drops the note he is carrying into a post box. In the Control Room, having completed his daily broadcast, the Supervisor, turns back the pages of his request folder and finds a message he has overlooked. He reads out its contents over the air: 'And here is a personal message for Number 6. It is from 113 . . .' Number 2 hears the broadcast as he is making a telephone call. Telling the caller that he will contact them later, Number 2 rests the receiver in its cradle and devotes his attention to the message being broadcast. '. . . and it reads, warmest greetings on your birthday . . . May the sun shine on you today and every day. And that concludes the personal messages. We continue with music . . .' Snatching up a file from a shelf below his control console, Number 2 flicks through its pages. Confirming his suspicions, he repeats the procedure with a second file. Slamming the folder closed he beckons Number 14 to follow him, and stalks angrily from the chamber, carrying his sporting stick. Observing the two men leaving the Green Dome, Number 6 continues his stroll with a wry smile.

Entering the Control Room with his lap dog at his heels Number 2 finds the Supervisor surrounded by assistants, each sitting at their observation posts. From his position on the ramp by the entrance doors, Number 2 calls 'What's going on here?' 'Going on, Number 2?' quizzes the Supervisor. 'That personal message for Number 6 . . .' 'What about it?' questions the bespectacled man, as everyone in the room turns to watch their superior. '. . . Do you all think I'm stupid?' barks Number 2. 'I . . . I don't understand sir,' replies the Supervisor. 'Don't you? Birthday greetings for Number 6 from 113.' 'That's right,' nods the Supervisor, confirming that the superior had heard the message correctly. 'It's NOT right! It's all wrong and you know it!' screams Number 2, losing his patience. He beckons for the Supervisor to come closer. The bespectacled man does so. 'It is not Number 6's birthday today . . .' 'Oh,' whispers the Supervisor, confused as to what is taking place. '. . . Yes "oh". And Number 113 doesn't exist!' snaps Number 2. 'Doesn't exist?' questions the man being admonished. 'An old woman . . . she died a month ago . . .' confirms Number 2. 'Well?' 'I swear Number 2, I . . .' 'You're innocent . . . you know nothing,' mocks the elder, taking the words out of the Supervisor's mouth. 'Nothing at all,' confirms the bespectacled man. 'And that message . . . May the sun shine on you today and every day . . . *You* don't know what it means?' 'It . . . means . . . what it says,' stammers the Supervisor. 'It isn't a coded message for Number 6?' accuses the superior. 'I've no idea,' pleads the other. 'You're finished,' screams Number 2. 'Finished?' whispers the Supervisor. 'I'm relieving you from your post as Supervisor.' Not wishing to tempt the elder's wrath further, the dismissed man slouches his way up the staircase. Pointing to another operator with his finger, Number 2 orders the junior to take over. 'Yes,' says the new Supervisor as the previous one joins Number 2 on the ramp. 'And steer clear of Number 6. Or you'll lose more than your job. Understand?' yells the red-faced elder. 'Yes Number 2,' says the newly-elected man. 'And that goes for all of you,' screams Number 2, as the deposed Supervisor is led away by Number 14. 'I'll BREAK THIS CONSPIRACY!' comes the departing shot as the metal doors slide to a close.

Inside his residence, Number 2 studies the personal message dictated by Number 6 for the *Tally Ho* newspaper. 'You say Number 6 put this personal ad in?' he asks, turning to Number 14. 'Yes sir, I checked as soon as I saw it.' Lowering himself into his oval-shaped chair, the superior reads the message aloud. 'Hay mas mal en el aldea que se suena . . . there is more harm in the Village than is dreamt of.' 'Something ought to be done about Number 6,' proposes the other. 'I can take care of him,' confirms Number 2. 'It's got to be done *soon*,' insists Number 14. 'Every day he's a bigger threat to you personally. Let *me* deal with him. He's undermining your authority. Give me the word.' Number 2 appears untroubled by the warning. 'He doesn't hide it. He's out to poison the whole Village,' says Number 14. 'He's a plant,' proposes Number 2. 'If anything happened to him, our masters would know who was responsible.' 'Leave it to me. They'll never connect you with it,' coaxes the lap dog. 'An accident. It's the *only* way.' Rising to his feet, Number 2 begins to pace the room. After several minutes, he turns back to his assistant and, with a sharp nod of his head, leads him from the chamber into the entrance hall of his home. 'What do you want?' he enquires, stopping

A Kosho contest to settle a dispute

in his tracks as Number 6 enters through the front door. '*I* don't want anything. *You* sent for me,' grins the newcomer. '*I* did?' 'Yes. You telephoned. You said you wanted to see me urgently,' quips the other with a smile. 'I didn't phone you,' contradicts Number 2. 'It was *your* voice ... *he* said he was Number 2. Someone in this village is impersonating you,' says the Prisoner. 'I have some calls to make. I shan't need you,' the superior informs Number 14. 'Right sir,' acknowledges the lap dog, as Number 2 leaves the two men alone. 'You're a troublemaker Number 6. Do you know what I'd like ... really like? To dust you down. I'd really enjoy that.' 'Well nothing's stopping you – Kosho?' grins the other. 'I challenge you.' '*I* accept!' Within the space of a second, the two men stand facing each other on the gymnasium trampoline mats positioned over the giant water tank. The contest begins, but Number 14 is prevented from using any foul moves when other Kosho opponents enter the gym and remain to watch the match. The contest over, Number 6 strips off his Kosho attire and heads for the General Store. Spotting several pigeons dancing on the roof of the premises, a wry grin crosses his face. Entering the establishment, he declares that he wishes to purchase a small notebook. 'Very good sir,' says the assistant, reaching behind him and placing a selection of writing pads on the counter. 'Will that be all sir?' 'No,' the customer replies selecting a small notepad, 'I'd like one of these.' He crosses to a selection of cuckoo clocks which are on display at a nearby stand. 'Ah yes sir ... yes sir, very good value. Special import. What about this type sir?' smiles the shop assistant, proffering an ornate timepiece. 'No. I'll take this one,' says Number 6, indicating the clock in front of him, which is sitting on top of a wooden box, the hinged lid of which the customer has been playing with. 'As you please sir. Now sir, that will be 42 units in all sir.'

'And a what?' asks Number 2, while receiving a telephone report from the shop assistant. 'A cuckoo clock sir. And that's not all. I think he was looking for a special one sir. He didn't want the one I picked ... he seemed to be searching for a specific box.' 'All right. Thank you,' replies Number 2, laying down the telephone. Puzzled by the Prisoner's antics, he considers what his quarry may be up to.

The specific box now sits on a table outside the purchaser's cottage. Lifting up the box, Number 6 places it on the gravel at his feet. Raising its hinged lid, he props it open with a thin rod which he removes from his pocket, takes a bite from the half-eaten sandwich that lies on a plate on the table top and throws the remainder of the bread into the back of the box. Picking up the cuckoo clock, he totes it carefully through the Village, mounts the steps leading to Number 2's residence and, peering around him, nestles the timepiece snuggly against the foot of the building's entrance door. Having watched these events with growing concern on the Control Room monitor screen, Number 2 takes the bait. He calls out in alarm: 'What's he up to with that clock...? It's a bomb, that's it ... it must be a bomb!' His trap laid, Number 6 descends the Green Dome's steps and returns to his residence. He has barely left the street when a Village buggy screeches to a halt below the Green Dome. Two men in helmets race up to the door and the 'bomb' is safely stowed away in a container of sand. Simultaneously, Number 6 has returned to his residence, collected his home-made pigeon trap (which now contains a bird, tempted into the snare during his absence) and carried the box and its prisoner into the woods. Meanwhile, in a sand-bagged dug-out, a thoroughly frustrated Number 2 joins an equally bemused Bomb Disposal mechanic to stare at the skeleton remains of the cuckoo clock which now adorn a table top before them – the technician's raised eyebrows clearly indicate his thoughts: is it Number 2, or the timepiece who is going cuckoo! 'Supervisor. Number 6 is now approaching Restricted Area,' calls out a camera operator. 'Let's have him on the screen,' orders the newly-promoted Supervisor. Seeing Number 6 approach the forbidden area, the senior operator telephones Number 2 and reports that the Prisoner is in the mangrove walk. 'He could be making for the shores, or the hills.' 'Don't lose him. I'm coming over,' orders the superior, as, deep in the woods, Number 6 lays the box he is carrying on the ground. Removing the notebook he bought earlier, from his pocket and pausing to consider the next part of his plan, he carefully writes several numbers onto the blank sheet. This done, he folds the paper several times, attaches it to the pigeon's leg and releases the bird into the blue. 'Track that bird,' orders the new Supervisor. 'Tracking sir,' replies an operator. 'Beam.' 'Beam on sir. Yellow ... tracking ... Orange ....' confirms the operator, as a pencil-like aerial rod eases its way through the hinged-top of a flag pole sitting on top of the Control Room roof. '... It's out of sight!' 'Get a fix. Radar,' orders the senior. 'We've got a fix sir,' confirms the man at the radar screen. 'Prepare to fire ...' 'What do you think you're doing?' exclaims Number 2, racing into the control chamber. 'But sir,' calls out the new Supervisor, indicating the monitor screen, 'that pigeon. Number 6 is sending a message!' Mumbling to himself, Number 2 orders the bird to be brought down. 'I want that message. Beam. Minimum strength.' 'Minimum strength,' repeats the other. 'Fire!' orders Number 2. Seconds later the lifeless bird is carried into the chamber and the note attached to its leg is handed to Number 2. Unfolding it and seeing the set of numbers, the elder gives orders for it to be deciphered right away. 'Yes sir,' calls out the female code expert, reciting the numbers to her assistant. '20, 60, 40, 47, 67, 81, 91, 80.' The decoding machine clatters out its reply and Number 2 is handed the result. 'Vital message tomorrow 06.00 hours by visual signal ...' he reads. '... Visual signal ...?'

The time on the Prisoner's wristwatch, which lies side by side with a looking glass on the waiting man's table, reads 5.36 am. Leaving his cottage while the rest of the Village sleeps – all that is except Number 2 and his Control Room operators, who have the Prisoner under constant surveillance – Number 6 makes his way down to the beach and heads off across the sand. 'Stand by observers ...' orders Number 2, following the man's progress as Number 6 kneels on the sand and begins to flash a message with the hand mirror. 'Get that Morse down ... get it down! Get in closer ... get in as close as you can,' orders Number 2. 'Who can he be signalling to?' queries the new Supervisor. 'We'll find out. Radar ... anything?' asks Number 2, shoving the assistant aside and crossing to join the radar operator. 'No sir ... not at sea,' says the man. 'There must be!' 'No sir. There's no ship sir,' confirms the radar man. Number 2 lowers his eyes. 'There must be an aircraft, helicopter ... something?' he yells, running to each operator in turn. 'There's nothing sir.' 'Under the sea ...' tries Number 2. '... a submarine? We'll try the sonar.' He races to the sonar operator. 'No sir,' he replies, 'there's nothing coming through.' Number 2 looks concerned. 'But he must be signalling to *someone*. Morse, did you get it?' 'Yes sir,' replies the operator staring intently at his monitor screen. At last. Number 2 grins. 'What's it say?' The operator looks silently over his shoulder. 'Well!?' exclaims the superior, demanding an answer. 'Pat a cake, pat a cake baker's man. Bake me a cake as fast as you can,' stammers the Morse operator. Number 2 is aghast. 'it must be a special code,' he mumbles to himself, crossing to the control console which is now pumping out its ticker-tape decoded result. '*Pat a cake, pat a cake* ...' reads Number 2. 'But this is what you put in!' 'And that's what came out sir,' confirms the female operator. 'It must be a new code,' insists the elder. 'And the computer's not programmed for it!' The girl looks startled. Number 6, meanwhile, joins Number 14 at his cafe table. 'Morning ... did you sleep well? I didn't. I had a terrible night...' he whispers to the man eating his breakfast. '... Insomnia, couldn't sleep, so restless ... and there's no point in lying in bed when you're awake ... is there?' Number 14 gulps down a mouthful of food. 'What are you talking about?' he asks. Ignoring him, Number 6 drones on '... So I got up, went out, had a long walk on the beach ... marvellous at that time of day, invigorating, the air, it's brisk and clear ...' 'You must be out of your mind,' suggests the diner. '... the rain on your face, the wind in your cheeks ... don't look now, the waiter's watching ...' Then, raising his voice he ends '... Yes, it's the only way. I'm so glad you agree with me.' The trap sprung, he leaves the bemused man staring after him. 'Get me Number 2. Quickly,' says the waiter, lifting his telephone receiver.

'You expect me to believe that?' growls Number 2, to the man standing in front of him – an ashen-faced and concerned Number 14. 'But that's what happened. He came over and ...' 'And asked if you'd slept well!' mocks the superior from his chair. 'Yes sir.' Number 2 laughs. 'The waiter said you were whispering.' '*I* wasn't, but he was,' pleads Number 14. 'What about?' challenges the superior. 'Well, he said ...' 'Yes!' 'Well he talked a lot of rubbish. Then he said the waiter was watching us ...' 'Why?' scowls the superior, rising to his feet. 'Why did Number 6 say that?' 'I don't know sir.' '*Don't* you. You're *working* with Number 6!' exclaims Number 2, his face a mask of suspicion. 'Me sir?' 'And I thought you were the one man I could trust,' the superior throws back, his voice sobbing with despair. 'But you can. I'm loyal.' 'Traitor!' screams Number 2, slapping the man heavily across the cheek. 'Traitor! Traitor!' he sobs, his shoulders hunched, his eyes welling with tears. Unable to believe what is taking place, Number 14 strides from the chamber, leaving the broken man behind. But Number 2 is not quite finished with him. As the mute Butler accompanies Number 14 to the door, an hysterical Number 2 races up behind them. 'You've lost, you and your friends!' he screams. 'I'll break the lot of you ... You too,' he yells, staring down at his black-coated manservant as Number 14 walks through the door in disgust. 'You're in this plot, aren't you?' The small man stares back blankly, unable to comprehend what is going on. 'Oh yes!' exclaims Number 2, raising his arm as if to strike the defenceless figure. 'Get out! Get out of this house!' Lowering his head, the Butler calmly walks to the double doors through which the superior has passed, pulls them closed and returns to his duties.

Leaning back in his chair, Number 6 is listening to a record when Number 14 races into his cottage. 'Turn that thing off,' orders the intruder. 'I beg your pardon?' grins Number 6. 'Turn it off I said,' insists Number 14. 'I'm listening. Music makes for a quiet mind,' quips the tenant as the intruder bends over him to flick off the record player. 'I'd rather you didn't,' grins the listener, grabbing the man's arm and throwing him effortlessly onto the carpet. Rising from his chair, Number 6 asks what's on the other man's mind. 'You put the poison in,' hisses Number

14, scrambling to his feet. 'Did I?' grins the tenant. 'With Number 2 . . .' continues the intruder. '. . . I'm finished!' 'Sorry to hear that,' mocks Number 6. 'I'll kill you!' yells the other, leaping at the Prisoner, his fist raised. 'Will you?' grins Number 6, stepping backwards to ward off the blow. The men enter into a vicious fight. Bedsheets are torn and scattered to the floor. Crockery from the tenant's kitchen is smashed to the floor as the kitchen divider gives way under the strain of the men's weight as they battle their way around the cottage. The fight is long and arduous until, with a final lunge from his opponent, Number 14 is sent crashing through the Prisoner's front door. Meanwhile in the Green Dome, the Butler is preparing to leave. Having packed his suitcase, he gathers up his raincoat and marches to the door – leaving behind a babbling superior, his bloodless hands clasped tightly to the large wheel of the penny farthing bicycle; his tormented face a mask of self-pity.

Number 2 stands alone, his face a mask of torment

'What are you doing here?' sighs Number 2 as the Prisoner strides into the chamber. 'I've come to keep you company. I hear all your friends have deserted you,' mocks the newcomer. 'You can't trust anyone anymore . . . Pity. It's odd isn't it . . .' he peers around the huge chamber, '. . . all this power at your disposal, and yet, you're alone. You do feel alone don't you?' 'What do you want?' sobs Number 2. 'To talk and to listen.' 'I have *nothing* to say.' 'That's not like the old Number 2,' grins Number 6, descending the ramp and approaching the trembling figure. 'Where is the strong man. The hammer. You have to be *hammer* or *anvil*, remember?' 'I know . . . who . . . you are,' stammers Number 2, crossing to face the newcomer. 'I'm Number 6.' 'No! *D6*.' 'D6?' grins the Prisoner breaking into laughter. 'Yes . . . sent here by our masters to *spy* on me,' babbles Number 2. 'Sorry, I'm not quite with you,' replies Number 6, striding away from the elder. 'Oh yes, oh yes, you can stop acting now, you know. I was onto you from the beginning. *I* knew what you were doing!' 'Tell me,' mocks Number 6 while pacing the floor, the superior trailing him like a lap dog. The roles are reversed now. 'All those messages you sent, and all the people you recruited. I knew you were a plant. *You* didn't fool ME!' 'Maybe you fooled yourself,' quips the other, raising an eyebrow. 'What does that mean?' 'Let us suppose for arguments sake, that what you say is true . . . that I was planted here.' 'By X04,' yells the elder. 'X04?'

'I know who you are!' (I'm Number 6.)

'Mmm,' returns Number 2, nodding his head in confirmation. He has his quarry on the run now. 'Oh very well then, by X04 . . . to check on Village security. To check on you . . .' 'You were!' '. . . What would have been your first duty as a loyal citizen? Not to interfere . . .' confirms the Prisoner. Number 2 bites his lip. '. . . But you did . . . *interfere* . . . You have admitted it yourself.' The elder's bottom lip begins to twitch. 'There is a name for that . . . sabotage!' Realisation dawning, Number 2 begins to sob. 'No.' Pressing home his advantage, the other takes on the role of interrogator. 'Who are you working for Number 2?' 'For us. For US!' pleads the distraught superior. 'That is not the way it is going to sound to X04.' 'I swear to you . . .' 'You could be working for the enemy. Or you could be a blunderer who's lost his head. Either way you've failed. And *they* do not like failures here,' insists Number 6, his words cutting deep into the other man's pride. Head bowed, his words racked with sobs, the defeated man sighs. 'You've . . . destroyed me.' 'You've destroyed yourself,' retorts the interrogator, shaking his head. 'A character flaw . . . you're afraid of your masters. A weak link in the chain of command . . . waiting to be broken.' 'Don't tell them. Don't report me,' pleads Number 2 through tear-stained eyes. 'I don't intend to. You are going to report yourself,' confirms Number 6, handing the broken man the instrument of his resignation – the ominous over-size red telephone – the superior's direct line to Number 1. Clutching the cordless receiver to his chest, the luckless man settles himself into his soon-to-be vacated oval chair. A drawn out sigh, then, regaining his composure, under the watchful eyes of Number 6, the out-going Number 2 reports to his superior. 'I have to report a breakdown in control. Number 2 needs to be replaced . . .' His battle won, Number 6 paces slowly from the chamber. '. . . Yes, this is Number 2 reporting . . .' confirms the man behind him, as he falls back sobbing into his chair. Glancing back, the Prisoner leaves and the bars slam closed.

MANY HAPPY RETURNS

Written by Anthony Skene

Guest stars

The Colonel	**Donald Sinden**
Thorpe	**Patrick Cargill**
Mrs Butterworth	**Georgina Cookson**

with

Group Captain	**Brian Worth**
Commander	**Richard Caldicott**
Gunther	**Dennis Chinnery**
Ernst	**Jon Laurimore**
Gypsy Girl	**Nike Arrighi**
Maid	**Grace Arnold**
Gypsy Man	**Larry Taylor**

Directed by Joseph Serf (Alias Patrick McGoohan)

IT IS MORNING. Sunbeams flow through the windows of the cottage denoted '6 - Private', their golden rays casting shadows across the resident's bedroom. Looking at his wristwatch, the Prisoner flings back his bedsheets, dons his dressing gown and crosses to the kitchen. Checking that his coffee percolator has water, he flicks on the switch and enters the bathroom with the intention of taking a shower. But the faucet is not working. Neither are the bath or wash-basin taps . . . nor the radio speaker in his lounge, which, for the first time since he became a resident of the cottage, sits on its shelf as silent as the grave. Strolling outside, he paces the veranda and views the Village. The square and the swimming pool are void of life. As far as he can tell, the Prisoner is alone – except for a solitary figure, a black cat, whose yellow eyes gaze in his direction. Discovering that his telephone is dead, he gets dressed and ventures outside. The Village is deserted. Empty coffee cups sit on top of the vacated cafe tables; the Village Store is closed, the cottages devoid of tenants. The Stone Boat carries no passengers, its blue, yellow and red banners blowing merrily in the wind. Save for the screeching of seagulls flying overhead, there are no voices. It seems as though the Village has died, very suddenly. Climbing to the bell tower, he scans the deserted horizon. He rings the bell, but the panoramic view remains unchanged. Back at ground level, he spots a deserted buggy. Its engine starts easily. Removing its ignition key, he strolls to the Green Dome. Unlike previous occasions, the entrance door remains closed. He raps on the barrier without success. Easing open the door, he passes into the lavishly-furnished hallway, expecting the Butler to appear. When no one arrives, he approaches the steel doors that lead to Number 2's seat of power. The barriers remain closed and he is forced to prise them apart by hand. The circular chamber and the superior's seat are deserted, an air of eerie silence hanging over the vast dome-shaped Control Room. Returning to the sunlight, he fires the buggy's engine and drives deep into the woods. The mountains rise before him. No Rover blocks his way, no Orange Alert is forthcoming. For the first time since being abducted, he sees the real promise of escape. With no one to stop him he hacks down some trees and builds a raft. Breaking into the General Store, he gathers together some supplies; food, a radio speaker, a camera and so on. Leaving an IOU for 964 units scrawled in chalk across the shop assistant's counter, he races outside to take several photographs of the strangely silent community. Back at the raft, he is about to depart when he is startled by the sound of breaking crockery. A look of alarm flicks across his face. Has he been discovered? Are *they* playing another cruel game – allowing him to believe that he was alone and holding back on interference until that last glorious second when, believing that escape was finally in his grasp, *they* strike. A barely-discernible smile crosses his lips as he turns and sees the black cat sitting on top of a cafe table, a smashed dinner plate resting at its feet. Hopping aboard his make-shift vessel, he poles himself out to sea.

Far out on the ocean, he removes the film cartridge from his camera, seals it into a plastic bag and stows it safely away. Dismantling the radio speaker, he removes a darning needle from a needlecase. When rubbed against the speaker's magnetic coil and attached to a home-made sextant, this serves as a compass. Torn into squares and folded, a copy of the *Tally Ho* newspaper becomes a seaman's log. On his seventh day at sea, he eats and shaves. On day 18, he adjusts the vessel's sail and collapses from exhaustion, waking as darkness descends and the distant throb of an engine pounds in his ears. Through heavy eyes, he perceives a movement on the raft beside him. A seaman is passing his boxes of possessions to his companion aboard a fishing trawler. Rescue at last, he believes, as his body is heaved forward. It is not to be. With a grunt, the stranger heaves the Prisoner's body into the murky cold ocean and clambers back onto the trawler. Munching on a slice of chewing tobacco, the seaman casts the raft off and walks to his bridge to fire the trawler's engine. He is unaware that the man he pushed overboard has swum to the trawler and is now descending below deck. Observing the seaman's companion carrying a tray of food and drink to the man at the wheel, the stowaway enters a cabin, prises open a crate and discovers a cache of guns. Hearing the sound of a radio playing in another cabin, he enters sliding the door shut behind him. It is the vessel's galley. He places a frying pan on the stove, fills it

Entering a cabin, the stowaway discovers a cache of arms

with rag and douses the dish with alcohol. Stretching out to pick up a box of matches, he strikes one and ignites the alcohol-drenched rags. Adding further strips of cloth to the inferno, he waits until the dish is well alight, then, smothering the flames with a dampened table cloth, he departs from the smoke-filled galley. Alarmed by the whisps of smoke from below, the seaman who dumped the Prisoner into the water races below where, hidden in a cabin, the Number 6 takes revenge for his untimely swim. In swift succession, the stowaway deals with the second man and both sailors find themselves trussed up with rope and pushed into a cabin. Slipping a length of chain through the cabin's door, the victor ascends to the bridge, grabs the controls and steers a new course.

Sometime later, the captives recover and struggle to loosen their bonds. Above them on the bridge, Number 6 sees a light flashing far out at sea, and sets a new course, heading for the beacon at full throttle. Free now, the men below decks attack the chained door. Unable to get through, they remove several items from a cupboard and smash their way through into the adjoining cabin. Unaware of what is taking place below him, the Prisoner races at full speed towards the shoreline which is now in view. Attacked unawares by the gun-runners, he gives as good as he gets. However, when one of the men runs below to return with a gun, he has no option but to dive overboard and swim for the shore.

Waking on a beach, the Prisoner surveys his surroundings. The rock-strewn sand stretches out before him, a chalky-white cliff face towers above his head. Confirming that he still has the waterproof bag containing the film cartridge in his trouser pocket, he sets forth to explore his new environment. He weaves his way carefully over the rocks and climbs to the plateau above. Pausing to get his breath, he looks down at a lighthouse on the beach and traverses the grassy cliff top until, wonder of wonders, he meets a man walking his dog. 'Where is this?' he asks. The man passes the unkempt stranger in silence, urging his dog forward, and continues his stroll. Following them, the Prisoner stops in his tracks as the man joins a woman and her male companion sitting around a campfire. The people are gypsies. The woman gets to her feet and approaches the stranger, inviting him in a foreign tongue, to join them. Finding herself ignored, she returns to the campfire, pours the newcomer a cup of bubbling-hot liquid and offers it to the man, indicating to the stranger to drink. 'Where is this place?' he tries. 'Ah . . .' says the woman in Romany tongue. 'A road. Where is there a road?' asks the stranger, sipping his drink. Unable to understand her reply, he sets off down the hill in the direction in which she points. Descending a grassy knoll, he is forced to take refuge in the trees as, to his astonishment, he sees an English policeman directing traffic along a country lane. Racing back up the hill, he rejoins the road at a spot a few yards further on. But again his escape route is blocked; this time by two uniformed policemen who stand by their patrol car stopping and searching the oncoming traffic. Noting that one of the stopped vehicles is an open backed removal van, he races back into the woods and crouches hidden in the trees some distance further up the road. As the removal van motors past him, he leaps from the trees. Racing after the vehicle, he hops over the van's tailboard and lands in the back of the van with a bump. Climbing to his feet, he snuggles down on a platform directly above the unsuspecting driver's head where, covered by a hessian sack, he drifts off to sleep. Hearing the sound of a siren, he awakens with a start and tumbles from the back of the removal van – to find himself standing precariously in the middle of a busy London street! A red bus drives by. A London taxi plies its trade a few feet behind him. He is home! Staring at the familiar London landmarks he can hardly believe his eyes. He has done the impossible. He has beaten them. He has escaped. He is a FREE man!

Making his way to the most familiar landmark of all, the white-painted front door of the elegant Georgian house that had once served as his residence, he tentantively raps its door knocker. The door is opened by an elderly maid. 'Yes?' she queries, staring at the unshaven, scruffily-dressed stranger. 'Who owns this house?' 'I beg your pardon!' 'I'm sorry. What I meant was I'd like to see your master.' 'My *mistress* is not at home,' snaps the maid. 'Do you mind if I wait . . .?' She slams the door in the man's face. Left alone on the doorstep, the man descends the steps and begins to walk away. At that moment, a familiar sound causes him to stop. Peering back up the street, he sees an attractive woman stepping out of a sporty customised yellow and green Lotus 7 sports car – the very machine which he had built with his own hands! Racing after the woman as she enters the house he asks 'What's the number of that car?' About to close the door, the woman thinks better of it and joins him on the steps, her eyes taking in his dishevelled appearance with a smirk. 'Terribly interesting,' she retorts. '*KAR 120C*. What's the engine number?' 'Do tell me,' mocks the woman. '461034 TZ,' he states. 'Marvellous!' she exclaims, nodding her head as the stranger continues his mysterious approach. 'I know every nut and bolt and cog. I built it with my own hands!' he confirms. 'Then you're just the man I want to see. I'm having a good deal of overheating in traffic. Perhaps you'd care to advise me,' smiles the woman. Entering her home, she invites the stranger inside. Easing his way past the woman, he enters the familiar surroundings, his eyes lovingly surveying his one-time home. 'This way,' she calls from her lounge. He joins her. 'Make yourself at home and I'll organise some tea . . . You would like some tea?' 'Very much.' 'I am Mrs Butterworth,' she establishes, removing her stylish motoring cap. 'And you are?' 'An exile.' 'A nameless exile?' 'Smith . . . Peter Smith,' says the guest looking around the lounge. 'Enchanting. Be comfortable and I'll be back in a moment . . .' smiles Mrs Butterworth, leaving to arrange for tea. '. . . and then you can enlighten me on the intricacies of KAR 120C.' Left alone in the room, the man lovingly runs his fingers over the oh-so-familiar objects. Crossing to the window, he eases back the curtains and stares out at the London skyline, recalling perhaps that the last time he did so, he ended up in a place . . . but no, all that is now behind him. Lifting the telephone and hearing the familiar post office dialling tone, he lays the receiver back onto its cradle as the woman reappears. 'Refreshments on the way. Now, tell me more.' 'What's the date?' he asks. 'Saturday, March 18, the woman confirms, selecting a cigarette from a silver cigarette box. 'Tomorrow's my birthday,' he says, pacing the floor. 'You are an odd fellow.' 'Yes . . . you er . . . you must think I'm crazy.' 'Who isn't these days,' Mrs Butterworth replies, placing the cigarette between her lips and igniting a match. 'Do you know, this er, this was my house,' he states. 'Really. In better days. Before I went away.' 'You must miss it,' she says igniting her cigarette and placing the dead match into an ashtray. 'The lease had 6 months to run,' he recalls. 'Then it's been renewed. I have it for 10 years, fully furnished.' 'Oh yes,' says he, pushing his hands into his trouser pockets as he crosses the room to join the woman. 'Is the inventory in order?' 'I'll bet . . .' he snaps. '. . . The only thing that's missing is a body.' 'Don't tell me that you've been prying into my private affairs.' she grins. 'Forgive me. I'm very sorry,' he pleads. 'Er, would you do me a very great favour?' 'Are you growing a beard?' she asks. 'No.' 'Pity,' she replies, crossing to stand by the fire hearth. 'I've always had rather a soft spot for bearded men. But I could never get dear Arthur to grow one.' 'Arthur?' 'My late husband. Navy you know. Unhappily, now deceased.' Hearing a knock on the lounge door, Mrs Butterworth calls for the person to come in. The maid enters carrying a tray bearing refreshments. 'Oh thank you Martha,' says her mistress, removing a flower vase from a table to accommodate the tray. 'Is this the gentleman you said called earlier?' 'It is madam,' confirms the maid, staring at the stranger with disdain. 'Her description of you was hardly flattering Mr Smith. You must learn to delve beneath the surface Martha, who knows what treasures we may find. Alright.' Thanking her employer, the maid leaves. 'Come and sit down Mr Smith,' smiles Mrs Butterworth indicating the cushion on the settee beside her. The man does so. 'Sandwich?' asks the hostess, proffering a plate. 'You're very kind, he says munching on the triangular slice of bread and accepting the paper napkin the woman hands to him. 'It's a pleasure,' she smiles, as the guest gobbles down each morsel in turn, followed in rapid succession by a three-tiered variety of pastries. 'That was the best fruit cake I've ever tasted,' he says dabbing his lips with the napkin. 'I'm a very good cook. It's one of my hobbies.' 'Mrs Butterworth,' says the guest rising to his feet. 'I asked if you would do me a very great favour?' 'Certainly.' 'Behind that desk . . .' he begins, indicating a piece of furniture on the far side of the room, '. . . there was an area of dry rot. It was made good about 12 months ago. The bathroom door is sliding, it opens to the left. The sink is on the right as you go in. The hot and cold taps on the shower were put in the wrong way round . . .' The hostess giggles. 'I had them changed. Don't be so silly, you haven't got to prove anything. I believe you.' 'Sorry, I'm not used to that,' he confirms. 'What can I do for you?' she asks. 'I would like to see, the lease of the house and the log-book of the car.' 'How mysterious . . .' says the tenant, rising from the settee to reach into a bureau drawer. Finding the log-book, she hands it to him. He points out that the document is new. 'Yours is the first name on it. There's no indication of the previous owner.' 'The estate agents arranged it all,' she explains rifling through the bureau to find the house lease document. 'They said the car was for sale. It was reasonable. And I've always had a taste for a little speed.' she smiles, handing her guest the lease to the property. 'The estate agents were Stumbell and Croydon?' he queries, reading the name at the top of the document. 'Most reputable. And a charming man dealt with me – Mr Croydon himself. Did you ever meet him?' 'No,' he confirms, 'That wasn't the firm that I did business with.' 'How odd?' she says, aware that his reply contained a hint of suspicion. 'Yes indeed Mrs Butterworth . . . You've been extremely kind in allowing me to intrude on your privacy in this way . . . I have to make two important calls. One in the country, one in town. So if you will please excuse me, I'll say goodbye.' He opens the door preparing to leave, but the woman calls out to him to stay. 'Mr Smith, you musn't . . .' 'I'm sorry, I have to.' '. . . You musn't go like that . . . Some of Arthur's things. You're very welcome. I've kept them all you see. Stupid but, even though there isn't a man about the place, I like to feel that there is. Do you understand what I mean?' she says, crossing to the lounge door. 'Yes I . . .' 'I just know that you're in some kind of trouble. Have you got any money?' 'No . . .' 'There you are you see. How are you going to get about?' Easing his way past her, the guest informs her that it is perfectly all right. He can manage. 'Thank you. Thank you very much indeed . . . you've been terribly kind.' 'Don't be silly . . .' says Mrs Butterworth chasing after him and grabbing his arm '. . . and independent and proud.' She manoeuvres the guest towards the staircase. 'Now go on up. You'll find everything you want in the bathroom. And I'll lay some of Arthur's clothes out for you . . .'

'That was the best fruit cake I've ever tasted'

After a shave and a change of clothes, the man is sitting behind the wheel of his beloved Lotus. '. . . on condition that you stop that nasty overheating,' continues Mrs Butterworth, leaning over the man at the wheel. 'It's a deal,' he replies. 'Bon voyage,' she calls, turning back to her home. 'Mrs Butterworth, you've been tremendously k . . .' 'No speeches,' she says, raising her hand, 'Off you go . . .' Then, pausing for a moment as the driver revs the vehicle's engine, '. . . Don't forget to come back.' 'I'll be back,' he calls, his reply lost in the throb of the powerful engine. 'I might even bake you a birthday cake,' she promises as the Lotus pulls away from the pavement. It is though he has never been away. His hair blowing in the wind, he guns the car's engine and accelerates through the busy London streets. Making a right turn, he once again drives into the underground garage, throws back the double doors of the establishment's secret ante-room and enters his superior's office. The room has not changed. The large map of the world still hangs behind the solid wooden desk behind which sits a man in a chair. Nor has its occupant, the bespectacled man to whom he handed in his resignation many months before altered. Unaware of the newcomer's arrival, the bald-headed superior sips from his tea cup and places it back on its saucer. Picking up a pen, he lowers his head over several sheets of writing paper lying on the blotting pad before him. 'Anyone at home?' asks the intruder, leaning over the desk to attract the man's attention. Raising his head, the superior answers the newcomer's request with a silent, but knowing smile.

In his lavishly-furnished home, the Colonel is inspecting the photographs the newcomer has taken of the Village. 'Pretty spot . . .' he comments, looking at each picture in turn. ' . . . Mixture of architectures. Italianate . . . Difficult. Certainly has a Mediterranean flavour. What do you think Thorpe?' he calls to a department executive standing beside a table in the adjacent room. Meanwhile, the man once known as Number 6, is patrolling the carpet between them with his hands clasped firmly behind his back. 'I think I wouldn't mind a fortnight's leave there. Prison for life eh?' replies Thorpe, placing duplicates of the photographs back onto a table. 'It's a far cry from Sing Sing.' 'I'm sorry to interrupt on an afternoon's golf Colonel . . .' interjects the newcomer, crossing to where the Colonel sits astride a balustrade ' . . . but this is not a

'Anyone at home?'

joking matter.' 'My dear fellow,' says the military man, getting to his feet, his eyes glued to the pictures he holds. 'You really musn't blame Thorpe. After all, you yourself on occasion could be, a little sceptical. That's why you were such a good man. Why we were so sorry to lose you.' 'The evidence is there,' says the newcomer. 'A set of photographs from ground level, of a holiday resort,' mocks the man known as Thorpe, as he adds a splash of soda water to his drink. 'And a schoolboy navigational log on the back of what *you* call the Village newspaper.' 'I'm sorry. It was the best I could do in the circumstances. You'd hardly expect the Village store to issue sextants would you!' exclaims the guest, raising his voice. 'Indeed, indeed . . .' the Colonel pipes up ' . . . if the place is as you say it was. The *Tally Ho* . . .' he adds, peering at the newspaper. 'A daily issue,' informs the newcomer. ' . . . Morning or evening?' 'Daily, at noon,' says the guest. 'What are facts behind Town Hall?' says the Colonel, reading out the paper's headline. 'Town Hall?' 'That's right,' confirms the newcomer. 'Town Council?' asks Thorpe. 'Correct.' 'Were you a member?' 'I could have been . . . It's democratically elected once a year.' 'Democratically,' queries the Colonel. 'That is what they claim,' answers the newcomer from across the room, his reply raising a smirk on Thorpe's face. 'And they're all *numbers*. No names. No names at all?' he challenges, tapping his fingers on the side of his whisky glass. 'Just *numbers*,' the man continues. 'I see,' says the military man, as the guest informs them that each inhabitant was a number in a village which is a complete unit of its own society. A place to put people who cannot be left in ordinary society. 'People who know too much or too little. A place with many means of breaking a man!' he ends, his voice showing signs of anger because their minds are closed to the evidence. 'Intriguing,' mocks Thorpe, raising his glass to his mouth in total disinterest. 'They have their own cinema, their own newspaper . . . their own television station,' growls the newcomer pacing the room. 'A credit card system and if you're a good boy and cough up the secrets, you are gracefully retired into the Old People's Home!' He turns to face the men. 'But er . . . no escape?' asks the Colonel. 'They also have a very impressive graveyard,' confirms the man. 'Which you avoided,' states Thorpe. 'The Village was deserted,' confirms the other. Why don't they believe him? 'Perhaps they were on the democratic annual outing,' quips Thorpe, casting doubt upon the man's version of events. Snatching up several photographs from the table, the man shoves them under the Colonel's nose, leafing through them as he confirms the evidence – evidence which the men appear to dismiss out of hand. 'The Town Hall . . . Number 2's residence . . . *My* house . . . the Old People's Home . . .!' 'My dear fellow, you really mustn't get excited,' calms the Colonel. 'You must forgive us. You see we have a problem . . . Tell him of our problem Thorpe.' 'You resign. You disappear. You return. You spin a yarn that Hans Christian Anderson would reject for a fairy tale,' condemns the Colonel. 'And we must be sure . . .' ' . . . People defect. An unhappy thought, but a fact of life. They defect from one side to the other . . .' '*I* also have a problem,' growls the guest. '*I'm* not sure which side runs this Village.' 'A mutual problem,' confirms the military man. 'One which *I'm* going to solve . . .' states the guest. 'Quite,' replies the Colonel. ' . . . If not here, then elsewhere,' threatens the other. 'Thorpe,' calls the military man. 'Sir?' 'Check.' 'Yes sir,' says the other rising

'You must forgive us. You see, we have a problem'

from his chair. 'Check every detail contained in our . . . ex-colleague's report,' snaps the Colonel.

'Of course I helped him. I'd help anyone in trouble, wouldn't you?' says Mrs Butterworth, seating herself next to Thorpe's assistant, who silently writes her reply into his notebook. Having shuffled the ashes of the gypsies' campfire with his boot, a policeman mounts his bicycle and departs from the scene. 'Never mind,' says Thorpe, addressing an unseen caller on the telephone. 'Keep checking and report when you have anything. All corroborated, apart from the boat,' he tells the Colonel who sits at his desk, the remains of his breakfast lying on a tray before him. 'The beach?' 'Gypsies,' confirms Thorpe. 'Romanys,' says the man once known as Number 6. 'What about the road-block?' confirming that the police patrol had nothing to do with their guest and they were looking for an escaped convict, the Colonel asks the guest if he can tell them anything more about the boat. 'No name?' 'Would *you* advertise if you were gun-running?' asks the man, emptying his coffee cup. 'No I would not. I most certainly would not. Would you Thorpe?' grins the Colonel to his junior. 'No,' answers the assistant, picking up his cup and saucer and crossing to a table where several other men have their heads bent low, studying the newcomer's *Tally Ho* log. 'Are you satisfied?' asks the log-owner. 'Let us say that the dice are heavily loaded in your favour,' the Colonel agrees. 'Right,' says the guest. 'Let's get to work.' He joins the men at the table. 'Commander, how's it going?' The elderly man dressed in naval officer's uniform gives his verdict. 'On the basis of your log, and allowing for the variance of your primitive device and the laggard speed of your craft, I estimate that you would have averaged some three and a half knots.' Agreeing that this was the case, the guest inclines his head as the naval man asks if he had fair winds. 'Mostly,' says the man. 'You'll appreciate that there is no allowance for tide.' 'No there couldn't have been. I had no charts nor any means of assessing them.' 'Precisely,' affirms the Commander. 'You slept for how long?' 'Four hours out of each twenty four.' 'Remarkable,' says the naval man. 'So, in 25 days at sea, you proceeded at an average of three and a half knots for 24 hours out of each 24, on a north easterly course, which would have put us at . . .' He looks at the map spread before him on the table. '. . . four hours sleep, 24 under fair sail. Maximum travel on a true course . . . 1,750 miles,' interjects an RAF Group Captain. 'Where was the lighthouse?' asks the man attempting to prove his story. 'Here,' says Thorpe, indicating a spot on a map pinned to a board and easel. '250 miles to the inch . . .' states the Group Captain, calibrating the mileage on a slide rule. His calculations complete, he draws a circle on the map with a compass. After further discussion, the RAF man pinpoints an area on the chart. If the Village exists, it lies somewhere on the coast of Morocco, South West of Portugal and Spain: an island perhaps. With over 1,750 square miles to search, its quite an undertaking. Nevertheless the ex-prisoner has got to discover the truth, and the authorities agree to give him every assistance – even if it means scouring every inch of the world. Early next morning, a milk float arrives at an aerodrome in the country. Inside a mission control room, the Group Captain confirms that clearance has been given for refuelling at Gibraltar. 'Good,' says the man once known as Number 6. 'Then we'll sweep as far as we can today, and again tomorrow.' 'And tomorrow and tomorrow . . . you're a stubborn fellow Number 6,' grins the Colonel. 'James, you call me that once again, and you're liable for a bout in the hospital,' threatens the ex-prisoner, dressed now in RAF flying gear. 'I won't be a minute,' calls the Group Captain from inside the changing room. 'Good luck,' smiles the Colonel shaking his ex-colleagues' hand, paying little attention to the milkman walking into the building behind him. 'Thanks,' says the other striding over to the reconnaissance plane. Watched by the Colonel and Thorpe, the man climbs into the jet and the pilot taxies down the runway. 'Interesting fellow,' says Thorpe. 'He's an old, old friend . . . who *never* gives up,' says the Colonel as the jet soars over their heads.

'Turn. Sweep back 15 degrees south-west,' the man in the cockpit directs the pilot, as he plots their course on a chart resting on his knee. 'Sweep nine degrees south-west. That could be it,' he urges, leaning forward in his seat as an island sweeps into view below them. 'Get closer. There it is . . . we've found it! That's it!,' he confirms as the Village is found nestled on the coast. Lowering his sun visor, the co-pilot prepares for a low level fly past. But the pilot has other ideas. Sliding back his visor and releasing his breathing mask, the man at the controls edges his hand towards the aircraft's yellow ejection lever. 'Be seeing you,' grins the milkman turning to stare at the man behind him. A tug of the lever and the co-pilot is ejected high into the clouds, his parachute opening atuomatically. Down, down he falls, watched by a solitary figure – the grinning black cat, who sits immobile on the wall of the cafe. Landing with a thump on the golden sand, the man releases his harness and climbs to his feet. Watched by the cat, he paces through the familiar streets and returns to his cottage. Pausing on the veranda, he scans the still-deserted Village, his face betraying his thoughts. This round is theirs. But there will be others. Turning, he walks into his residence. As he steps into the lounge, the shower which he had turned on before he had left gushes forth a fountain of water. The lights come on. The coffee percolator begins to bubble away and the black cat creeps into the room – followed by Mrs Butterworth, carrying the Prisoner's birthday cake! 'Many happy returns,' she grins, as crossing to the window, Number 6 peers outside to see a procession of villagers parading the square!

Author's Note: The first episode to break the tradition of showing the identity of the current Number 2 during the opening credit sequence – necessary, of course, to achieve the 'twist in the tail' finalé (although the voice used for Number 2 is that of a male – actor Robert Rietty).

Courtesy of stock footage from *Arrival*, Script Editor George Markstein 'returns' as the man behind the desk.

Number 6's birthday is given as 19th March – McGoohan's own birthdate.

Slides are being projected onto a screen which stands mounted on an easel before the doors of an office. The majority are of landscapes: a scenic Scottish loch, the Eiffel Tower in Paris, a rugged, wind-swept coastline. Viewing the screen sit two men, a silver-haired civil servant (and head of the British Secret Service) named Sir Charles, and a man whose head is barely visible over the rear of a high-backed chair. A third man is operating the slide projector. 'Cipher, coding, optics – still known as computers, experts in every field . . . and yet we're still left 36 dreary and badly photographed colour shots,' complains the man in the high-backed chair. 'Yet I'm convinced they contain the clue we want,' says Sir Charles. 'Have you tried superimposing?' 'Yes we have sir,' replies the other. 'But as you'll appreciate, the permutations on 36 runs into millions.' 'Well, coming to them relatively fresh, one of us may get a sudden flash,' proposes the slide operator. 'That you say is Loch Ness?' asks Sir Charles, peering at the screen. 'Yes sir. We've pinpointed the position exactly,' confirms the other, shuffling in his chair. 'Not an inspired photographer, however brilliant a scientist,' quips the silver-haired man. 'Extraordinary order of filming isn't it . . . Loch Ness, the Yorkshire Moors, Dartmouth, the Eiffel Tower, Beachy Head . . . What's Number 6?' A man's photograph is flashed onto the screen. 'Hopelessly over-exposed . . .' comments Sir Charles '. . . I wonder if there's a reason?' 'Well there are nine on the roll very over-exposed, and as many under, the rest are correctly exposed,' confirms the man in the high-backed chair. We see his face now, and learn his codename: another civil servant called 'V'. 'I hate to mention this Sir Charles, but er . . . it is possible that there is no clue to be found in these shots.' 'How do you work that out?' asks the silver-haired man. 'Breaking a code or a cipher is a finite problem, but as I said, with these we don't know that there is a problem, and if there is, on what level of reasoning it is set.' 'We just haven't thought of it,' proposes Sir Charles, 'and I don't accept that it is impossible to do so. Do we know where Seltzman is?' He turns to look back at the blurred image of the man on the screen . . . .

DO NOT FORSAKE ME, OH MY DARLING

Written by Vincent Tilsley

Guest stars

Janet	**Zena Walker**
Number 2	**Clifford Evans**
The Colonel	**Nigel Stock**

with

The Butler	**Angelo Muscat**
Seltzman	**Hugo Schuster**
Sir Charles	**John Wentworth**
Villiers	**James Bree**
Minister	**Kynaston Reeves**
Danvers	**Lloyd Lamble**

and

Camera Shop Manager	**Lockwood West**
Potter	**Frederic Abbott**
Cafe Waiter	**Gertan Klauber**
Old Guest	**Henry Longhurst**
1st Young Man	**Danvers Walker**
Young Guest	**John Nolan**

Directed by Pat Jackson

A helicopter hovers over the Village and lands softly on the lawn beside the swimming pool. Pictured on Number 2's monitor screen, Number 6 walks from his kitchen and enters his lounge carrying a coffee cup and a slice of toast. Biting into the bread, he crosses the room to peer out of his window then turns to stalk the room like a caged cat. 'Relax, relax old boy . . .' murmurs Number 2 '. . . it won't be long now.' Having raced through the streets and deposited its passenger outside the Green Dome, a Village taxi drives away at speed. Inside the building, Number 2 rises from his oval-shaped chair to greet the man flown in by the helicopter. 'Ah, Colonel. Had a good trip?' he asks, shaking the newcomer's hand. 'Yes thank you,' says the guest, descending the ramp, his eyes taking in the bizarre surroundings. Asking the newcomer if he's had breakfast, Number 2 leads the middle-aged man to his control console. 'I'd appreciate knowing my duties as soon as possible,' says the Colonel. 'You've no idea why you're here?' grins the superior. 'All I know is I was sent here by the highest authority,' returns the other, anxious to proceed. 'You were indeed. You should be very proud.' 'I'm gratified certainly . . . and now, if you'd be kind enough to explain what I'm supposed to do?' Draining the last drop of coffee from his cup, then dismissing the mute Butler with a nod of his head, the superior motions for the newcomer to look at the monitor screen, on which is pictured Number 6 still pacing his room. 'What sort of opinion do you form? . . . of that fellow,' asks Number 2. The Colonel watches the man's actions with interest. 'Anybody who spends his time doing that, must be rather stupid,' he comments. 'You couldn't be more wrong, because *he's* our most interesting citizen from every point of view,' says Number 2. 'Particularly yours.' 'Why's that?' 'You'll find out,' grins the superior, crossing to join his guest. 'Tell me, have you heard of Professor Seltzman . . . Professor Jacob

Seltzman?' 'I don't seem to recall the name . . . should I?' asks the Colonel. 'No, in your line of business I suppose not,' confirms Number 2. 'Doctor Seltzman is a great neurologist who became fascinated with the study of thought transference.' 'I've actually seen it done, in India,' says the newcomer. '. . . Where Seltzman studied for many years. As you know the advanced Yogi is capable of living in a state of suspended animation for months, his mind and body disassociate . . .' says Number 2. '. . . Now what Seltzman did, was to take this dicipline several stages further, and with scientific aid, he was able to transmit the psyche of one person into *another*.' 'The mind of one man into another. Impossible. I don't believe it!' exclaims the Colonel. 'Where is this Seltzman?' 'Nobody knows,' sighs Number 2. 'The only man who may because he, had the last contact with him, hmm, is our friend,' he concludes, leaving the other to stare at the man pictured on the monitor screen. 'Are you asking me to believe that it's possible for me to become you and you to become me?' asks the Colonel, turning back to the superior. 'Not exactly, but near enough,' confirms Number 2. 'I don't believe it!' challenges the guest. 'Colonel, if I told you that ten years ago that you could've flown a rocket around the moon would you have believed that?' 'No, I suppose not . . . but *why* all this interest in Seltzman?' 'Colonel,' replies Number 2, enjoying the game, 'You must be aware that all major powers have in their prisons one or two of each other's spies . . .' 'Yes.' '. . . From time to time diplomatic swaps take place . . . imagine the power we could have if the spies we returned had the mind of *our* choosing. We could break the security of any nation. Let me show you one or two other things that will interest you.' Leading the Colonel out of the chamber, Number 2 shows him in to an examination room. 'Now we call this our amnesia room, d'you like the title? With it we can erase the memory back to any point in time we choose . . .' instructs Number 2, crossing to where a man lies strapped to an operating couch, his head connected by wires to a machine, on which is projected the silhouette of a soldier. 'This man you see, was extremely cooperative, he told us all we needed to know in three days . . . with hardly any persuasion . . . so now we can wipe out all unhappy memories of the Village, and put him back into circulation to gather more information.' A doctor arrives to check the patient's pulse. Elsewhere, four uniformed guards push their way into the Prisoner's cottage. 'And this . . .' continues Number 2, leading the Colonel to a row of banked electrical machinery, '. . . is a Seltzman machine . . .' A struggling Number 6 is dragged from his cottage by the four guards and thrown, without ceremony, into the back of a canopied buggy trailer. '. . . Let me give you a dummy run,' continues Number 2, handing the Colonel a pair of tinted goggles. Indicating to a technician to switch on the machine, the superior gives a running commentary as the bank of machinery buzzes into life and the room is bathed in a piercing blue light. 'A device with which Seltzman finally succeeded in switching the minds of two people . . .' informs Number 2. Watching in astonishment, the Colonel can scarcely believe his eyes as the room itself appears to pulsate and a pink vapourish cloud begins to form over two empty operating couches sitting at the rear of the room.

Back before his monitor screen, Number 2 stares at the image of a drugged Number 6 who lies on one of the operating couches. His eyes are covered by opaque goggles and wires are attached to the side of his head. 'Sleep well my friend, and forget us . . . tomorrow you will wake up a new man,' whispers the superior wryly.

'This man you see was extremely cooperative'

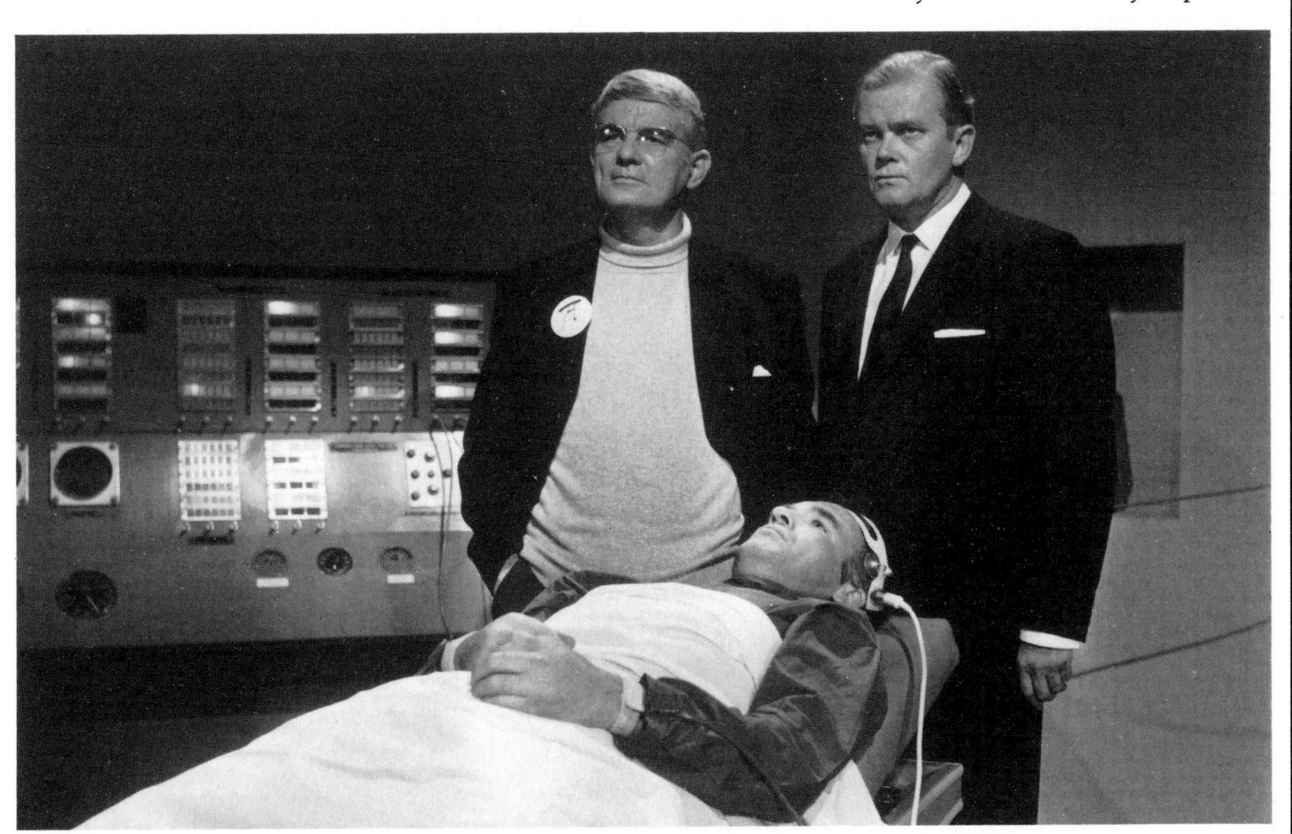

'Hmm,' growls the figure in the bed (we do not see his face). Humming, he stares at his wristwatch, throws back the bedsheets, slips on his dressing gown and walks to the window to peer through the venetian blind. A familiar London street is seen. 'Yes, not a bad day,' he says. 'Let's see . . .' He spots a framed photograph of a pretty young girl. '. . . oh yes, Janet's birthday present . . .' He lifts the picture. '. . . Hope she likes it . . . can always change it if she doesn't.' Replacing the photograph in its position next to the telephone, he crosses over to his day-to-day jotter sitting on top of the writing bureau. 'What's on for today? Let's see . . . car service, dentist's appointment, no no, we'll have to cancel that because Sir Charles' lunches go on forever, but who can blame him . . . he's the boss.' (Although we have yet to see his face, the voice we hear is definitely that of the Prisoner.) Passing into his entrance hall, he catches sight of his reflection in the mirror there – and stops dead in his tracks. He has the face and body of the Colonel! Back in his control room, with the mute Butler in attendance, Number 2 concentrates hard on the image of the drugged Number 6 pictured on his monitor screen. '. . . *Seltzman machine . . . a device with which Seltzman finally succeeded in switching the mind, switching the mind . . .*' drones a voice in the Prisoner's brain. '*Relax . . .*' begins Number 2, as scenes from the drugged man's past flicker through the patient's mind: 'I am not a number, I am a person . . .' The soothing voice urges him not to be aggressive. '*You mustn't resist . . . Take it easy, take it easy . . . it will all be won in the end . . . The thing to do now is keep calm . . . Keep your head. . .*' 'I will not be pushed, filed, stamped, indexed, briefed, debriefed, or numbered,' warns the image on the monitor screen. '. . . *Just bear in mind your ultimate objective . . . We want information*' drones the voice. '. . . Information!' exclaims Number 2. '*Seltzman . . . Seltzman . . .*' the voice tears at his brain '. . . *Proceed as our friend would have done . . . relax . . . good . . . now go boy . . . go . . . This is the time . . . Now . . . Move or leave it . . . move move move . . . Seltzman. . .!* Will the voice never end?

It does, abruptly, as the doorbell behind the Prisoner confirms that he has a caller.

AUTHOR'S NOTE: Once again, life for the Prisoner becomes more complicated than usual. Like it or not, he now occupies the Colonel's body. In order to make the plot more lucid, from this point onwards, the actions and dialogue of Number 6, will be attributed to the Colonel's given name – Oscar.

With a final glance at his reflection, Oscar opens the door. His caller is Janet, the girl in the photograph. 'His car,' says the girl, nodding in the direction of the pavement. 'Is he back? . . . is he with you?' Confused, Oscar gulps. 'Yes,' he confirms as the girl walks past him. 'Darling, darling,' she calls, entering the house and climbing the stairs. The man holds his head. What can he do? How should he act? 'His' mind is in another man's body. 'Where is he?' asks the girl behind him. 'Janet . . . however fantastic what I'm going to tell you may sound, you must believe me . . .' 'Who are you? How do you know my name?' asks the confused girl. 'What are you doing here any . . . How did you get hold of his car? Why . . . why did you tell me he was here? Who are you?' 'A friend,' he returns weakly. 'Well then, where is he? Why did he leave without a word to *me?*' 'Leave! But he saw you, he told me he saw you last night.' 'Last night? I didn't see him last night.' 'But he had dinner with you, after your fitting.' 'What fitting?' asks Janet, perplexed by the man's words. 'Your dress, for the party, your birthday party, he even told me the colour, yellow silk.' 'Yellow silk? The only y . . .' she stares back at the other in amazement, '. . . that was a year ago. Yes, I took him to the final fitting . . . I haven't seen him since.' 'A year!' exclaims Oscar. 'A year . . . what's happened?' 'You couldn't have seen him . . . even if you had, he couldn't have made *that* mistake,' confirms Janet, following the man into the sitting room. 'No, but *I* could have . . .' he falters. '. . . I *must* have got it wrong.' 'Yes you must have . . . What are you doing here? How did you get in anyway?' 'Miss Portland, you must be aware of the sort of work he did?' 'Obviously, working for my father,' she confirms. 'So it won't come as a surprise to you to learn that . . .' He falters, biting his lip '. . . it may not be possible for him to get in touch with you for a year, or even longer.' Lowering her eyes, she replies 'Thanks, that's a big help.' Sighing, she turns to leave. 'Miss Portland,' he calls 'I may have a message for you soon.' 'When?' 'I'll bring it to your birthday party,' he says, as Janet leaves. Catching sight of his reflection in the hall mirror, Oscar angrily smashes the looking glass into fragments with his fist.

Having returned to her home and entered her father's study, Janet finds Sir Charles talking to two men. 'Father, I must have a word with you,' she calls, ignoring the guard posted by the door. He points out that it is not a very convenient time and that he sincerely hopes that she is not about to make a practice of bursting into his room unannounced. Told by his daughter that her business is both important and personal, Sir Charles asks the men to give them a few minutes alone. 'Now my dear,?' he asks sitting at his desk. 'You know where he is . . . all this time you've known and you've let me go through this hell. You sent him on a mission, he can't get in touch with me.' 'I presume we're talking about your fiancé,' says Sir Charles. 'His house, his car, he's lent them to a friend,' she says. 'A friend? Tell me about him . . . what sort of a man is he?' asks her father. 'He's perfectly ordinary . . . Is he able to get in touch with me?' 'I honestly don't know.' 'Do you mean you haven't sent him on a mission?' 'No,' shrugs her father. 'And you must realise I'm telling you more than I should. I shouldn't even tell you that.' 'You mean even you don't know where he is?' asks Janet. 'I have no idea,' her father replies shaking his head. 'But you must know someone who does.' 'There again I can't help you.' 'It's awful. I don't know whether you're telling me the truth or not,' she accuses, turning her head away in disgust. When her father remains passive in his seat, Janet leaves. At that moment, outside 'his' residence, Oscar leaps into the yellow and green customised Lotus 7 which stands parked at the curb. Revving its engine, he sets out at speed and weaves the machine through the busy London traffic, following the route indelibly etched in his mind – a mind which now occupies the body of another. The drive to the underground car park is accomplished in minutes, as is the purposeful march along its dimly-lit corridor. The metal 'exit' doors offer no resistance, nor does the man sitting beneath the map of the world – a new face this time, a younger man climbing his way up the ladder of seniority – who offers little beyond a token 'Who are you? What are you doing here?' The young man finds himself being grabbed by the collar and hoisted from his chair by the intruder who demands that he gets him Sir Charles Portland at once! Supported by his jacket lapels, the executive knocks over his tea cup as his fingers snake out across his desk to press an alarm button.

Their roles are now reversed, with the man back in his seat and Oscar standing erect before the desk. His determination unchanged, despite the two burly guards who stand but a few feet away, the intruder's daring knows no limits. 'You're still as pompous as ever Danvers,' Oscar grins to the man behind the desk. 'Where did you get my name?' demands the seated man. 'Jonathan Peregrine Danvers. Born in Bootle. Took elocution lessons . . . came to London in 1948 as a junior clerk. Was moved to this department some three years later, mainly at the request of the typing pool . . . Am I going to see Sir Charles? Well . . . or would you prefer me to go on . . . I'm sure these 'gentlemen' would be most intrigued to hear of your little jaunt to Paris in March 1958 . . . Let me see now, what was her name . . .' Danvers is saved from further embarrassment by the arrival in the room of another man. Walking calmly to Oscar's side, he demands the intruder's name. 'Code or real?' taunts the intruder. 'Code.' 'In France, Duval. In Germany, Schmit. You would know me best as ZM 73, and *your* code number is PR12. Do you want more . . . Seltzman,' grins Oscar. 'Alright, thank you,' says PR12, dismissing the two heavies who stand at the door. 'Danvers, I must ask you to leave.' 'Yes sir,' says the man behind the desk, rising to follow his companions out of the room. 'What do you know about Seltzman?' asks the superior when the men are alone. 'He invented the device that makes it possible to put one man's mind into another man's head,' states the intruder. The one denoted PR12, is aghast, particularly when the other slips a photograph of Number 6 from his pocket. Aware now that the intruder knows something, the superior escorts him into an elevator. Several stories above their departure point, the two men step into a corridor. Having shown his pass to the guard at an office door PR12 and his companion are allowed to enter. Ushered into Sir Charles' study, Oscar marches to the man's desk. 'Sir Charles, at last . . . I am ZM73.' You *claim* to be ZM73,' challenges the silver-haired man. 'And I can prove it!' 'Do so,' bids Sir Charles. 'I could pitch this on a very personal level Sir Charles . . .' 'Oh don't spare my feelings,' grins the other 'speak as freely as you wish.' 'Very well,' says Oscar. 'I will confine myself to simple domestic details, of no interest to anyone accept the family . . . Details incidentally which couldn't possibly be known to anyone except ourselves, would you accept that . . .?' 'Yes. I suppose so,' says Sir Charles. The newcomer proceeds with his claim: Sir Charles is a rosarian and it was while he was pruning his baccara, the one down by the little goldfish pool, that ZM73 asked for the hand of his daughter. He remembers that Sir Charles dropped his secateurs – he had never understood why, because it could not have been all that much of a surprise. The next day Sir Charles had taken him to lunch at his club. They had their favourite dish, jugged hare. But still Sir Charles refutes his story. 'I don't dispute the accuracy of your statement, it's correct in every detail. The trouble is, you see, there's nothing you can tell me which may not have been told to you by the person you claim to be under sedation or hypnosis,' says Sir Charles. 'It could have all been recorded and you could have learned it parrot fashion.' 'Ask me the minutest details of anything you know that we did together,' urges Oscar. The same problem applies, the other confirms. 'I could never convince you then,' states Oscar. 'Only sufficiently to intrigue me . . . to make sure that you are watched and followed every inch of wherever you go,' confirms the silver-haired man. 'It's a waste of somebody's time,' growls Oscar. 'He'll be paid for it.' 'Thank you, thank you very much,' says Oscar, making his way back to the elevator alone, the words of his alter-ego urging him onward. '*Where is he? . . . where is he? . . . where is he? . . . Did he perfect the reversion process? If he didn't . . . it's a pity.*' Driving back to his home, he overtakes a long black saloon – a hearse. Are *they* after him again? A false alarm. The hearse has followed a different route . . . perhaps so, but why is he now passing the ominous vehicle again as he brakes the Lotus to a stop outside his home – and what dark business in the street does the gaunt-faced undertaker have, the one standing by the parked hearse just a few feet down the road? Entering the house, the words of his alter-ego begin anew. '*Before I know it, I'll be inside for forgery . . . Talking of forgery, is my handwriting still the same? Let's see, lets try it . . .*' he checks the Prisoner's handwriting against his own. They are the same. The alter-ego laughs '*. . . That's rather interesting isn't it . . . that's something . . . Well let's be grateful for small mercies . . . Now, money. Unless the rats have been at it . . .*' He opens a safe, secreted behind his television set. '*. . . good . . . still intact . . . fresh as ever. Splendid.*' Oscar counts the wad of bank notes he has removed from the safe. '*. . . That should be adequate.*' Placing the bank notes into his wallet, Oscar picks up the framed photograph of Janet. An idea.

'Are you sure he's being followed,' Sir Charles asks PR12, as the superior enters his boss' study. 'We've attached a homing device to his car, our man will be there by now,'

Entering the Portlands' mansion, Oscar finds the party in full swing

confirms the junior. It is dark when a tuxedo-suited Oscar enters the Portlands' mansion. A party is in full swing and a waiter hands him a glass of champagne. Of course, it is Janet's birthday. Draining his glass, he elbows his way through the guests and escorts Janet to the dance floor. 'I didn't invite you,' she says, as they glide around the floor. 'Our friend lent me his card, a year out of date . . .' 'You've seen him?' 'Not exactly,' he grins. 'Look. Do you work for my father. Did he send you here?' 'No, but I've no doubt that he knows that I'm here . . . When I arrived they were playing a waltz, the first I danced with my love . . .' The girl stares at him in astonishment. '. . . my dear beloved in Kitzbuhel.' This cannot be happening. 'How do you know all this? Where is he? Please,' pleads Janet. 'I have a message from him . . . before he went, he left something with you for safe keeping in case of trouble. A slip of paper.' 'Yes, yes I have it,' she says, unable to comprehend how 'he' can know so much about 'him'. 'Do you want to see him again? Will you get it . . . I'll be in the arbour,' he urges, ending their dance and retreating through the French windows. 'May I?' asks a young man, inviting the girl to dance. '*Was she just trying to get rid of me? Will she come? Will she have the receipt?*' whispers his alter-ego as Oscar waits in the garden. But Janet does arrive and she has the receipt. 'I'm sorry I was so long . . . here it is,' she apologises handing Oscar a scrap of paper. 'What was the message?' 'Simply this . . .' he replies, raising his hand to caress her cheek. Following this with a peck to each cheek and one to her nose, he embraces the girl and they share a long passionate kiss. Pulling away, she steps backwards, her thoughts unable to grasp what has happened. 'Who else could have given you *that* message?' he asks over his shoulder. 'Nobody . . . but . . .?' 'Couldn't you say, nobody but you . . . I need your faith.' Janet turns. 'Nobody but . . . *you*,' she concedes. She knows now. As difficult as it is for her to understand, she knows.

Bright and early the next morning, Oscar makes his way to a high street camera shop to collect an order 'he' left there 12 months earlier: a roll of film which he had left to be developed into transparencies. Handed the receipt, the camera shop owner confirms that the order had been collected by a Mr Carmichael – a clerical error. However, discovering his mistake the man had returned them, so no harm has been done. 'How very good of Mr Carmichael,' says Oscar. 'It's very kind of you to take it that way sir. Alas, no business can be entirely free from the occasional clerical error. Is there anything else sir?' 'Yes.' 'What is that sir?' 'Can I get a photograph taken?' asks Oscar. 'A photograph?' 'Yes. A passport photograph.' 'I'm afraid our photographer's away on holiday at the moment sir,' replies the shop owner. 'Hmm, he would be.' However, the other is happy to oblige – as long as the customer does not require a flattering study, but one that will be satisfactory for the passport authorities. 'Thank you,' says Oscar. 'It's a pleasure sir. This way . . .' grins the camera shop owner leading the customer into a back room.

'He has collected the transparencies sir,' confirms PR12, reporting to Sir Charles. 'Condones my conviction . . . somewhere they contain a clue and our own bright boys have missed it,' states the superior. Followed back to his home by Potter, one of Sir Charles' men, Oscar parks his Lotus at the curb and enters his home. 'XB4,' reports Potter, from his car parked outside the house. 'He's gone inside . . . and now the living room curtains are being drawn.' The lookout is ordered to stay at his post and follow his quarry when he leaves. Having erected a projection screen in his living room, Oscar moves to his desk, pulls a writing pad towards him and writes two rows of figures on the blank page. One above the other they read: SELT and ZMAN. This done, he counts on his fingers and writes the number five above the letter E. A further finger count and the number 20 is placed above the letter T. Muttering aloud he whispers, 'Miss out the one M . . .' then, counting aloud on his fingers, '. . . A, b,c,d,e,f,g,h,i,j,k,l,m – 13, and N must be 14 . . .' The letters M and N on the paper before him are numbered 13 and 14 respectively. Shuffling the numbered slides into a certain order, he begins to lay each one by its equivalent number on the writing pad. This done, he sets aside the unwanted slides and places the remainder into the projector, superimposing one on top of the other. By using a special set of dark lenses which are snapped into place over his reading glasses, he reads off the words that are now magically brought into view on the screen, KANDERSFELD, AUSTRIA. Shutting off the projector, he locates the town in an Atlas, destroys his notes and stows the projector away. 'Hello sir,' reports Potter from his car, 'the curtains are now being opened . . . he's coming out of the house and getting into the Lotus.' 'Follow him,' orders Sir Charles.

'Our route is definitely Dover,' reports Potter, following the Lotus as its speeds down the A20 to the ferry port. Using the electronic bug planted on Oscar's car, the pursuer follows his quarry aboard. A short time later, Oscar steers the Lotus into the forecourt of an Austrian cafe. 'Welcome to the village sir,' greets a waiter. 'What would you like to order?' 'I took some photographs, look . . . here's one,' says the customer, handing the waiter one of his colour slides. 'Is he still here?' 'Yes. Herr Hallen sir,' confirms the other. 'Where is he now?' 'In the barber's shop I suppose,' grins the waiter, pointing to a building across the street. Entering the establishment, Oscar is greeted by a grey-haired old man wearing a barber's smock. The man greets him in a foreign tongue. 'Good afternoon, Herr Hallen. The waiter at the cafe told me I could get a shave here.' 'That is correct sir,' confirms the barber, lapsing into foreign dialect again as he motions for the customer to sit in a chair by a sink. 'Please sit down mein herr.' 'Your English is very good,' says Oscar lowering himself into the seat. 'Yes,' replies the other, explaining that he learned his trade in London, but returned to the village in which he was born. 'Herr Hallen, I may as well come to the point,' says Oscar, resisting the man's attempts to drape a smock around his shoulders. 'I don't want a shave, I want your help, desperately . . .' 'In what way sir?' asks the other. 'We have met before. But you couldn't possibly remember me because the first time we met I looked like this.' He hands the other a photograph of himself. (The Prisoner). 'It is not possible!' exclaims the man. 'You see, Professor Seltzman, your invention works . . . only too well.' 'I am simply a village barber,' tries the other. 'Don't play tricks on an old man, I beg of you.' 'Believe me, Herr Professor, you're the last person in the world I would choose but somebody's played a wretched trick on me. Do you recognise that face?' 'Of course, he was a friend . . . But anyone who has that photograph could claim to be him.' 'For what reason?' asks the customer. 'Perhaps you will tell me,' says the other returning the photograph. 'I understand,' says Oscar, rising to his feet. 'Incognito, until I can prove that I *am* that man. When everything I tell you can be countered by you. By saying that I have extracted the information by fair means or foul.' 'Yes, that is so,' says the barber. 'Herr Professor, would you admit that, as with fingerprints no, two handwritings could be the same?' 'I would.' 'Then the only way that I can prove to you that I am that man, depends on whether or not you kept that letter I sent you over a year ago from London when you were staying in Scotland.' 'If you really are who you say you are, you would not have expected me to keep it. Would you?' challenges the other. 'No . . .' sighs Oscar. 'It's a hopeless situation.' 'If I had kept it I would have been very stupid, silly.' 'You've made your point, I accept it,' sighs the customer accepting his fate. 'But you overlook one thing . . .' grins the other '. . . Sentimental people *are* sometimes stupid, very stupid. Wait please,' he smiles, disappearing from the room. Potter, meanwhile, guided by the blips from the hidden bug, is approaching the village at speed. The barber soon returns, carrying with him a letter. Having written the man's Scottish address on his note pad, Oscar tears off the page and hands it to the Professor for comparison. The handwriting matches the envelope the customer mailed to his friend 12 months earlier. 'My poor young friend . . . but *who*?' 'I don't know,' replies the other. 'The motive is clear. You will lead them to me, that is what they hope. Do you think your people have done this to you?' 'No, I'm sure . . .' Oscar says. 'Then it must be your enemies.' 'My enemies presumably having my other half.' 'Precisely. If you are taken by the side that hasn't you must learn to accept yourself as you are.' As they speak, Potter enters the village and parks his car at the cafe across the street. 'As both sides want my reversal process it will be a close race,' says the Professor. 'Then the reversal process *does* exist?' 'In theory, but put into practice, it could be dangerous. Very,' warns the elderly man, leading Oscar to the window. Drawing back the curtain and seeing Potter heading across the street towards them, the Professor asks his friend if his face is familiar. 'Potter,' confirms Oscar. 'We must not be taken by *him*.' Then hide behind this door,' urges his friend, leading the other into a room at the rear of the shop. Closing the door behind him, Oscar stares down into the darkened cellar below. 'Come in, come in,' calls the Professor, as Potter stalks into the shop. 'Don't move please, Professor,' warns the thug, ignoring the man in the chair. Having searched the shop thoroughly, he notices the door at the rear of the premises. Sliding his gun from its holster, Potter rams open the door. Grabbing the thug's arm, Oscar pulls him into the cellar and the men fight on the staircase. Downwards they tumble, picking up where they left off on the cellar floor. Snatching up a chair, Potter brings it crashing down onto his opponent's head, but still Oscar fights back, the fury and strength of his punches sending the other reeling backwards. The fight is hard-fought and culminates with both men lying unconscious – overcome by the clouds of acrid gas emitting from a strange gun held by a third man, who, having descended the staircase unseen, grins as the men fall backwards into oblivion.

'Ah, Herr Professor,' greets Number 2, as Oscar and the scientist are ushered into the dome shaped chamber. 'Welcome to *our* humble village. Had a good trip? At least let me offer you some breakfast,' grins the superior, turning to the po-faced Butler. 'You have kidnapped me for one reason . . . my answer is no!' challenges the Professor. 'You are livery this morning Professor,' laughs Number 2. 'Surely neither of us wants to prolong this interview,' says the scientist. 'Life has not brought you sweet resignation,' quips Number 2. 'Nor has it for many other scientists. Rutherford, for example. How he must regret having split the atom.' 'Yes . . .' mocks Number 2, '. . . almost as bad as splitting two human beings. Unlike all the king's men, only you can put them together again.' 'Don't rely on it,' warns the Professor. 'Why make this stand now. You must have known what you were doing when you invented the wretched process,' states the superior. 'Only people like you have made it wretched.'

The fury of Oscar's punches send Potter reeling

'Can you really leave this poor man with his mind wrongly housed,' challenges Number 2, indicating Oscar. 'Surely you owe him some slight responsibility.' Pausing for a moment to glance sideways at his friend and then at the monitor screen on which is pictured Number 6 – his head strapped to a concoction of wires, his eyes unseen behind the black-tinted goggles – the Professor gathers his thoughts. 'I will do it . . . on certain conditions,' he concedes. 'I'm sure they will be reasonable,' grins Number 2, putting on his glasses. 'For once *I* am dictating,' snaps the scientist. 'Heil . . .', mocks the superior, raising his arm in a Nazi salute. 'I will do it . . . but alone, under this condition only,' states the Professor. 'I accept,' nods Number 2. 'Very well. I shall need time to prepare myself. In 12 hours . . .' stipulates the scientist, departing from the chamber with his friend. Alone, the superior's lips draw back into an insidious grin. Twelve hours later, the experiment gets under way, watched from his Control Room by Number 2 and a group of white-coated observers. 'All cameras turn . . . make a note of everything he does,' orders the superior, as the Professor enters the laboratory to begin the reversal process. Viewed on the monitor screen, the scientist flicks on the bank of machinery. Then, placing an electrode device over his head, he sits down in a chair positioned between Oscar and his alter-ego, who are strapped to the operating couches within arms-reach of the scientist. At the flick of a switch, a milky-pink cloud begins to form over the head of Number 6, while a blue haze shimmers above Oscar's head. The power is increased and a flickering array of electrical disturbance channels its way across the divide between the recumbent men; the man in the chair forming a three-way link between them. But the power is too great. With trembling hands, the Professor slumps forward, his teeth biting his lips, his face a mask of torment. 'Emergency . . . examination room, immediate treatment,' screams Number 2. *'Emergency, emergency,'* echoes a voice over the public address system. Within seconds, two male orderlies race into the laboratory and place the Professor's unconscious body onto a stretcher. *'Emergency, emergency,'* screams the voice from the public address system as an ambulance races away from the building. 'He must not die . . . I need him,' orders Number 2, to the group of medical people attending the scientist's body. 'Thank you Colonel,' he says to Oscar 'Your help has been invaluable.' 'I trust I've been of service,' comments the other. 'Yes. You'll be suitably rewarded . . . the helicopter is waiting for you.' Slipping on his jacket, the Colonel leaves. 'You assured me that he was in good health,' whispers the Professor, raising himself from the couch. 'You must contact Number 1, and tell him that I did my duty . . .' With a final gasp of breath, the patient slumps backwards onto the stretcher. 'The *Colonel* . . .?' hisses Number 2, concerned by the dead man's words '. . . the man who is just flying out of here . . .?' He stares to the ceiling as the helicopter passes over head. '. . . Is not who you thought it was,' confirms Number 6, sitting erect on the couch. 'I don't believe it . . . I *watched*, I saw *everything*,' whispers a resigned Number 2. Stripping off his goggles, and tearing the wires from his person, Number 6 delivers the coup de grace. 'The good doctor's mind now inhabits a body perhaps not to his liking . . . the Colonel's . . . Dr Seltzman had progressed more than any of us had anticipated. He *can* and *did change three minds at the* same time.' The ashen-faced superior stares back at him in total amazement. 'He's now free to continue his experiments in peace,' concludes Number 6, as the helicopter soars high over the Village. With the Colonel dead in the Professor's body, Number 2 has lost both the game and his post!

'The man flying out of here is not the man you thought it was'

AUTHOR'S NOTE: A different pre-credit scene and slightly different title sequence appear in this story.

The letter to Professor Seltzman is addressed in McGoohan's own hand and the address on the envelope 'Portmeirion Road' was an in-joke. All McGoohan's scenes were done in a one day shoot.

Originally filmed under the working title *Face Unknown*.

A lone rider gallops across the prairie, his mount given free rein to increase its speed. At his desk in a nearby town sits a Marshal, pen in hand, filling in a report. As if by magic, the Prisoner appears before him, his dark-piped blazer replaced by a thigh-length buckskin range coat, his legs protected by western-style riding breetches, a low-slung Colt 45 strapped to his right hip. Staring at the Marshal from beneath the brim of his stetson, the intruder flicks out his hand and a badge lands squarely on the lawman's desk – but not, as could be expected, one bearing the numeral '6', but a star-shaped Sheriff's badge of office. Returning the newcomer's stare, the lawman pays scant attention as the intruder unbuckles his gun belt and slams it forcefully down on the desk to join the Sheriff's star. Heaving his saddle to his shoulder, the Prisoner leaves and sets out on foot across the hills. Descending a slope, he finds his way blocked by a cowboy toting a gun. Ignoring the man, he attempts to move past him but finds himself looking up the barrell of the man's revolver. The saddle, thrown with lighting speed, hits the cowboy square on the jaw, sending him reeling backwards down a grassy knoll. In a flash the Prisoner is upon him and the two men fight. Knocked to the ground, the Prisoner crawls to his knees – to find himself facing five other men. His refusal to concede brings punches raining down on his head and he is forced to his knees in an onslaught of flailing fists . . .

Having handed in his tin star, he sets out on foot

LIVING IN HARMONY

Written by David Tomblin

(from an original story by David Tomblin and Ian L. Rakoff)

Guest stars

The Kid	**Alexis Kanner**
The Judge	**David Bauer**
Cathy	**Valerie French**

with

Town Elder	**Gordon Tanner**
Bystander	**Gordon Sterne**
Will	**Michael Balfour**
Mexican Sam	**Larry Taylor**
Town Dignitary	**Monti De Lyle**

and

Horse Dealer	**Douglas Jones**
1st Gunman	**Bill Nick**
2nd Gunman	**Les Crawford**
3rd Gunman	**Frank Maher**
1st Horseman	**Max Faulkner**
2nd Horseman	**Bill Cummings**
3rd Horseman	**Eddie Eddon**

Directed by David Tomblin

POUNDED INTO unconsciousness, the man's body is strapped to a horse which gallops away to a nearby town. His saddle thongs are sliced and the helpless man is dumped onto a dusty street. Their work done, the horsemen ride away. Climbing groggily to his feet, he dusts himself down and stares around the town. Its streets are deserted save for one man, a Mexican who sits with his back to a watering-trough. 'Welcome to Harmony, stranger,' calls the man, as the newcomer hoists his saddle onto his shoulder. 'Harmony. Never heard of it,' states the Prisoner. 'Not many people have senor, it's sorta exclusive,' grins the other. 'So am I,' quips the stranger. 'Where is this town?' 'You'll find out senor, it's not wise to ask too many questions.' The stranger makes to leave. 'Hey hombre,' calls the Mexican, inclining his head in the direction of the cantina behind him, 'you look like a man who could use a drink . . . why not try the saloon.'

Carrying his saddle, the newcomer enters the saloon. As he does so, the place becomes silent: the pianist removes his fingers from the keys; the drinkers and card players look at him in astonishment. Ignoring their stares, he crosses over to the bar, dumps his saddle at his feet and is joined by a pretty girl. 'Regulars get the first one on the house,' she says as the bartender slides a glass of whisky down the bar. 'I'm not regular,' he quips staring at the glass. 'I'm Cathy.' 'Nice name,' he returns reaching for the drink. A shot rings out and the glass disintegrates. 'Come and join me Sheriff,' shouts a voice. 'Whisky,' he calls, ignoring the voice. The bartender fills a new glass. Downing it in one gulp, the Prisoner turns, his eyes trained on a grey-haired man – the town Judge – who sits at a table playing solitaire. Crossing to the card-player, he pauses for an instant to stare at the young man who stands at the Judge's side – the baby-faced gunslinger who shot the whisky glass from his fingers. Without warning, he sends the youngster reeling with a powerful right hand to the jaw, then pulls up a chair and joins the card-player. 'You know me,' he says. 'You shouldn'ta done that. A man needs all the friends he can find,' warns the Judge. 'I don't know you,' states the Prisoner. 'I know you. I know all about you. That's why you're here,' insists the card player. 'Where?' asks the newcomer. 'Here,' says the other gulping back his drink. 'Cathy, bring us more whisky.' At that moment, the young man the Prisoner punched recovers consciousness. The gunslinger staggers to his feet, grabs his top hat, dusts it and, given a barely perceptible nod from the Judge, leaves the saloon. 'He's good. Sensitive, but one of the best . . . but he's mean,' the card player relates. 'You've got plenty of those,' mocks the stranger. 'I could use some more . . . like yourself for instance.' 'I'm not for hire.' 'You've turned in your badge.' 'And my gun,'the Prisoner confirms. 'What were your reasons?' '*My*' reasons,' replies the other with a grin. 'You've already taken a job. Who with?' 'With whom?' mocks the other. 'Look,' grins the Judge, '*I'm* offering you a job. Harmony's a good town . . .' The saloon doors swing back and three newcomers swagger up to the bar and order drinks. ' . . . Runs smooth and peaceful. Now let's be friendly,' says the card player. 'Red two on black three,' quips the Prisoner, laying a red deuce on the card player's hand. Drawing another card from the pack, a black ace, the Judge grins. 'Think it over.' 'I already have . . . ' says the other, easing back his chair. 'And?' ' . . . I'm moving on,' grins the Prisoner, climbing to his feet and crossing to the bar where he left his saddle. Picking it up, he starts to leave. He stops, thoughtfully. Drops the saddle and walks back to the men at the bar. Removing a gambling chip from his pocket, he holds it under the nose of one of the men and flings it to the bar. Then, hoisting the saddle onto his shoulder he leaves.

'How much?' he asks, indicating a horse tethered to a post outside the stable. 'Sold,' replies the stable keeper from his rocking chair. 'The bay?' tries the Prisoner, looking at a second horse, 'How much?' '$5,000.' 'The rest?' 'They're expensive,' mocks the other. 'How's business?' quips the Prisoner, making to leave. Before him stands the town elder. 'Well stranger, fancy living in Harmony?' 'Not

'Harmony's a good town . . runs smooth and peaceful'

my kind of town,' retorts the other, walking next to the man. 'It's a good town,' says the elder, picking up the stranger's step. 'Enjoy it,' grins the other. 'Why. What's wrong with out town mister?' 'Maybe I don't like the way it's run,' replies the other. 'Oh if you just do as the Judge says, he'll look after you.' '*I* look after myself.' 'It's a good town,' the elder insists. 'Keep it!' the Prisoner exclaims, as Mexican Sam (the man who welcomed him to Harmony) grabs his saddle and heaves it to the ground. 'So you don't like our town huh. You insult us,' roars the Mexican, turning to address the group of townsfolk who have appeared on the scene. 'Are we going to let him do this?' he growls. 'He's insulted our town,' yells a resident. As the stranger picks up a length of timber to stave off their attack, a man with a gun appears on the scene. Firing the weapon in the air, he points the Colt at the stranger's chest. 'All right folks. We'll take care of him . . . now git.' At gun-point, the Prisoner is taken to the Sheriff's office. Inside he finds the Judge, sitting calmly at his desk. 'Change your mind yet?' he grins, as the crowd gathered outside scream for the stranger's head. 'Charge?' asks the Prisoner. 'Protective custody,' grins the Judge. 'Lock him up and bring Johnson out here . . . We mustn't disappoint the crowd.' Two men step forward and drag the Prisoner to a cell. As the bars slam shut in his face, another man is pulled from the adjoining cell and thrown screaming into the street. 'There he is,' yells Mexican Sam, as the crowd surges forward. Dragged beneath a tree in the town square, a noose is thrown over the man's head. His hands are tied behind his back and the lariat is thrown upwards, its trailing end looped over a sturdy branch. 'Stop it . . . stop it!' screams Cathy, arriving on the scene and racing to the intended victim's side. 'You can't hang my brother, he's done nothing wrong . . . you promised . . . ' she screams, as the blood-crazy crowd surges forwards to get a better view of the hanging. ' . . . Let go of me, let go!' the girl screams as two cowboys drag her away, her words lost in the roar of the crowd. Screaming, she faints as a blood-thirsty cowboy whips the horse from under her brother. Watching this from his cell window, the Prisoner lowers his eyes. Behind him, the young gunslinger he had earlier knocked cold, calmly quenches his thirst from a bottle.

Drunk now, and finding it difficult to maintain his equilibrium, the top-hatted youngster plays a game of now-you-see-me-now-you-don't with the Prisoner, goading the man by leaping into sight with his revolver raised in threatening manner and then back again to snatch his Colt from its holster with lightning speed. Observing the young man's antics with total disregard, the Prisoner calmly rolls himself a cigarette and sits unmoved on his bunk. After a few minutes, Cathy arrives carrying a bottle. 'I've brought you a drink Kid,' she smiles, placing the bottle on the desk next to the youngster's feet. Lowering his boots from the desk, the Kid, who is mute, walks behind her. 'You know I've always liked you Kid,' smiles the girl, as the baby-faced gunslinger grabs her and kisses her passionately on the lips, his hands clutching at her dress. 'Hey, how about pouring me one?' grins Cathy, pulling free of his hold. As the youngster searches the desk for glasses, Cathy slips the keys to the cells from a hook on the wall and hides them inside her dress. The glasses found, the mute pours her a drink and attempts to kiss her again. 'Not now Kid, I've got to get back to the saloon,' she teases. 'I'll drop by later.' Before he can offer any resistance, she quickly walks out of the door. Stunned by this new development, the Kid begins to sob, while outside in the alley, Cathy places the keys she has stolen onto the window ledge of the Prisoner's cell. Intoxicated, the Kid curls up in a chair and drifts off to sleep. Donning his stetson, the Prisoner gently unlocks the door of his cell and slips out into the darkness. Having saddled a horse at the stable, he is about to depart when Cathy arrives carrying a canteen of water. Advised by the girl that there is only one way out, due north, the fugitive rides off into the night.

Returning to the jailhouse and finding the Prisoner gone, the Judge throws the Kid from his chair. Dazed from his drinking bout, the mute goes for his gun, but his employer slaps his face several times. Galloping away from the town, the Prisoner is lassoed by two lookouts. The lariat is tied to the pommel of a rider's horse and the Prisoner is dragged back to the town. 'Let justice be done,' grins the Judge, banging his glass on a table as the fugitive is thrown at his feet. Anticipating some fun and games, several cowboys line up their chairs in front of the Judge who, banging his gavel hard on a table, calls for order. 'Order! The court is now in session,' grins the Judge. 'What's the charge?' sneers the Prisoner. 'Against *you*, none,' smiles the Judge. 'You were only held in protective custody. You're free to go.' Turning, the Prisoner joins Cathy at the bar and pours himself a whisky. 'The people of Harmony against Catherine Johnson,' calls the Judge. 'The accused step forward.' The words burn into the Prisoner's brain. Turning to face the court, he pours himself another drink as the girl at his shoulder steps forward to face the Judge. 'You are accused of aiding a criminal to escape. How do you plead?' 'But Judge, you just said that he wasn't a criminal, he was just being held in protective custody,' a bystander pipes up. '*She* didn't know that!' snaps the Judge, quelling the outburst. 'How do you plead?' Cathy says nothing. Sometime later, the jury returns. 'Have you reached a verdict?' barks the Judge. 'We have your honour,' confirms a town dignitary. 'Do you find the defendant guilty or not guilty?' 'Guilty!' comes the reply. 'I will pass sentence later. Take her away.' Cathy is taken off to the jail and all, save the bartender, the Prisoner and the Judge leave the saloon. 'When you work for me, I'll let her go,' grins the latter, joining the Prisoner. 'You're a bad judge,' whispers the other. 'We'll see, we'll see,' grins the arbitrator, edging his way past the one he wishes to employ. Turning back to the barman, the Prisoner calls for another drink.

Placed on the far end of the bar counter, a top hat and a Colt 45 are swept along the bar to rest at the Prisoner's right wrist. It is the Kid. Peering at the newcomer from beneath his stetson, the Prisoner sighs, draws himself to his full height and turns to face the gunslinger. As if by magic, a gun appears in the Kid's hand. A shot rings out, and the Prisoner flinches as the bullet grazes his cheek. Another shot, and a trickle of blood appears on the man's left hand. 'Hold it!' cries the Judge, re-entering the saloon. 'I've been looking for you Kid . . . decided to give you your old job back. Go take care of the jail.' This pacifies the gunslinger, who, sliding his gun back into its holster, reaches across to the bar to pick up his top hat. 'You'll need two of these to take care of the woman,' taunts the Prisoner, sliding back the Kid's gun. A look of anger crosses the Kid's face. Snatching up the Colt, he aims it at the man standing at the bar. 'There's always another time Kid,' warns the Judge, grabbing the gunman's wrist. Placing his topper squarely on his head, the youngster leaves the saloon. 'The Kid's real fond of Cathy. But he does tend to get *over*-affectionate,' the grey-haired man admits. 'If anything happens, it will be paid for,' threatens the Prisoner, elbowing his way past the man. 'Nothing could happen . . . if *you* were Sheriff,' grins the Judge.

Watching the girl pacing the floor of her cell, the Kid licks his lips in anticipation of the pleasure in store. Entering the jail and seeing the gunslinger ogling Cathy's every move, the Prisoner snorts in disgust when the Judge shoves a sheriff's badge under his nose. 'Let her go!' he exclaims, snatching the star from the other man's hand. 'Let her out Kid,' orders the Judge, walking into the cell block. The youngster stares back in silence. 'I said let her out!' warns his employer. Gritting his teeth, the Kid rises from his chair and unlocks the door to Cathy's cell, his intense stare never leaving the face of his master. 'Don't give me any problems,' snarls the Judge as the girl joins the newly-elected Sheriff. 'I'm sorry,' she says. 'It's alright,' he confirms as the girl leaves the office. 'She's safe now. Safe for as long as you work for me . . . ' the Judge tells the Prisoner. ' . . . But enough of that. We don't want to start off on the wrong foot. You're gonna like this job, it's most rewarding . . . ' he says, leaving the Prisoner to bandage his hand. ' . . . No Sheriff, you won't regret joining my outfit.' 'No, but *you* may,' goads the other. 'You're just sore at the moment. Here, put this on, you'll feel better,' says the Judge, offering the other a gunbelt he has fetched from his desk. 'Nothing but the best.' 'I agreed to wear the badge. But not the guns,' states the Sheriff, knotting the bandage he has taped round his wrist. 'It's a start. But you'll find this a rough town without a gun,' warns the other, placing the gunbelt back on his desk. Later, while out on his rounds, the Sheriff is confronted by a cowboy. 'Mornin' Sheriff . . . I'm Zeke. I don't carry no gun either, but then *I* don't need one.' The Sheriff attempts to push his way past the man, but Zeke blocks his way. A mistake. Within seconds the cowboy lies flat on his back, his head resting on a pile of logs. Two others arrive, but Zeke calls them off. 'He's mine!' he screams, picking up a short piece of timber with the intention of clubbing the other into the dust. A long fight ensues and Zeke is decisively thrashed. The others join in and the Sheriff is attacked from all sides. In the saloon, the Judge rejoins his card school. 'The boys are just teaching him it's not safe to walk around without guns,' he grins, puffing on his cheroot. Outnumbered, the Prisoner gives a good account of himself as one after the other, Zeke and his companions rain blows to his jaw. Watched by the townsfolk, the men fight their way across the street until, tired and exhausted, the Sheriff is clubbed to the ground. Down but not out, he drags himself to within reaching distance of his remaining assailant (the others litter the street) crawls to his feet, and throws one final punishing knockout blow to the other man's jaw. Grabbing his groggy opponent by the shirt, he throws him sideways into the horse trough and then into the dirt. Back in his office, Cathy enters to help him bathe his wounds. 'Are you hurt?' 'Nothing a bit of water won't take care of,' he says splashing water to his face. 'I'm sorry, I'm blushing . . . I didn't think I could blush anymore,' she sighs. 'It's alright.' 'Get out or they'll kill you,' she pleads. 'The last time I got out, they dragged me back and er . . . I can't refuse that kind of hospitality. Can I?' 'You saw what they did to my brother.' 'That's one of the reasons I'm staying . . . ' 'He was a stubborn man too,' Cathy interjects. 'I'll be in the saloon tonight . . . Regulars get the first one . . . ' 'On the house,' he finishes as the girl leaves.

Things in the saloon are rowdy. A cheroot between his lips, the Kid stands at the bar, his eyes glued on Cathy,

Watched by the townsfolk, the Sheriff throws a final punishing blow to his opponent's jaw

who is enjoying a drink. At a table in the corner, two old-timers engage in an arm-wrestling contest, the man who spoke up in defence of Cathy emerging the winner. The loser, a small man, leads the victor to the bar. 'Come on bartender, let's have some whisky . . . Drink up, they're on me,' he calls throwing his arm around Cathy's shoulder. 'C'mon Cathy, you're going to have one on me,' he slurs. 'Okay Will, but don't let your wife catch you,' she teases. Witnessing this, the Kid removes the cheroot from his lips and purposefully rams the cigar into the drunken man's neck. Staggering away in pain, Will turns on his attacker. Seeing the Kid standing silently by the bar, the lethal Colt strapped to his hip, the small man stops in his tracks. Inclining his head to one side, the Kid stares back in silence. As one, everyone in the room races for cover, all save Cathy, who, approaching the youngster cautions him to wait. But he shoves her aside. Drawing his gun, Will makes no attempt to shoot, the Kid doing likewise. Backing towards the bar in a mock expression of defeat, the youngster draws with frightening speed and shoots the man through the heart. Looking silently at the crowd, the gunslinger turns to leave. At that moment, the Sheriff enters the saloon. 'Will drew first Sheriff,' confirms a bystander, as the Kid leaves the saloon. 'You're the Sheriff, it's up to you,' calls a voice from the crowd. 'It's time you did something . . . Get some guns on.' 'You're wearing the star, you know Sheriff, c'mon,' challenges another as, watched by the Judge, the lawman leaves. Later that evening, the man who spoke the loudest, pays the Sheriff a visit. 'Some of us have been talking Sheriff . . . ' 'Yeah,' replies the lawman. ' . . .

You're the only man who stood up to the Judge. So we're with you.' 'Yeah?' 'We'll help you clean up this town,' confirms the visitor. 'You're-going-to-help-*me*-clean-up-the-town,' quizzes the lawman. 'We can't do it by ourselves,' the other concedes, 'and Sheriff, neither can you.' 'Get yourself some coffee,' smiles the lawman.

'Whisky,' calls the bystander, a few minutes later as he enters the saloon. 'That one's on me,' calls the Judge over the man's shoulder. 'Come over Jim,' he bids from his table. The Sheriff's new ally joins him. 'Jim, you disappoint me . . . your choice of friends, Jim, *old* friends are the best friends. What were you talking to the Sheriff about?' The newcomer remains silent. 'Well if you won't tell me, I'm sure you'll tell the boys,' warns the Judge, signalling for his men to join them. They do so and beat the man to death! Returning from his rounds, the Sheriff finds Jim's body propped up in his chair. He snatches up his gunbelt. Checking that the Colt is loaded, he rotates its chamber and slips it snugly into its holster. He will make them pay – but not with a gun. Flinging the gunbelt aside, he stalks from the jail-house and enters the saloon. 'And *still* he doesn't wear guns,' observes the town elder from his seat next to the Judge. 'We're leaving tonight,' the Sheriff whispers to Cathy. 'But I told you, the pass is guarded. You'll never make it with me,' she states. 'Be on the edge of town . . . after the saloon closes,' he says, dismissing her warning. 'I'll be there,' she promises. 'The Kid wouldn't be too happy if he saw them with their heads together like that,' says the Judge to the man sitting next to him. 'I think someone should tell him.'

Under the cloak of darkness, the Sheriff rides into the hills where, having crept up behind a lookout, he slugs the man guarding the pass. Spotting the relief lookout sitting beside a camp-fire, he throws a lasso over the limb of a tree and swings into the campside, his feet connecting squarely on the chin of the second man who, knocked unconscious, is trussed up in his sleeping blanket. Back in the town, meanwhile, Cathy finds her way blocked by the Kid. 'Get out of my way,' she yells as the baby-faced gunslinger stares silently into her face. 'You're crazy. Now get out of my way!' she exclaims as the Kid tries to kiss her. Biting his lip, she breaks free of his hold and tries to escape from the saloon. But there is nowhere to run. Grabbing her firmly by the throat, the crazed assassin throttles her to death! Having waited for Cathy to join him, the Sheriff creeps back into the town. Seeing the Kid leaving the saloon, he races inside and finds Cathy's body. At dawn, he buries her in the town's graveyard, his solitary figure silhouetted in the early-morning sunlight, taking on the spectre of vengeance. It is war now, and they will be made to pay. Entering the jailhouse, he strips off his jacket, washes his hands and buckles the gunbelt to his hip. Tightening the holster's drawstring firmly to his calf, he slides open the Colt's chamber, spins the gun's chamber with his palm, flicks on the safety guard and replaces the revolver back in its holster. Placing his badge on the desk, he purposefully steps through the door, his jaw set, his eyes cold. The Kid stands before him, his hands held tightly at his side, shadowing the pearl-handled Colt strapped to his thigh. They stare at each other in silence until, drawing together, they fire simultaneously. Rotating the gun, the Kid slides his Colt back into its holster – and keels over dead! Walking past the dead figure, the Prisoner enters the saloon, grabs a bottle and a glass from the bar, and squats at a table. 'You *beat* him! And he was the fastest I've ever seen,' grins the Judge, entering with his henchmen. 'The fastest you will

Patrick McGoohan rehearses a scene

ever see, I just quit!' barks the Prisoner downing his whisky. 'You aren't quittin' while I've got Cathy. Just get it clear, *you* work for *me*, guns an' all,' threatens the other. 'You haven't got Cathy any longer . . . she's dead.' 'But he was only supposed to . . . ' '*Rough* her up a little bit!' snarls the Prisoner, leaping to his feet. 'Wait' calls the Judge, as the ex-Sheriff turns to leave. 'You work for me whether you like it or not! *Nobody* walks out on me . . . I'm not lettin' you join some other outfit . . . I'll *kill* you first.' Looking around him, the Prisoner weighs up the opposition: before him stand two of the Judge's gunslingers. Another peers down from the balcony. 'You've got five seconds to make up your mind,' warns the Judge, carefully edging his way out of the firing line. 'One . . . two . . . three . . . four . . .' Staring at the man on the balcony, the Prisoner draws, fires and leaps for cover behind the bar. The shot finds its target. The gunslinger above him tumbles down the stairs. Another falls backwards over a table, his face etched in agony as the Prisoner's lead pierces his heart. As the gunman's bullet strikes him in the chest, the third gunslinger is thrown backwards through the saloon window. Now for the Judge. But the Prisoner is too late. Drawing a gun from beneath his jacket, the Judge fires twice, the bullets entering the Prisoner's head. Clutching his ears, he falls backwards to the floor . . .

Still holding his head, the Prisoner wakes up on the sawdust-covered floor of the saloon. His western attire has magically vanished and he is dressed once again in his familiar Village blazer. Scrambling to his feet, he tears off the strange ear-muffs which cover his ears. Staring around the saloon and seeing the Judge, he leaps at his enemy, grabbing the man by the throat – but the figure is nothing but a lifesize cardboard cut-out. Confused, he races outside to snatch up the two-dimensional cut-out of the Kid. A cardboard horse waits in the street to carry him away. Is he going mad? Terrified, he races back into the saloon and out again, pausing to slump over a hitching-post hewn from a tree. A *wooden* hitching post! Wood! He runs his hands along its length. It is real! Hearing the sound of a brass band playing in the distance, he races towards the direction of the sound. Running down a tree-covered country lane, he finds himself staring down at – the Village! A visit to the Green Dome and the nightmare becomes clearer. Cathy is there, or at least a girl wearing the ubiquitous Village clothing and a badge numbered '22'. Aware of what has happened, he retreats from the control room, leaving the girl behind – together with the Judge and the Kid, who are now exposed as numbers 2 and 8 respectively. 'Interesting that he could separate fact from fantasy so quickly,' states Number 8. 'I told you he was different. I *knew* it wouldn't work!' exclaims Number 2. 'Fill him with hallucinatory drugs! Put him in a dangerous environment! Talk to him through microphones.' 'It's always worked, and it *would* have worked *this* time, if you hadn't . . . ' Number 8 begins. 'But it DIDN'T did it?' interjects an angry Number 2. 'Give him love, take it away. Isolate him. Make him kill, then face him with death . . . He'll crack. Break him, even in his mind, and the rest will be easy. I should never have listened to you!' 'It would have worked, if *you* had kept your head and not created the crisis too soon,' challenges Number 8. 'How could I control it? Tell me that. You said yourself we would get involved and do what we would in a real situation.' Throwing back his head, Number 8 laughs. 'Well then, don't blame my method just your own damned lack of self-control.' 'It's alright for *you*. *I* have to answer for this failure,' says Number 2. Standing by the penny farthing bicycle, 'Cathy' begins to sob. 'It seems as though I'm not the only one who got involved,' says Number 2, as the girl numbered '22' races out of the chamber. Sighing, with a shrug of his shoulders, Number 8 concedes defeat.

Elsewhere, the girl enters the dummy saloon of the town called 'Harmony'. Walking to the staircase, she positions herself at exactly the spot where 'Cathy' lay when the 'Sheriff' found her. Having followed her, Number 8 now stares at the woman through the gap beneath the stairs. 'What are you doing here Number 8,' asks the one numbered '22'. Receiving no reply, she descends the staircase. 'The *game's* over Number 8,' she calls to the man in the shadows. For her perhaps, but the other has played his role too well. Edging into the light,

The Sheriff faces the townsfolk. (Scene does not appear in tx version)

he paces slowly towards the girl – his face a distorted mask of terror. Number 8 is the Kid again, reliving the role he played so well. In a flash, his hands are at the girl's throat, his nerve-shattering scream ringing in the ears of Number 6, who, strolling through the town, races into the saloon. Seeing the crazed youngster throttling the girl, he punches the maniac to the floor. Too late. Kneeling at the girl's side her dying words cut through his soul. 'I wish it had been real,' she gasps. Having driven to the town in a buggy, Number 2 dashes into the saloon as the Prisoner lays the girl's head gently to the floor. Turning to greet the newcomer in silence, Number 6, climbs to his feet as the superior looks first at the girl and then to the Kid, whose glassy-eyed stare convinces the superior that his colleague is insane. 'Keep away from me Judge, keep away ... ' screams the Kid, climbing the staircase. 'I'm getting no more ... not going to hit me ... no more,' he screams racing along the balcony. 'No mo...re ... ' he yells, throwing himself to his death at the superior's feet. Leaving Number 2 staring at the girl's body, the Prisoner walks out in the darkness.

AUTHOR'S NOTE: The standard title sequence, with its newly-shot western style resignation sequence, was without the usual *The Prisoner* title theme. However, much against McGoohan's wishes, several UK television companies superimposed the words 'The Prisoner' over the title credits when the story was transmitted.

This was the only story that was NOT aired in the United States when the series premiered on American television. Five sequences hit censorship problems and were either edited or deleted altogether: Johnson's hanging, the no-holds-barred fight with Zeke, the Prisoner being dragged back to Harmony and both sequences in which 'The Kid' strangles Cathy.

This episode marks the only credited appearances of stuntmen Frank Maher and Les Crawford as the 3rd and 2nd gunmen respectively.

THE GIRL WHO WAS DEATH

Written by Terence Feely

(from an idea by David Tomblin)

Guest stars

Schnipps **Kenneth Griffith**
Sonia **Justice Lord**

with

Potter **Christopher Benjamin**
Killer Karminski **Michael Brennan**
Boxing M.C. **Harold Berens**
Barmaid **Sheena Marsh**

and

Scots Napoleon **Max Faulkner**
Welsh Napoleon **John Rees**
Yorkshire Napoleon **Joe Gladwin**
Bowler **John Drake**
Little Girl **Gaynor Steward**
1st Little Boy **Graham Steward**
2nd Little Boy **Stephen Howe**
(Alexis Kanner ... uncredited appearance as Young Man with Camera)

Directed by David Tomblin

LIKE ALL GOOD fairy stories, our tale begins with a book whose colourful pages are turned back to reveal a picturesque English scene – a cricket match being played on a village green. Spectators sit around the perimeter and applaud as the man at the wicket swings back his bat and scores a four. The score-keeper, a man named Potter, registers the hit on his scoreboard, then taking a pair of binoculars from his sports bag, he fastens his sights on a pair of shapely legs. They belong to a pretty young blonde who sits away from the crowd in a deckchair. From the tips of her shoes to the parasol she holds aloft, she is dressed entirely in virginal white. Shifting his attention to the batsman, Potter smiles as the whiskered man gives him a wink. Awaiting the next ball, the batsman steadies himself as the lady in white eases herself from her chair and walks to the edge of the green. To raucous applause, the batsman receives the ball with a whack, and sends it skittering away to the deep clusters of grass which determine the boundary. A six! Ecstatic, Potter registers the score on his board as a fielder races after the ball. Unseen by either players or spectators, the leather-bound cricket ball is exchanged for an identical one. Snatching this up, the fielder runs back onto the green and pitches the ball back to the bowler who, catching it neatly in his hand, takes several determined paces past the umpire to ready himself for his next delivery. The spectators are agog; Potter watches in anticipation, the girl in white grins. Steadying himself, the bowler surges forward, his arm aloft, his face a mask of grinning teeth. The ball leaves his hand, the batsman whacks it – and in a busy London street, the Prisoner reads the stop press newspaper headline: 'Col. Hawke – English, Murdered at cricket match ... one short of his century!' Placing the newspaper under his arm, the Prisoner walks several paces down the street, stopping at an outdoor stand where a shoe-shine boy is plying his trade. It is Potter, the ex-scorekeeper and ex-Secret Agent (retribution for failure travels swiftly it appears). 'Busy Potter?' quips the newcomer. 'It's our form of Siberia,' grunts the shoe-shine man, confirming that he is serving his punishment for allowing the batsman to be killed. 'What was the Colonel up to?' asks the other. 'Doctor Schnipps. Crazy scientist. For the last 26 years he's been building a super rocket . . . to destroy London.' 'Where?' 'Well that's just what the Colonel was about to find out,' returns the other, scouring the newcomer's brogues with a wire brush. A transmitter device in his shoe box indicates that someone wishes to talk with him. 'Excuse me,' says Potter, placing a receiver to his ear. 'Where do I start?' asks the other. 'You're to go to the Magnum record shop. Booth 7. The chief will speak to you there.' 'Chin up Potter,' quips the Prisoner. 'It was so damned unsporting,' pleads the shoeshine, 'It certainly wasn't cricket,' confirms the other, handing his ex-colleague a bank note. 'Keep the change.' Leaving, the Prisoner fails to see the girl in white watching his progress from inside a shop window. The Prisoner enters the record shop, asks the assistant for a record and enters booth numbered 7. Placing the disc on the turntable provided, he listens to the voice of his chief. 'Mission. Find and destroy Professor Schnipps' rocket. There is very little *I* can give you I'm afraid, the opposition have been one step ahead of us all along.' 'Thank you very much,' quips the listener. 'What was that?' asks the record. 'Nothing.' 'Standard disguise. Take over where the Colonel left off . . . ' orders the voice.

The Prisoner does so. Wearing a false moustache and side-whiskers, he stands at the wicket dressed as a batsman. The girl in white sits as before, her parasol raised over her head. Marking his crease, the Prisoner accepts the ball and scores a run. The bowler tries again; the batsman lifting the ball aloft and sending it soaring to the boundary, where, as before, the ball is exchanged for an identical one. Repeating his actions, the fielder races after the sixer, grabs it in his hand and throws it back to the bowler. A toothy grin, and the bowler retreats to his bowling crease. The Prisoner's score rests at 99; the girl in white stands by a tree. Lowering his bat to protect the middle stump, the batsman prepares to accept the next ball. His arm aloft, his face set in a toothy grin, the bowler races forward. Leaving his hand, the ball soars through the air towards the batsman, who, *catching* it in his gloved hand, throws it high in the air, where it explodes above the trees. Racing after the bomb, the batsman finds nothing but a lace handkerchief draped over a bush. It carries a message scrawled in lipstick: 'Let's meet again – at your local pub!'. Having parked his sports car on the forecourt, the Prisoner enters the pub and orders his usual from Doris, a barmaid. He removes his white raincoat, hangs it on a coat stand and returns to the bar. Sitting on a stool, he sips from his beer glass – a drink with a difference. When drained of its nutty-brown liquid, the glass contains a message written on its base: 'You . . . have . . . just . . . been . . . poisoned!' 'Same again sir?' asks Doris. 'No thank you,' he replies, 'one of those is quite enough. Brandy.' The girl hands him his drink. ' . . . Whisky, Vodka, Drambuie, Tia Maria, Cointreau, Grand Marnier . . . ' he orders, gulping down each drink in turn. 'SIR!,' cries Doris, 'You'll make yourself sick.' Counting each empty glass before him, with a wry smile, he staggers from the bar and stumbles to the washroom – holding back the door to allow the girl in white to ease past him, her arrival heralded by an 18-inch long white cigarette holder. Having emptied the contents of his stomach, he splashes cold water onto his face and reaches for the towel dispenser. This, too, carries a message: 'Upset Tummy? Try Benny's Turkish Baths around the corner!' Wearing his phoney moustache and sideburns, the Prisoner sweats it out in a steam box. The girl in white is there too. Dressed in the briefest of mini skirts, the perspiration trickling down her shapely legs, she carries a broom handle as she creeps from her steam-box and slides the pole through the handles of the cabinet in which the Prisoner sits humming merrily away. Unseen through the billowing clouds of steam, she places a perspex globe over the man's head. Catching sight of the retreating figure's shapely ankles, he kicks out in anger, splitting the broom handle in two and engineering his release. Dressed now in a Sherlock Holmes ensemble of dog-tooth cape and deer-stalker hat, he is about to chase after the girl, pausing at the door first. Crossing swiftly back to the steam box vacated by the girl, he again finds a message inviting him to follow her to Barney's Boxing Booth, front row. The message ends in a PS: 'Who would be a goldfish.' The fairground is in full swing as he enters the large marqueé and squats in a chair at the ringside. The master of ceremonies issues a challenge: 'Ladies and gentelmen. It is my pleasure to introduce to you, for the first time in this country, at 207 pounds, the Polish giant, Killer Karminski . . . ' Stepping into the boxing ring, a huge brute of a man bows to the crowd. ' . . . And now Ladies and Gentlemen, another hand I want for a gallant and courageous opponent who has undertaken to go three rounds with the Killer . . . A man of mystery . . . in the front row . . . Mr X.' He points at the Prisoner. The spectators go wild, and two men step forward to divest the Prisoner of his Edwardian motoring cloak. Climbing into the ring, he removes his coat and sits on the stool in his corner. 'Good luck young man,' says an old lady behind him, dressed in a black funeral dress, a black shawl pulled tightly around her shoulders (we have seen her before – clad entirely in white). A second enters the ring and straps a pair of gloves over the Prisoner's hands. The referee calls the opponents together in the centre of the ring. 'Now I want a good clean fight,' he orders. 'No kicking, butting or gouging – except in moderation . . . and when I say break, break. Don't forget eh. May the best man win. Go back to your corners . . . ' Before he can do so, the Prisoner is stripped of his dark sunglasses! 'Seconds out. Round 1,' calls the master of ceremonies. As the boxers close on each other, the girl in white takes her seat in the crowd. A sharp jab to the stomach throws the Prisoner, followed by a second punch. About to throw a blow at his opponent's head, the Killer blocks his arm. 'Take it easy sorr, will you . . . me face is me fortune . . . You might knock it back in shape,' grunts the Killer in a sharp Irish brogue. Coming between them the referee intervenes, splitting the two men apart as the Prisoner's glove is about to clip his opponents's nose. A right to the jaw and the Prisoner reels backwards to the ropes. He rallies, closing on his opponent in a bear hug. The girl in white grins, the Killer grunts. 'Let's go to the Tunnel of Love,' he gasps, dancing with his opponent around the canvas. 'The what?' growls the Prisoner, planting a solid right hand into the man's solar plexus. 'The tunnel of love . . . ' gasps the Killer, returning the blow. 'Who . . . gave . . . you . . . the . . . message?' asks the other, peppering the Killer's face with forceful left hooks. 'The lady . . . ' grunts his opponent, giving as good as he gets. 'Who was she?' seeks the Prisoner, landing a punch in the man's midriff. 'I don't know.' 'Who . . . *was* she?' challenges his opponent. 'Didn't I tell you,' utters the Killer, closing in for the kill. 'I don't *know*!' His glove, lands squarely on the other's waistline, bringing a gasp from the Prisoner. 'In the tunnel of LOVE!' exclaims the Killer, following up his advantage by swinging a vicious right cross to his opponent's jaw. Beaten now, the Prisoner collapses to the canvas and smiling, the girl in white leaves the marqueé.

Wearing his Sherlock Holmes attire, his false moustache and side-whiskers back in place, the Prisoner sails through the fairground's Tunnel of Love. Hideous white masks adorn the rock walls and the vessel floats past the immobile figure of the girl in white, her arm raised erect as she stands motionless, disguised as Aphrodite. As the unsuspecting passenger floats past her she calls to him. 'Hello . . . No don't turn around. I have you covered. The tunnel of love is very fitting, because I'm beginning to love you . . . in my way. All my life I've been looking for a worthy opponent. *You* have passed my first little test brilliantly. You will be hearing from me again. Auf Wiedersehen.' She laughs. He turns quickly. The girl is nowhere in sight, but a tiny white box has been placed in the rear seat of the boat. Hearing the girl's hysterical scream, he flings it into the water behind him. It explodes, the force of the blast drowning her hideous laughter.

Beckoned on by the girl, he sees her board a roller-coaster and disappear from view. Climbing into a roller-cart, he finds himself alone, high on the fun-machine: the girl now stands watching him from the ground. She blows him a kiss from the merry-go-round, but by the time he boards the ride the girl has disappeared again. Catching sight of her racing through the crowd, he follows, seeing her board a caterpillar ride. He polevaults a fence and jumps into the seat beside her, but when the canvas hood is raised at the end of the ride, he is sitting with a stranger, the girl in white mocking him from the pay booth. A slap from the woman beside him and he is off and running again, following his beautiful but deadly quarry as she hails him again from the seat of her roller-coaster carriage. Leaping aboard, he begins to climb, hand-over-hand, towards her, his cloak flowing in the wind as several seats in front of him, the girl stands precariously aloft swinging her arms in pantomimic defiance. Faster and faster speeds the ride, climbing high up the tracks and plummeting down at speed to the water-splash. Wilder and wilder become the girl's antics until, having dropped into the carriage behind her, the Prisoner is about to grab her when she turns. She is a stranger – as is the young man with a camera who magically appears from behind her and threatens the pursuer. 'Here, what's your game Sherlock Holmes . . . I'll spread your nose all over your face . . . I'll bust you up and down this fairground . . . you'll never pick up your teeth with a broken arm. I'll tear off your leg and I'll beat you over the head . . . ' shrieks the man, placing a protective arm around the girl's shoulder. Staring downwards, the Prisoner sees the girl in white beckoning him from the ground.

Back on the ground, he spots her again standing before

'Hello. No, don't turn around, I have you covered'

a carousel, her face hidden beneath a billowing web of white lace. But is it his quarry or another dupe? The reappearance of the young man with the camera suggests the latter, so the Prisoner makes a hasty retreat. A mistake. As the pursuer makes his exit, she pulls back her veil - it is *she*. The youth with the camera plants a kiss to her lips and the girl races away to her gleaming white sports car – pursued by the Prisoner who, failing to impede her progress, strips off his disguise, climbs into his speedster and roars off in pursuit. Within minutes he is behind her as they race along a motorway. Supremely confident, the girl raises her hand in salute, beckoning him on – but to what? Entering a country lane, the cars speed on, he endeavouring to overtake, she raising a telephone to her lips. 'I love you madly. I love the way your hair curls on the back of your neck. You'll make a *beautiful* corpse!' she confirms, her words being piped into the pursuer's car. 'I'm going to do you the honour of letting you die *superbly* . . . ' Gritting his teeth, the pursuer changes gear, his foot going down hard on the accelerator. Looking over her shoulder, she stretches out her hand, her finger pointing at his vehicle. As her hand sways back and forth, so does his car. She draws a circle in the air, his car appears to follow suit, doing a 360 degree turn, although its wheels never actually leave the ground. What magic is this? ' . . . But not yet darling. There's more fun to come . . . ' she purrs, as her car streaks around a bend in the road. In an attempt to follow, for a second he loses control of his car. Reversing, he continues his pursuit, losing the girl in a maze of roundabouts and country lanes.

Having located her parked car on the outskirts of a deserted village, he climbs out of his vehicle and peers up and down the street. A shopsign denoted 'Candlestick Maker'. Another a baker, a third a butcher. 'I'm glad you came,' echoes her voice 'This is to be our love tryst. You may not see my face, but you may know my name . . . *my* name is Death!' She laughs as he wanders through the streets endeavouring to locate the building from which the voice emanates. 'I'm sorry my father could not be here to greet you, but he's busy with his rocket. Besides, he did not wish to play gooseberry. *You* are a born survivor, *I* am a born killer. *We* were made for each other . . . ' Above him, pinned to a wall, he spots a loudspeaker. ' . . . But I fear this is where it must end. Your reflexes cannot save you now. It will come swiftly, suddenly . . . when your luck runs out . . . ' He finds himself standing in front of the door of the building. ' . . . With my love . . . ' He crouches, his shoulder ready to crash down the door. 'Come, come inside my darling . . . ' He bursts through the flimsy door, landing inside on the dilapidated floor of the room. Crouching, he crawls to peer through the vents of a door that leads into an adjoining room. Flinging the door back on its hinges, he dives to the floor as a machine gun erected on a bracket rotates and spits its bullets into the rotted timbers of the wall behind him. Crawling on his hands and knees, he makes his way towards the weapon, placing his hands over its infra-red trigger control to halt its chattering progress. ' . . . Is your heart pounding,' continues her voice. ' . . . Your hand shaking? That's *love* my darling! My father was a great man, but the war ended before he was recognised . . . ' Listening to her words, he begins to disconnect the machine gun from its moorings. ' . . . But when London lies in ruins he will be a God . . . ' The machine gun is free now. Ramming it firmly into his hip, he turns its barrel towards the walls, raking his way through them with a clip full of bullets and leaps through the opening he has made. Spotting a figure standing in the darkness, he sends a spray of bullets into its chest. It is a dummy assembled from sacks and a balloon. Angry, he races forwards, the floor giving way under his feet. He falls, but the gun saves him, its barrel jammed tight across the gaping jaws of a pit. 'Nice of you to drop in . . . ' quips the voice. ' . . . I can see you're having a swinging time, but that's not quite what I had in mind . . . ' He stares into the pit below his feet. The heels of his shoes are barely fractions of an inch away from a bed of iron spikes, their tips filed into jagged points, inviting him to be skewered. ' . . . Perhaps this will help . . .?' At her cue, the spikes begin to rise, threatening to pierce the soles of his feet. ' . . . You'll soon get the point . . . ' mocks the voice. ' . . . Incidentally, they're electrified . . . ' He attempts to haul himself upwards, but succeeds only in bringing a discarded wardrobe drawer crashing to the floor. It is release enough. The drawer falls neatly over the spikes, forming the base of an elevator which, much to the girl's disappointment, raises him out of the pit. ' . . . Ingenious. Nobody has ever thought of that before. You really are the most entertaining love I've ever had . . . ' Recocking the machine gun, he rakes bullets into the walls of the room. ' . . . That was ill-mannered *and* dangerous. I might not have been able to inform you that the rest of this floor is mined . . . Very small, but very sensitive. And quite deadly . . . ' she warns as he lays down the weapon. Snatching up a brick, he flings it several feet away and the floor disintegrates in a puff of smoke! ' . . . Oh, I almost forgot, they will all explode anyway in 90 seconds . . . ' Using the drawer beneath his feet as a platform, he pulls himself onto a pipe above his head. ' . . . That's the hot line,' informs the voice, as the scalding hot pipe sears at his hands. ' . . . Or had you noticed . . .?' Blocking out the pain, hand-over-hand he approaches the door and leaps across to an adjoining pipe. Gathering momentum, he swings backwards and forwards and leaps into the adjacent room. The floor behind him explodes into sheets of smoke. ' . . . You've been through the butcher's and the baker's, now you're in the candle-stick makers . . . ' drones the voice as the man drops to his feet. ' . . . only he never made candles like these. These are *my* invention . . . ' Rising from the rubble, he traverses the room. It is decked out with thousands of candles. 'They have a cyanide derivative mixed with wax. As the candle burns, it gives off a cyanide gas. Every candle in this room is breathing poison into the air . . . ' He attempts to escape, but two steel doors crash down from the ceiling blocking his path. He races to the door, the windows; these too are blocked. ' . . . I do so believe in double glazing, don't you? Keeps out the noise . . . of course it does keep out the air too . . . Oh a last word of advice. If the candles are blown out, they explode . . . ' Choking now, the man is about to blow out the candle in front of his face. Hearing the girl's warning, he stops in mid-breath. Picking up a candle-snuffer he raises it above him to the chandelier and fluffs out its wick. The result is devastating – the device being blown apart. ' . . . And that's just one of the little ones. I warned you your luck would run out. I've got to go now. I'm glad it's to be this way. I *hate* quick farewells, don't you?' mocks the girl. But he is not outsmarted so easily. Gathering together as many of the candles as he can, he places them en masse next to the steel exit doors. Witnessing this the voice tells him that she has noticed that mice get irrational in just the same way when they are about to die. 'In this village in the past, when a great man was dying . . . ' she continues, ' . . . they sounded the death knell. I think that was a charming idea . . . ' By now, the Prisoner has collected a pair of bellows from the corner of the room. Standing behind a counter, he sends a jet of air from the device and . . . an explosion ensues, allowing him to race through the wrecked door and out into the street. He immediately comes under fire as the girl in white, attired now in a snow-white version of a World War I battledress, a spiked soldier's helmet adorning her head, eases back the trigger of a Gatling-gun. Racing into a blacksmith's shop, the Prisoner slams the doors closed behind him. 'Alright darling, you win . . . ' greets her voice from a speaker positioned on the wall over his head. ' . . . I've *just* realised something. I don't want to kill you anymore. You are the *best*. If I kill you, what will be left for *me*? Life would be a bore . . . Why don't you join us, my father and me. We'd have a wonderful time together. You would be a constant challenge to me . . . ' He, too, has realised something: no matter what she says, he is now fully aware that she does intend to kill him – he is aware, too, that his enemy is a girl, although he doesn't know her by her given name (Sonia), but only by the name she has given herself : 'Death'. He realises, too, that he has a chance of escape. Behind him in the blacksmith's shop stands a bulldozer – if only . . . ? 'Come and join me in the bell tower,' she suggests. 'What do you say darling? Don't let silly pride stand in your way . . . ' He doesn't. Having fired up the bulldozer's engine, he leaps behind its controls and releases the throttle. In an instant, the massive wooden doors of the building are smashed aside and the Prisoner is free – free to elevate the bulldozer's steel shovel to act as a shield against the bullets, the mortar bombs, and World War I hand-grenades that his enemy unleashes as he steers the machine towards the bell tower. 'Wheee, wheee. Wheee!' she grins, as the bulldozer grinds to a halt, its gears ripped apart by the onslaught. Staring upwards, he sees with alarm that the girl has the sights of a huge bazooka trained at his chest. 'Bye bye lover . . . ' she grins, releasing the weapon's trigger mechanism. In a heartbeat, the bulldozer is blown apart, its tattered burning remnants littering the street. As the tower bell chimes its death knell, the girl calmly powders her nose. Placing a white leather helmet to her golden locks, she descends from the bell tower to savour her opponent's defeat. Behind her, the Prisoner rises from a manhole and follows her from a safe distance.

Seeing the girl climb into a helicopter, he races after the machine and firmly grabs the aircraft's landing gear. As the machine soars skywards, he crawls up into the

'Don't let silly pride stand in your way'

helicopter's skeleton tailpiece and holds on for dear life. Unaware of her stowaway's presence, Sonia lands the machine in a field where, as the engine cuts out and its rotor blades grind to a halt, the Prisoner runs away from the machine and seeks refuge in some bushes. Pursuing her, he follows the girl over a hill, before losing sight of her in the rocks. Climbing to the top of the hill, he sees a lighthouse out at sea. But how can he reach it? The drop below would test the nerve of even the most ambitious climber – 100 feet of sheer rock face. A nearby cave appears to offer a solution. Entering its darkness, he urges his way forward along a passage, which empties into a large room hewn from the rock. In front of him stands an impressive bank of machinery; to the left of the cavern stands a row of bunk beds. The walls are adorned with pictures and reproductions, each representing a Napoleonic scene. Hearing a sound behind him, he seeks refuge behind a rock as a man dressed in a scarlet Napoleonic uniform descends a ladder leading from the area above. 'From glen to glen, and down the mountain side . . . The summer's gone and all the roses dying . . . ' sings the newcomer, crossing to a record player and placing its needle on a record. ' . . . 'Tis you 'tis you must bide and I must go,' pipes the Prisoner, knocking the stranger unconscious with a blow to the head. Removing the unconscious man's uniform, he puts the scarlet tunic over his own coat. Above him, in a room decked out with machinery, stands a row of half-a-dozen men, each wearing the scarlet finery of Napoleonic times. Parading before them walks 'Napoleon'. It is Professor Schnipps, the scientist intent on blowing up London. Inspecting his troops and noticing that each man has their hand concealed beneath his tunic in true Napoleonic fashion, he races down the row hitting each man in turn, removing their hands at a blow. Regaining his dignity, he walks over to his daughter Sonia, who is now dressed as Marie Antoinette. 'Everybody's doing it now you see . . . You're quite sure you killed him?' he asks. 'Father. Who taught me?' she sighs. 'You're a girl after my own heart. If only your dear mother could see you now . . . Good old Josephine,' he sobs, wiping a tear-stained eye. 'Tell me again about her last cavalry charge,' asks Sonia. 'Not now child, we have work to do,' he says, turning back to his troops. 'Gentlemen,' he begins, addressing the fairy tale soldiers, 'In one hour's time, London will be entirely in ruins . . . ' Meanwhile the Prisoner has broken into the armoury and dealt swiftly with its guard, dumping the man's body down a safety-hatch. Gathering up each rifle in turn, he flicks back their firing pins and begins to prise open the bullets he has ejected onto a table. Above him,

The intruder punches the armoury guard

'Napoleon' continues to relay his plan of battle. ' . . . And then of course, as I was saying, there will be no more Trafalgar Square, it will be Napoleon Square . . . and of course, Nelson's Column will go to become Napoleon's Column . . . and er . . . and then my little girl here will be taking over Bond Street . . . ' 'Oh,' cries a delighted Sonia. ' . . . and you merry lads can have . . . Chelsea Barracks . . . ' One of the troops mutters something under his breath. ' . . . Ungrateful swine!' yells the Professor ' . . . and then we'll be taking over the entire regions . . . Is the Scottish Marshal here?' 'Present,' nods one of the men. 'You keen on soccer?' growls Schnipps. 'Oh aye sir, I am, I am . . . ' 'Like Wembley Stadium?' 'Oh aye, aye I would,' gushes the Marshal as the leader pushes his finger into the man's chest. 'It's yours . . . Welsh Marshal?' 'Here sir . . . What a great day for the Nationalists sir.' 'Thank you Marshal Jones,' grins the Professor. 'Irish?' 'He's gone down stairs to the armoury sir,' says the Scot. 'He'll not be long.' Schnipps grits his teeth. 'Blast O'Rorke . . . what on earth does he do down there?' O'Rorke, of course, is unconscious, courtesy of the man now replacing the 'doctored' rifles back into the weapons rack. This done, the Prisoner begins to ease the fuses out of several hand-grenades. However, as he is tipping the black explosive powder into the tubular *handles* of the grenades, one of

'The countdown has now been started . . . ' confirms 'Napoleon' Schnipps, switching on his control machine and arming the red trigger button. Sonia, however, glancing behind her and aware that her father has overlooked something (he is, after all, a 'nutty' professor), taps him on the shoulder and draws his attention to the fact that the rocket's guidance system *wasn't* really armed! 'Mmm,' sighs her exasperated father, attempting to regain his dignity. Turning back to his troops, he picks up where he left off. ' . . . As I was saying, the countdown has already started. In a few minutes we transfer to the speedboat and control the final phase of the operation from the sea. O'Rorke will . . . where is Marshal O'Rorke? Find him at once. All of you!' As one, the men trip over each other as they bump into one another and attempt to go their different ways, each of them stumbling down the staircase in total mass confusion. Staring at them Schnipps cannot help but mumble 'Oh . . . it's Waterloo all over again.' 'Oh,' smiles Sonia, stroking his brow. Finally regaining some semblance of order, the men descend the stairs where, believing the man at the table to be one of their companions, one of them asks if he has seen O'Rorke. 'No,' returns the Prisoner. 'But he must have come through here,' says the Scottish Marshal, who demands to know what O'Rorke is up to. 'I don't *KNOW*!'

'This one won't backfire darling'

the Professor's soldiers descends the staircase behind him. Identifying the intruder by his trousers (the Prisoner has donned only O'Rorke's tunic and tri-corn hat) the newcomer creeps up behind the stranger – and receives a blow to the head for his pains. He, too, joins O'Rorke in the safety hatch.

grins the Prisoner, swinging the grenades he is holding over his shoulder and laying two of the troops out unconscious. Turning, he easily slips through the arms of the other men as, panicking, they stumble over themselves in their attempts to grab him. Knocking them out, he flees through the door and descends the outside of the lighthouse via a metal ladder. Above him, running around in circles of confusion, the men each grab a rifle from the weapons rack. Seeing the intruder racing along the pier towards the motor launch, the Scot orders the men to fire. As one they do so – and fall backwards into the armoury as the 'doctored' rifles explode in their faces! Having climbed back up to the armoury, the Prisoner eases his way upwards to the room above – to find himself staring down the barrel of a gun held by Sonia. 'This one won't backfire, darling,' she warns.

'Mountaineering rope,' confirms Sonia, tying her enemy to a chair. 'It would hold an elephant.' 'I must remember that the next time I go climbing with one,' quips the Prisoner. 'Oh I'm afraid there won't be a next time for you darling. I'm going to give you the most original death in history . . . You're going for a rocket ride,' grins the girl. 'Oh the rocket. That reminds me . . . Where is it?' asks the bound man. 'It is here,' grins 'Napoleon' Schnipps, with a wave of his hand, ' . . . all around you.' 'All around us?' quizzes the Prisoner. 'The light . . . house itself is the rocket!' confirms Schnipps, Sonia and the Prisoner as one. 'You've guessed,' mocks the Professor. 'I say, you're not the Duke of Wellington are you? Ah, well I guess you're surprised to meet me. Don't you think it's clever? Aren't I an extraordinary man?' 'Crazy,' grins the bound man. 'This is the nose cone we're in now,' confirms Sonia, indicating the lighthouse walls with her hand. 'So you see, when the rocket reaches London, you'll be the first to know. Won't that be exciting?' she grins, staring at the man tied to the chair. 'I'll just go to pieces,' he jokes. A red warning light flashes on the control panel. 'It's time to go aboard the boat,' grins 'Napoleon', confirming that the flight pattern is set and all that remains is for them to fire the 'lighthouse' when they get out to sea. 'Bon voyage darling . . . ' waves Sonia, as she follows her father down the staircase. ' . . . Think of me when you hit town.'

'Warning' says the red sign below the flashing danger signal that rests before the man bound to the chair. 'When red light is flashing, it is strictly forbidden to enter upper chamber.' The clock on the control panel reads .2 minutes to countdown as the Prisoner struggles to unfree his hands. Far below him Sonia and her father fall over each other to cram documents into their briefcase. 01.78 registers the countdown clock as the man above them struggles against his bonds. 'Please hurry. It's less that 2 minutes to blast off,' urges Sonia. 'I must have my papers . . . these are the history,' insists the Professor, shoving further sheets of paper into his brief-case. 01.55 . . . 01.41 ticks the countdown. Pausing for a second, the Prisoner eases the back of his chair upwards. It springs free with a pop (like everything else connected to Schnipps' plan, his attempts to defeat our hero are doomed to failure). Easing his bound wrists over the back of the chair's backrest, the Prisoner stands and the bonds fall free of his wrists. Stripping off his Napoleonic tunic, he crosses to the control console, manipulating its dials, levers and buttons until sparks begin to emit from the machine and a dense cloud of smoke pours from its innards. Grabbing up the coil of the mountaineering rope which Sonia laid aside, he hurriedly climbs the ladder to the lamp-house room. Far below him lies the sea. Tying one end of the rope to the inspection gantry's guard rail, he casts the rope over the side and carefully eases himself over the railing, before descending hand-over-hand to the rocks far below. Their packing complete, Sonia and her father race from the documents room and prepare to descend to their boat. Pausing with his foot on the top rung of the metal ladder, 'Napoleon' races back inside. 'What is it?' asks his daughter. 'I forgot to turn the gas off . . . ' 'Oh father!' she says. Peering below and seeing the man they left above them leaping into the motor launch, Sonia calls on her father to stop him. Racing together back into the armoury, she grabs a hand-grenade while he picks up two rifles. 'Not those . . . ' cries Sonia, handing her father a grenade, ' . . . these!' Armed with a grenade apiece, they race back to the door, prime the devices and fling them into the boat – and stare in amazement as the Prisoner throttles the motor launch out to sea. Bemused when the hand-grenades fail to explode, Schnipps and his daughter stare at each other in astonishment as their lives and hopes are blown away when the booby-trapped grenade *handles* they hold explode in a sheet of flame. Out at sea, the man on the boat stares back as the lighthouse disintegrates into a million pieces.

'And that is how I saved London from the mad scientist,' a seated Number 6 tells three children, who squat before him in a nursery, their eyes trained on the cover of *The Village Story Book* which he now lays aside. 'Go on tell us more . . . just one, one,' scream the children. 'No, no more for tonight, it's way past your bedtime,' grins Number 6, rising from his chair to gather up a little girl sitting on a rocking horse. 'Come on now to bed . . . there's a good girl,' he soothes, placing the girl onto her cot. 'You will come tomorrow, please, please,' sobs the infant. 'Yes yes, we'll see . . . ' 'Oh promise you will come,' cry the others, hopping into their bunks. ' . . . We'll see,' smiles the storyteller. 'Come tomorrow, yes tomorrow,' chant all three, snuggling beneath their sheets. 'You will come?' 'Sshhh . . . sleep . . . I'll come tomorrow,' whispers Number 6 ' . . . I don't think I have any other important appointments,' he grins, staring at the Village surveillance camera, on which Number 2 (Schnipps) is avidly watching his every move. Switching off the monitor screen, the superior turns in his chair with a shrug. 'He might drop his guard with children . . . he might give something away . . . ' he sighs, to the girl dressed in black (Sonia) standing behind him with her arm resting on the saddle of the penny farthing bicycle. 'Well it was worth a try Number 2,' she confirms, realising now that their plan has gone wrong. 'He told them *nothing*! He told them a blessed fairytale . . . ' sighs the disillusioned superior. 'That one wouldn't drop his guard with his own grandmother,' he roars, pointing to the monitor screen with his umbrella. 'Goodnight children . . . *Everywhere*,' mocks the image of Number 6 from the screen which has magically switched itself back on – to show a picture of the little girl's toy doll . . . a grinning red-faced clown!

AUTHOR'S NOTE: Reappearance of actor Christopher Benjamin as 'Potter', John Drake's contact man in the *Danger Man/Secret Agent* story *Koroshi/Shinda Shima*.

The countdown mechanism that triggers the rocket, was actually a stock shot originally filmed for the Gerry Anderson *Thunderbirds* series. The same shot reappears in *Fall Out*.

ONCE UPON A TIME

Written by Patrick McGoohan

Guest star

Number 2 **Leo McKern**

with

The Butler **Angelo Muscat**
The Supervisor **Peter Swanwick**
Umbrella Man **John Cazabon**
Number 86 **John Maxim**

Directed by Patrick McGoohan

DESCENDING THE ramp of Number 2's Green Dome residence, the mute Butler parks the breakfast trolley he is wheeling by the side of the superior's control console, reaches out his gloved hand and depresses three buttons from its vast array. In a fraction of a second, a curtain covering the monitor screen behind him slides open, a table magically appears from the depths and Number 2's oval-shaped chair rises from the floor; the shell of the seat now contains a spherical white ball – a Rover. The manservant places cutlery on the table before the pulsating balloon and puts a tray containing toast and coffee on the console's counter top. The silent Butler then picks up and shakes a small dinner bell. In the space of a breath, a second black leather chair rises from the depths, followed by Number 2, his head bowed, his hands clasped firmly behind his back. Crossing to the breakfast tray, he removes a silver cover from one of the plates and tastes the food. 'Wait!' he calls to the retreating servant. 'Remove it!' The Butler stand immobile. 'I told you to REMOVE IT!' screams Number 2, crossing to the other man's side. The manservant begins to clear away the breakfast tray. 'And *you* can remove that *thing* too . . . ' snarls the superior to someone (Number 1?) on the telephone. ' . . . I'm not an *inmate*! You can say what you like. *You* brought me back here. I told you the last time, you were using the wrong approach. I do it *my* way, or you find somebody else . . . ' Spotting the Butler about to carry the breakfast tray from the chamber, he holds the telephone receiver behind his back as he asks the little man to leave the coffee. 'The coffee, LEAVE IT,' he screams replacing the receiver to his ear. 'How many times do I have to *ask*?' he inquires as the chair containing the Rover descends back into the floor and the manservant leaves. Pouring himself coffee, he turns to view the monitor screen on which Number 6 is pictured prowling his cottage while eating breakfast. 'A likely lad . . . ' says Number 2, standing directly in front of the screen. ' . . . Why do you care? Take it easy, relax . . . why do you care . . . ?' he yells pointing his finger at the figure on the screen. Crossing back to his control panel he picks up a telephone and asks to be connected with the Prisoner. 'Why do you care?' he asks when the connection is made. 'I know your voice,' returns Number 6. 'I've been here before . . . Why-*do-you*-care?' 'You'll never know,' replies the other, laying the telephone receiver back on its cradle rest and walking out of the cottage. He pauses on the doorstep to clap his hands twice, and the door obeys his command and swings to a close behind him. '*Wait and see*,' whispers a determined Number 2. Outside in the Village, Number 6 bumps into a man strolling by the swimming pool. 'How?' asks the Prisoner raising his hand in mock greeting. 'Don't do that,' says the man with the umbrella. 'What?' 'Enquire,' whispers the other. 'What's your number?' asks Number 6. 'What?' enquires the man. 'Your number. What is it?' urges the Prisoner. 'Be careful,' warns the man staring around him. '1,2,3,4,5,6,7,8 . . . ?' 'Quiet,' urges the one being questioned. '9,10,11,12,13,14,15,*16*?' screams the Prisoner, his raised voice echoing around the deserted square. In the Green Dome, Number 2 is scanning the pages of the Prisoner's 'Progress Report', as scenes from Number 6's past life are flashed at speed across the monitor screen. '*Going to escape and come back* . . . ' says the voice from the screen, ' . . . *wipe this place off the face of the earth, obliterate it and you with it* . . . ' The screen changes ' . . . *This is what they did to you, is this how they started to break you before you gave them what they were after* . . . ' continues the voice. ' . . . *I've resigned. I will not be pushed, filed, stamped, indexed, briefed, debriefed or numbered* . . . ' This continues for quite some time until, tired of the game, Number 2 grabs a telephone as the man on the screen ends with ' . . . *I want to call a witness – a character witness*.' 'Degree *absolute*,' snarls Number 2 to his unseen superior 'I require approval . . . If you think he's that important . . . there's certainly no other alternative! You *must* risk either one of us. I am a good man . . . I *was* a good man . . . but if you get *him*, he will be BETTER! . . . and there's no other way. I repeat, no *other WAY*! Degree absolute, tonight please . . . ' he orders, as the man on the screen behind him repeats his challenge that he will not be pushed, filed, stamped, indexed, briefed, debriefed or numbered.' 'A week! That's not long enough . . . ' barks Number 2. ' . . . you don't want me to damage him . . . ' Apparently he is given no choice ' . . . Very well then . . . Tonight!'

That evening, he marches into the main Control Room. 'Degree absolute . . . you're under orders,' he snaps to the Supervisor. 'What period?' requests the bespectacled man as the superior races down the staircase to join him. 'One week!' 'Emergency?' asks the Supervisor. 'Well it has to be hasn't it,' sneers Number 2. 'Mind if I check?' asks the other. 'You check NOTHING!' growls Number 2 patrolling the floor. 'Recall all subsidiary personnel.' 'First shift, early release. Time sheets as normal. Double night time . . . double night time,' the Supervisor barks to his staff. As one the majority of the controllers in the chamber leave their posts and exit from the room. Sitting down in front of a control viewing console, Number 2 pulls back on its control stick and the sleeping figure of Number 6 appears on the screen. 'Blow up Channel 3 . . . ' orders the superior. 'Channel Three,' snaps the Supervisor. 'Check profundity,' calls Number 2. '1,2,3,4,5, 6, . . . first waveband clear,' confirms the bespectacled assistant. 'Repeat and increase,' comes the demand. '1,2,3,4,5,6 . . . still clear,' confirms the Supervisor. 'Third waveband . . . slow . . . and hold on 5,' states Number 2. '1,2,3,4,5 . . . 5,5,5,5,5 . . . ' calls the assistant through clenched teeth. On screen, the Prisoner tosses to and fro in his bed. 'Diminish . . . !' the superior calls. '5,5,5,5,5 . . . 5,' the bespectacled man replies, his words softening with each number called, '5 . . . 5 . . . 5 . . . ' Number 6 calms down, his head nestling snuggly into his pillow. 'Safe enough,' nods Number 2, walking briskly from the room. 'I'll take over.' 'It's a risk . . . I'd hate to see you go,' says the Supervisor, aware of the risk the superior is running. 'It's all yours. For one week,' throws back Number 2. 'Get moving. Degree *Absolute*. OPERATE!'

The lampshade above the Prisoner's bed begins to descend from the ceiling until it completely covers the sleeping man's face. As the lamp begins to oscillate and increase in intensity, Number 2, who is now standing by the side of the man's bed, leans over the sleeping figure and begins to recite a nursery rhyme. 'Humpty Dumpty sat on a wall. Humpty Dumpty had a great fall. All the king's horses and all the king's men, couldn't put Humpty together again ... ' Stepping backwards, he enters the Prisoner's lounge, his voice increasing in intensity. ' ... Jack and Jill went up the hill, to fetch a pail of WATER. Jack fell down and broke his crown and JILL came tumbling after ... ' Seated now in the sleeping man's lounge, he settles back and begins to sing. 'Oh the grand old Duke of York, he had 10,000 men. He marched them up to the top of the hill, and he marched them down again ... ' The figure in the bed sleeps on, the light above his head increasing in its intensity, pulsating in time with the superior's reversal to the lines of *Humpty Dumpty*, his childish babbering sinking deep into the Prisoner's brain – but to what purpose? It is morning, and Number 2 throws back the curtains and squints out into the sunshine. Throwing his blazer over his shoulder, he changes his mind and lays the jacket onto a chair then crosses to the sleeping man's bed. Lifting the lampshade from his head, he shoves it aside then whispers an invitation into the sleeping man's ear. 'Want to go walkies,' he grins as Number 6 leaps from his bed and turns to face the intruder. 'Wash and dress quickly, and I'll show you some nice things,' he quips, handing the man his dressing gown. With a childlike grin, Number 6 retreats to his bathroom – the promise of goodies in store ringing in his ears. A few minutes later, his hand clutching an ice cream cone, his body slumped in a wheelchair, the Prisoner is wheeled into the Green Dome by the mute Butler. Licking his ice cream, he looks on blankly as the manservant disappears into the floor and Number 2 beckons him to join him at the control console. They, too, descend into the floor where, led by Number 2, the lap dog follows his minder through several corridors until they reach a steel door set into the rock. The barrier slides open and Number 2 steps into the darkness. Beckoned inside, the Prisoner finds himself surrounded by a rocking horse, a child's swing, an infant's play pen, a blackboard and other toys; items one would associate with a well-stocked children's play room – all save an ominous huge metal cage which contains a replica of his own cottage kitchen. (From this moment on, Number 6 will be put through days of savage and relentless interrogation, his regressed mind to be taken back through his early childhood, as Number 2 leads him through the seven ages of man. Only one can return – the victor; the loser to remain a prisoner of life – or death.) 'This is it,' confirms Number 2. 'For better or for worse ... who knows? One week ... one teeny weeny week my boy. Neither of us can leave. Till death do us part ... And I brought it upon myself ... Who knows?' he says, setting the time lock on the massive steel door and drawing a heavy curtain over the exit. 'Come ahead son, let's see what you're made of ... find out what's in that noddle of yours ... ' He marches past the Butler, who now stands in the children's playpen shaking a baby's rattle. 'All the world's a stage and the men and women merely players. They have their exits and their entrances, and one man in his time plays many parts ... ' Donning a pair of white plastic spectacles, the lenses of which are narrow slits, he turns around to push a portable control, tape-recorder console towards the playpen occupied by the Butler. ' ...

'Till death do us part. And I brought it upon myself'

His acts being seven ages ... ' A piercing white light spotlights Number 6 who stands by the playpen with a childlike grin, staring intently at the antics of the silent manservant. Turning to the blackboard, the superior wipes it clean with a damp cloth. ' ... William Shakespeare, he summed it all up ... so they say. At first the infant, mewling and puking in the nurse's arms ... Be still!' he calls, distracted by the Butler, who, also adorned in the weird-looking spectacles, flings the rattle at the onlooker and climbs out of the playpen. ' ... Even as a child there is something in your brain that is a puzzlement. I intend to discover it ... ' He turns to write on the blackboard. 'A ... find missing link ... and when I have found it, I will refine it, tune it, and you will play our game ... ' he threatens, pointing at Number 6, who, shaking the rattle, stares intently at the piercing blue light beaming down on his head. 'B ... put it together ... and if I fail ... then ... ' He writes the word 'BANG' on the blackboard. Laying down his chalk, he walks past the Butler whose short legs are now dangling several inches from the floor as he sits on the swing. Taking the rattle from the Prisoner's hand he looks down at the kneeling man. 'I am your father ... do I ever say anything that makes you want to hate me?' Number 6 climbs to his feet, joining the superior as they walk around the floor. 'We're going for a walk aren't we ... ?' suggests Number 2, taking the other by the arm. ' ... Into the park isn't it? I always speak well of your mother don't I?' The two men climb onto a seesaw, the Prisoner falling flat onto the seat of his pants when, in his childlike innocence, he takes his seat before the superior can do likewise. Up and down they rock, the Butler swinging in time with their momentum. 'See-saw Marjorie Daw ... ' coaxes Number 2 ' ... Jacky shall have a new master ... ' 'See-saw,' picks up Number 6. (Margery Daw.) 'Jacky ... ' (Shall have) ' ... a new master.' (A new *Master*.) 'Master.' (Jacky.) 'Master.' (Jacky.) 'Master.'

(Jacky.) Faster and faster they go. 'Master,' says Number 6. 'Mother!' 'Master.' (Father.) With the word 'father' Number 6 stops the see-saw abruptly and steps off. Thrown to the floor, a distraught Number 2 picks himself up and grins as the other says 'Brother.' 'Friends,' nods the elder. 'Brother . . . brother . . . ' queries Number 6 timidly. 'Friends,' confirms Number 2. 'Friends . . . push!' grins the other, walking to the swing. 'Friends,' confirms Number 2, from over his shoulder. 'Friends push . . . push,' smiles Number 6, placing his hands on the Butler's shoulders and easing him forwards. 'School!' growls the superior. 'School?' 'School,' says the other, as the manservant vacates the swing and walks over to the console. He presses a button and the tape-recorder begins to revolve. ' . . . Creeping like snails, unwillingly to school . . . to school, school . . . school . . . school,' states Number 2, pushing the Prisoner who now sits on the swing. The Butler, meanwhile, has crossed to a cupboard and placed a straw boater on his head. Taking out a headmaster's cape, mortar-board and cane, he hands the attire to Number 2 and places the boater on the head of the man on the swing. Dressed now in his robes and square hat, the superior coughs out an order. 'Report to my study in the morning break,' he yells to the man on the swing.

To the sound of organ music (played by Number 2) the Prisoner stands at a mock-up door denoted 'Headmaster'. Escorted inside by the Butler, the manservant stands to attention behind the superior's back, while the 'pupil' waits to be chastised. 'Take off your hat in my presence,' barks Number 2, looking over his shoulder. 'Sorry sir,' says the pupil, removing his boater. 'You were talking in class . . . ' accuses the headmaster. 'No sir.' 'You refuse to admit it.' 'I wasn't sir,' begs the pupil. 'Do you know who was?' 'Yes sir.' 'Who was it . . . ?' questions the man sitting at the organ. The pupil remains silent. 'This is the ninth day since the incident,' challenges the headmaster. 'You have been in my study every morning at this time and still you refuse to cooperate. TODAY IS YOUR LAST CHANCE! It wasn't *you*?' 'No sir.' 'You know who it was?' 'Yes sir.' 'Who was it . . . ?' Again no reply. ' . . . This is cowardice!' 'That's honour sir,' challenges the pupil. 'We don't talk about such things,' states the headmaster. 'You should teach it sir.' (You're a fool) 'Yes sir, not a rat.' (Rat?) 'Rat.' Lifting his fingers from the keyboard in front of him, Number 2 swings round to face his accuser. 'I'm a rat?' he barks. 'No sir, I'm a fool . . . ' smirks the pupil, 'not a rat.' The superior gulps. 'Society,' he begins. 'Yes sir?' ' . . . Society is a place where people exist together . . . ' (Yes sir) ' . . . That is civilisation . . . ' (Yes sir) ' . . . The lone wolf belongs in the wilderness . . . ' (Yes sir) ' . . . and you must not grow up to be a lone *wolf*!' (No sir) 'You must *conform*!' (Yes sir) 'It is my sworn duty to see that you *do* conform!' (Yes sir) 'You will take SIX . . . ' grins Number 2. (Six?) ' . . . of the best.' 'I'm not guilty sir,' replies the pupil. 'TEN!' snaps the superior. (12!) 'What?' hisses the headmaster. 'Twelve sir . . . so that I can remember!' 'Huh,' shrugs Number 2. At a nod from the superior, the Butler passes through the door. Swishing the cane in the air, the servant closes the door behind him as Number 6 bends over the organ stool to receive his 12 whacks.

'And so we come to another graduation day. A joyous moment for any boy . . . but especially for our prize pupil . . . ' states Number 2, getting to his feet from his throne-like chair positioned on the top of a stage. Peering down at the duly chastised pupil, he continues his graduation speech. ' . . . As we launch him into the rapids of adulthood, we look back on the ups and downs of his childhood and view with some satisfaction, the fine specimen you see before you now. Have you anything to say?' 'Nothing,' replies the Prisoner. 'Nothing? Nothing at all?' 'Thank you for everything,' replies Number 6, peering down at the diploma he has been given. 'Congratulations my boy, you will do very well. *We* are proud of you. Proud that you have learned to manage your rebellious spirit. Proud that your obedience is absolute. Why did you resign?' (What's that sir?) 'Oh come along boy . . . why did you resign?' (From what sir?) 'Now my boy, you know perfectly well what I'm talking about . . . ' grins Number 2, descending the steps to face the pupil. ' . . . Why did you resign?' (I can't tell that sir.) 'Was it Secret . . . ?' (Secret sir?) ' . . . and Confidential?' (No sir.) 'Top Secret?' (No sir.) 'Top Secret!' (State Secret.) 'Yes!' urges Number 2. (State Secret sir.) 'Top. State. Confidential . . . !' screams Number 2, grabbing the lapels of the pupil's jacket ' . . . Why? Why? Why did you resign?' 'No . . . No-ooo!!!' screams Number 6, throwing the interrogator around in circles. 'Alright boy . . . alright boy . . . ' calms Number 2 ' . . . Leave school boy . . . just tell me, no more school . . . Tell me why DID YOU RESIGN?' Grunting, the Prisoner grits his teeth, draws back his fist and, with a vicious right hand, sends the other reeling to the floor. Leaping on top of the man, he grabs at his throat. As the two men wrestle and tug at each other's clothes, the Butler walks past them, places the bamboo cane into the cupboard, and returns to the men carrying a billy club. 'State . . .

'State . . . Confidential . . . Secret' Ugh!

Confidential . . . Secret!' screams the Prisoner as the club descends onto his head, knocking him sideways to the floor. Walking to a lamp, the silent servant pushes it across the floor and returns to help Number 2 gather up the unconscious man. Placed on a table top, Number 6 lies helpless as the superior lowers the perspex hood of the lamp level with the unconscious man's head. 'I'm beginning to like him,' puffs Number 2, his breathing pattern taking on the rhythm of the pulsating lamp.

'A.B.C.D.E. say them' orders Number 2, to the man sitting on a rocking horse. '1,2,3,4,5 . . . ' begins the Prisoner. (Six!) 'Five.' (Six!) 'Five.' (Six!) 'Five.' (Six!) 'Five.' repeats Number 6. Six-five they continue until, breaking the pattern, Number 2 tries another tack. 'Six of One!' 'Five,' counters the Prisoner. (Six of One.) 'Five.' (Six of One!) 'Five . . . ' On and on they go, neither man prepared to concede ground. 'Six of One, half-a-dozen of the other . . . ' snaps Number 2. 'Pop goes the weasel . . . pop, goes the weasel,' counters Number 6. (Pop.) 'Pop.' (Pop.) 'Pop.' (Pop.) 'Pop, pop, pop . . . ' each throws back in turn. 'Pop protect,' yells Number 2. 'Protect?' quizzes the other. (Protect Pop.) 'Pop.' (Protect pop, pop protect.) 'Pop.' (Protect other people.) 'Protect,' repeats Number 6, staring into the blue light over his head. (People's own protection.) 'Protect other pop,' grins Number 6, as the superior circles around the rocking horse. (Protect other people.) 'Pop.' (Why?) 'Pop.' (Why?) 'Pop.' (Why, why, why, why, why?) 'Pop pop pop-pop,' grins the man on the horse. (Why pop?) ' . . . goes the weasel,' sings Number 6. (WHY? WHY? WHY? WHY? WHY?) 'Half a pound of tuppenny rice, half a pound of treacle. That's the way the money goes, pop goes the weasel . . . ' (Why? Why? Why?) 'Half a pound of pop . . . ' grins the Prisoner. (Why pop?) 'Pop.' (Why pop?) 'Pop.' (Why pop?) 'Pop pop . . . ' 'Why?' asks Number 2. ' . . . POP!' grins the other.

Magically, the two men continue their verbal sparring in boxing gear, with Number 2 as the teacher and the Prisoner as the trainee. 'Pop,' says Number 2, protecting his chin from his opponent's swing. 'Too much swing boy . . . swings are for kids boy . . . not too much swing . . . keep 'em down . . . keep 'em short . . . again, again, again . . . Good boy . . . he puffs, warding off the Prisoner's blows as he backs across the room to stand with his back at the blackboard. 'Hit me . . . Hit me!' he challenges, dropping his guard. 'Like this?' lunges his opponent, swinging his gloves wildly at the superior's head. 'Too much swing boy . . . swings are for kids boy . . . ' confirms Number 2, throwing back a right. 'Don't move that right and leave the left asleep boy – Hit me! . . . Hook, hook, hook, hook . . . good that's it boy . . . it's the left boy, keep the left or I'll kill you boy . . . I'll KILL you boy . . .!' Their remaining words are lost in mumbles as the two close in on one another, Number 6 throwing wild jabs, the superior warding off each blow with a supremely timed counter-punch. 'Take it easy boy . . . you're the champ boy . . . take it easy . . . ' grunts Number 2 as the men stand face to face, the perspiration trickling down their faces. 'I made you . . . you're the champ boy, champ, champ . . . eh?' Number 6 is sitting exhausted in the children's playpen, being fanned with a white towel by the Butler. 'Pop . . . pop . . . pop . . . ' he murmurs as the piercing blue light burns into his eyes. 'That's it boy,' calms Number 2. The other stares blankly into the tutor's face. 'Son . . . tell me boy, why did you resign boy? Tell me son . . . you're the *champ* boy . . . the champ . . . ' The superior's words burn into the exhausted pupil's brain. 'Tell me boy . . . tell me something, *why-did-you-resign-boy* . . . ?' Clenching his gloved fist, the Prisoner holds it squarely under the other man's nose. A lightning upper-cut, and Number 2's head is jolted back!

It is épées now. A fencing lesson. 'That's my boy . . . that's my boy, touché . . . light and easy young man . . . no muscle . . . finesse . . . good, nice and easy . . . good! . . . But you ran . . . mustn't run young man, don't hit and run . . . don't treat it as a game young man . . . You're the champ . . . Kill! Kill! Kill . . . !' Countering his opponent's

thrust, the Prisoner sends Number 2's duelling weapon soaring to the back of the room. Removing his head guard, the superior stares at his opponent, daring Number 6 to end the game. ' . . . Now kill!' pants the superior as the other plants the top of his epee sharply to Number 2's throat, easing him backwards to the mock-up door. 'Afraid to prove you're a man . . . ' gasps Number 2 ' . . . Your resignation was cowardice wasn't it?' Circling his opponent's head with the epee's tip, the Prisoner thrusts his arm forward. 'Ah!' yells Number 2, as the weapon flicks past his ear and rattles into the door, the force of the lunge removing its safety cap. Drawing back his arm, the one being challenged places its razor-sharp point to the tip of the superior's nose. 'Kill!' grins Number 2. 'Kill boy . . . you can do it boy, you're the one-man band . . . ' The words penetrate the Prisoner's brain. Tearing off his face guard, he gives his opponent a bemused stare. ' . . . but you won't step over the threshold because you're scared . . . go on *kill*,' defies Number 2. Emitting a fearful scream, Number 6 rams his épée into the superior's shoulder. 'You missed boy . . . ' mocks Number 2 ' . . . You still can't do it.' 'Sorry . . . sorry,' pleads Number 6. 'Sorry . . . ' growls

'You have no respect for tradition'

the wounded man. ' . . . You're sorry for *everybody* . . . is that why you resigned?'

Day lengthens into night, night into day . . . and day after day the ruthless penetrating questioning continues, each man pitting his wits against the other, the macabre charade continuing unbroken against the ludicrous backdrop of the children's nursery and the huge metal cage in which the two men now sit, attended by the silent onlooker, the Butler, who serves them breakfast. Washed and refreshed after their last encounter, Number 2 begins the interrogation anew. 'I like it here,' he says, sitting at the breakfast table and toasting Number 6 with a glass of claret. 'Always use it for interviews. Nice and quiet . . . yes, well, I must say I am considerably impressed. Of course, naturally I shall have to discuss with my directors, but you seem admirably suited. Just to bring matters up to date . . . why exactly do you want this *job*?' 'It's a job,' whispers Number 6. (No other reasons at all?) 'No.' (You have no respect for tradition?) 'Pardon?' (No respect for tradition for an old established firm of bankers?) 'I was very good at mathematics.' (So were we all, otherwise we wouldn't be in it, would we?) 'I don't mean that.' (What do you mean?) The Butler crosses behind them to pick up the coffee perculator. 'I mean I can work.' (Tell me what hours.) 'I don't care.' 'Why?' asks Number 2, as the mute manservant places the coffee pot next to the Prisoner's right wrist. 'Well, it's the way I'm made,' replies Number 6 quietly. 'Oh excellent,' confirms Number 2, placing his hand on the other's shoulder. 'Are you ready? C'mon, c'mon . . . ' 'Ready for *what*?' asks the other nervously. '*You* are to meet our Managing Director!' exclaims Number 2. 'Right away?' cries Number 6, leaping to his feet and crossing the room to hop into a children's motorised toy car. Snuggling into its seat, he motors his way across the chamber, bringing the vehicle to a halt beside the mock-up door. As ever, the mute manservant appears and swings it open for him, bringing Number 2 into view, who now sits behind a bright yellow desk, reporting to someone on the telephone. 'It is approved and passed into the minutes,' he orders, slamming down the receiver as the man in the toy vehicle appears before him. 'Yes *sir*?' barks the superior, staring at the newcomer. 'I'd like a job,' replies Number 6. '*You* have it!' 'Thank you,' grins the Prisoner turning to leave. 'Wait a minute . . . !' calls the other, ' . . . Close the door . . . come here . . . come, come, come . . . ' he whispers, as the successful applicant approaches him with caution. 'Just . . . hmm . . . just one slight matter . . . ' 'Yes?' 'We've been watching *you*.' 'Have you?' 'Yes . . . you're . . . you're just right,' confesses Number 2. (Right for here?) 'Yes, of course, my dear boy . . . you don't expect a man of your talents would be wasted in licking stamps do you?' (Never.) 'Never. No *you're* with us.' (To death do us part.) 'Exactly.' 'This is a cover?' asks the Prisoner. (Exactly.) 'For . . . ?' (Ssh . . . Secret.) ' . . . Good.' (This *is* a cover.) 'Secret?' (Secret work.) '*Top* Secret, Confidential job . . . thank you . . . ' smiles Number 6.

Back at the controls of the motorised car, Number 6 zig-zags around the nursery. Dressed in a policeman's uniform and giving an occasional blast of the whistle in his mouth, the Butler directs the motorist around the room, their madcap antics accompanied by the tape-recorded sounds of London traffic. Round and round drives the childlike Number 6 until, braking his car in front of the tiny policeman, he stares in bewilderment as the constable

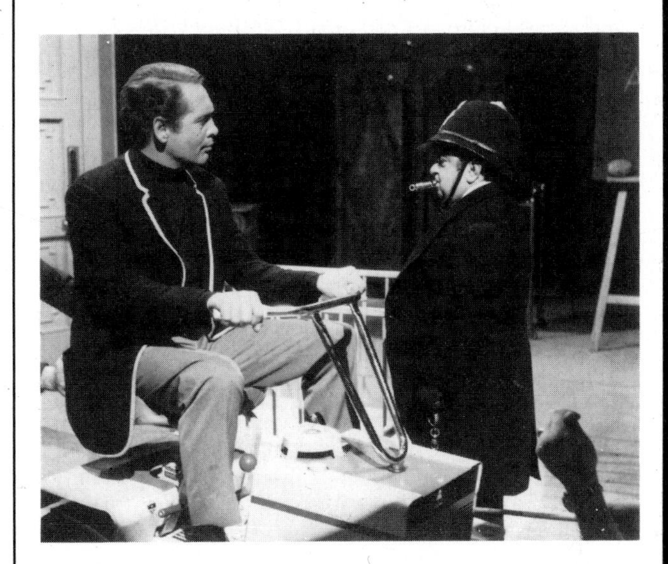

Number 6 stares in bewilderment as the 'constable' halts his progress

dangles a pair of handcuffs before his face. Number 2, dressed now in the scarlet robes of a judge, a shoulder-length white wig perched on top of his head, sits before the spinning wheel of a wooden children's toy, harkening to the defendant's plea. 'I am very good. I'm no angel . . .' pleads Number 6, his head bowed in abject apology ' . . . but I'm very good at mathematics.' 'Two and two?' snaps his lordship. 'Four!' 'Congratulations,' grins Number 2. 'Ask the manager.' (Manager?) 'The bank manager. He knows I'm good at figures,' says the defendant. (How many DEAD?) 'What?' (You were driving at *great* speed.) 'Yes, but nobody was hurt.' (In a restricted zone.) 'I had to.' (Had to?) 'Yes . . . I had a reason.' (Good, good. Tell me the reason.) 'I was on a mission . . . matter of life or death.' (Life or death eh?) 'Yes.' (Whose life or death?) 'I'm not allowed to say.' (Why?) 'It was secret business.' (Confidential . . .) 'State Confidential.' (. . . of the *highest* order . . .) 'Yes,' grins Number 6, warming to the game. (. . . International . . . *State Secret* business) 'Yes, yes indeed.' (Tell me.) 'Can't!' (*Can't?*) 'Such . . . such . . . b . . . b . . . business is above the law!' 'Above the law,' throws back the judge, challenging now, he means to get to thebottom of this. 'Above the law,, yes . . . ' (Tell me.) 'Never!' (You're GUILTY . . .) 'Yes?' (. . . of speeding on a public highway, no excuses!) 'Ask the manager,' pleads Number 6 as the Butler flicks the uppermost wheel of the toy sitting on the desk before his lordship. 'Alternating even numbers,' grins the Number 2. 'What?' 'Test.' 'Test?' queries the defendant. 'Test, alternating even numbers. Go . . . ' 'Two' says the Prisoner. (Two.) 'Four.' (Two Four.) 'Four.' (Six!) 'Four, four . . . ' repeats Number 6, lifting up his hand to block out the light. (Six!) 'Two . . . two . . . ' stammers the defendant banging his fist on a table ' . . . four FIVE!' (Six!) 'FIVE!' screams the Prisoner. (Two, four, *six*!) '*Five* . . . that's me,' seethes Number 6. 'Two, four, SIX, that's you . . . Six, you are *six* . . . alternating *even* numbers, go . . . 2,4,6,8.' 'Guilty,' whispers the Prisoner, lowering his head. 'Unrestricted murder on the public highways . . . Thinks he knows it all . . . too fast. Why did you risk the murder of innocent human beings by exceeding the speed limit?' 'I'm good at figures,' mocks the defendant. 'Don't you like it?' 'I'll work any hours of the day,' confirms the Prisoner. 'Fine 20 units.' 'I appeal.' 'What?' blusters Number 2. 'I appeal.' (Not allowed.) 'I can't pay.' (20 units!) 'I *can't* pay.' (Nothing?) 'Units are not for me.' '*You* are a *member* . . . of the Village!' bawls Number 2. 'No!' denies the defendant. '*You* are a *unit* . . .' 'No-oo!' ' . . . of *society*.' 'No-ooo!' screams the defendant. '*Contempt*!' '*No*.' '*Contempt* of Court.' 'I accept . . . ' nods the condemned, ' . . . I accept the ruling. Thank you.' 'Six days in jail,' sentences the Judge, leaving his chair to cross and hug the defendant. 'I was rebelling, my lord,' sobs the Prisoner. 'Six days,' says the other, grabbing the distraught man's arm. 'I was rebelling against the figures, my lord.' 'Six days. Take him away.' With the manservant's aid, Number 2 drags Number 6 down a table top, sweeping all before them as the condemned man is thrown into the cage. 'I shall appeal against unfair treatment,' swears Number 6 as he is forced into a chair and the metal door is slammed shut in his face. 'You've had the same treatment as everybody else,' growls Number 2. 'That's why I'm going to appeal,' yells the Prisoner grabbing the metal bars. 'Let me out. This is unfair treatment! Why, why, why did I resign? Am I a sick man . . . ?' mumbles Number 6 as the superior storms across the room to the Butler.

Wakened by the manservant, Number 2 struggles off the table top on which he has been sleeping. Although still tired, he quickly regains his composure, buttons up his blazer and mounts the steps leading up to the cage. Steadying himself by holding on to the bars, he paces backwards and forwards before the man locked inside, stopping to stare into the Prisoner's face. 'Why did you resign?' he grunts. 'For peace,' grins the handcuffed man. (For peace?) 'Let me out,' shouts the Prisoner pacing the cell floor. (You resigned, for peace?) 'Yes. Let me out.' (You're a fool.) 'For peace of mind.' (What?) 'For PEACE OF MIND!' barks the man in the cage. (Why?) 'Too many people know too much.' (Never!) '*I* know too much.' (Tell me) 'I know too much about *you*.' (Don't.) 'I *do*.' (Don't.) 'I *know* you,' growls the prisoner, pacing the floor of his cell like a caged tiger. (Who am I?) '*You* are an enemy.' (I'm on *your* side.) 'Yeah.' (Why did you resign?) 'You've been told.' (Tell me again.) 'I know *you*.' (You're smart.) 'In my *mind* . . . ' (Yes?) ' . . . in my mind, *you're* smart!' growls Number 6, pointing an accusing finger at the other's face. (WHY DID YOU RESIGN?!) 'There . . . you see,' sobs Number 6. (Why did you resign?) ' . . . Know who you are?' mocks the Prisoner. (What?) 'A fool!' (What?) 'Yes . . . ' (No, don't.) ' . . . Yes, you're an idiot.' (I'll kill you.) 'I'll die,' whispers the caged man, staring defiantly into the other man's face. 'You're dead,' mocks Number 2. Grabbing the bars, Number 6 rattles them in anger. 'Let me out,' he pleads. 'Dead!' exclaims the other. Racing to the kitchen cabinet behind him, the Prisoner grabs a carving knife from a drawer, and hands it to the superior through the bars. '*Kill* me,' dares Number 6. 'Open it,' orders the superior. 'Open it!' mocks the man in the cage as the silent figure of the Butler places the key into the locked door. 'Open the door,' repeats Number 2 with a sigh. Raising the knife to his shoulder, the tip of the blade a threat to the Prisoner's life, Number 2 enters the cage and holds the tip of the carving knife to the other man's neck. 'Kill,' mocks Number 6, falling backwards to the floor. 'Kill me lying down.' 'Get up you fool.' 'You can't?' challenges the Prisoner. 'In the was *you've* killed.' 'Yes.' 'You killed for fun!' 'For *peace*,' swears Number 6. 'DO AS I SAY!' orders the man with the knife. 'I did as I was told,' mocks the man on the floor.

Sometime later, dressed in pilot's flying helmets, Numbers 2 and 6 are sitting on a wooden beam high above the floor, their legs dangling above the head of the Butler who sits at the controls of a dry-ice machine which is pumping dense clouds of silky-white smoke into the nursery. 'Twelve seconds to zero,' Number 2 warns his co-pilot. 'Stand by to release. All set?' 'Set,' confirms Number 6. 'Eleven,' says Number 2, commencing the countdown. (Eleven.) 'Ten.' (Ten.) 'Nine.' (Nine.) 'Eight.' (Eight.) 'Seven.' (Seven.) 'Six.' (Five.) '*Six*' (Five.) 'Six!' (Five!) 'Six!' (Five.) 'Six!' (Five!) 'SIX . . .! Fire . . . ' screams Number 2, as the sound effects controlled by the manservant simulate the sounds of exploding bombs. 'Three.' (Three.) 'Two.' (Two.) 'One.' (One.) 'Zero go . . . zero go . . . zero, zero, go, go, go, . . . overshot you fool, wake up . . . ' yells Number 2. ' . . . Coming in again on the re-run, let 'em go as soon as the turn's completed . . . stand by . . . ' (Stand by.) 'Approaching . . . let go . . . Now!' 'Bombs gone,' confirms Number 6, pressing the make-believe bomb release button. 'Good boy . . . bull's-eye . . . We're hit . . . bail out, bail out . . . ' yells Number 2, leaping from the beam. After a slight pause, his co-pilot follows him. Back inside the cage, the Prisoner is being questioned by Number 2, who has now adopted the role of a German officer. (German dialogue, accompanied by the sounds of

'Bail out. Bail out. Bail out!'

German troops saluting their Führer.) 'I do not wish to kill,' confirms Number 6 in a German accent. Marching in time with the music being piped into the cell by the tape-player, the superior continues his cross-interrogation in German. 'The aircraft was hit. I had to bail out, over your territory,' pleads Number 6, with a shrug of his shoulders. 'It's not my fault . . . I cannot help bailing out!' The two men continue their conversation in German. 'My arrival is a fact, but I have to tell you nothing,' mocks the Prisoner. The superior replies in German. 'Zero go . . . ' shrugs Number 6. 'How dare you . . . ' snaps Number 2. ' . . . Go, go, go, go-oo,' laughs the Prisoner. 'Zero, zero go!' 'I'm a friend,' confides Number 2. 'Yes.' 'Why did you resign? I'm a friend . . . I'm a friend.' 'Eight,' replies Number 6. (Why did you resign?) 'Eight.' (Why?) 'Six.' (Six?) 'Yes . . . Four.' (No.) 'Two!' grins the Prisoner, leading the superior out of the cage. (No!) 'One.' (NO!) 'Zero . . . go.' (No!) 'I'm hungry.' 'What would you like?' asks Number 2. 'Supper.'

In a reversal of their roles, Number 2 now lies on a table, as Number 6 hovers over him like a hawk. 'You chose this method because you knew the only way to beat me, was to gain my respect,' coaxes the Prisoner. 'That is correct,' nods Number 2. 'And then I would confide?' 'I hoped that you would come to trust me,' nods the other, dancing his fingers over his ample tummy. 'This is a recognised method?' probes the interrogator. 'Used in psychoanalysis . . . the patient must come to trust his doctor totally.' 'Sometimes,' mocks Number 6, bending over the reclining man's head, 'they change places.' 'It is essential in extreme cases,' giggles Number 2. 'Also a risk.' 'A grave risk,' laughs the other. 'If the doctor has his own problems.' 'I have,' confirms the superior with a grin. 'That is why the system is known as "degree absolute"?' coaxes the Prisoner. 'It's one or the other of us,' giggles the superior. 'Why don't you resign?' The man lying on the table laughs. 'Very good,' giggles Number 2, raising himself aloft. 'You're very good at it.' Easing himself to the floor, Number 2 crosses over to where the Butler is playing the organ. 'Play something cheerful,' he requests. 'I'd like to know more,' says the Prisoner. 'You'll have every opportunity before we're through,' confirms Number 2, gazing around the room. 'Join me,' he calls, racing into the cage. Number 6 enters the cell. 'There you are,' grins the superior handing the Prisoner a glass of whisky. 'Straight?' 'One-hundred per cent proof,' confirms the elder, recorking the bottle. 'No additions?' 'My word of honour,' grins Number 2. 'Cheers,' toasts the Prisoner raising the glass to his lips. 'Mind if I er, look around our home from home?' 'Not at all,' chortles the elder. Offering to show his guest around, the superior leads him back into the nursery area. 'This delightful residence is known as the Embryo Room. In it you can re-live from the cradle to the grave. Seven ages of man, William Shakespeare.' 'Last seen all, that ends this strange eventful history, of this second childishness and near oblivion,' quotes Number 2. 'Sans eyes . . . ' whispers the superior. 'Yes.' ' . . . Sans teeth . . . ' 'Yes.' ' . . . Sans taste . . . ' 'Yes.' ' . . . Sans everything.' 'Correct,' confirms Number 6, placing his hand on the other man's shoulder. 'No there's no way out until our time is up . . . If we can solve our mutual problems, that will be soon . . . You can take my word for it,' confirms the weary elder. 'Naturally I would,' grins the Prisoner. 'Let me show you the DOOR!' invites the other. Racing across the room, he tugs on the curtain pull and the deep blue curtains slide apart to reveal the massive steel door. 'We are protected from intrusion in a most efficient way. No one can interrupt our, shall I say, deliberations? Totally encased in solid finest steel,' confirms Number 2, rapping his fist on the door. 'Behold the clock!' he yells, indicating its red dial, its triangular white minute hand denoting that only five minutes are left before the time-lock releases the door's locking mechanism. 'FIVE MINUTES!' he exclaims, resetting the dial to open at a new phase of their relationship. 'That is, if we are still here?' 'Are we likely to move?' quips the other. 'It's possible!' yells Number 2, racing back into the cage to refill his empty whisky glass. 'Somewhere nice?' mocks Number 6, following the superior to the bars of the cell, but remaining poised at the door. 'Built in bars?' he whispers, sliding the cell door almost to a close. 'Also self-contained,' grins the superior, walking around the interior. 'Kitchen, bathroom, air conditioning. Food supplies for six months. You could go anywhere in it . . . It even has a waste disposal unit.' 'It *moves*?' quizzes Number 6. 'It's detachable,' confirms the elder. 'What's behind it?' grins Number 6, sliding the cell door closed with a clunk. 'Steel . . . steel,' nods Number 2, as he leaps at the door. Too late. The one outside has turned the key in its lock and handed it to the Butler, who, bowing to the victor, carries it away. 'Ah . . . ha,ha,ha,' laughs the one locked in the cage. 'He thinks you're the boss now,' yells Number 2 in the direction of the silent manservant. 'I am,' gloats the Prisoner. 'I'm Number 2. I'm the *boss*! Open this door!' yells the one in the cell. 'Number 1 is the boss,' says the one standing outside. 'No!' 'Three minutes,' goads Number 6. 'You're scared.' 'No.' 'You can't take it.' 'FOOL!' exclaims Number 2, thumping his fist on the bars. 'Yes, a fool . . . but not a rat,' quips the other. '*You're* scared,' challenges the one in the cage. 'Want me to come in?' 'Keep out!' warns the elder. 'Let you out?' mocks Number 6. 'Stay away,' calls the one inside. 'Wanna come out?' grins the Prisoner. 'KEEP OUT!' screams Number 2. 'You're mine,' threatens Number 6, descending the steps to urge the Butler to open the cage. As beckoned, the mute manservant approaches the cage. 'STOP HIM . . . !' screams the elder, as his once loyal companion inserts the key into the lock. 'Two minutes,' confirms the Prisoner. 'STOP HIM,' pleads the hysterical Number 2. '*Two* minutes . . . thank you,' grins Number 6 sliding open the door to the cage. 'You're free!' he snaps, indicating that the superior can leave. 'No, I'm Number 2 . . . ' stammers the elder. 'You are number nothing,' sneers the Prisoner. 'I am Number 2!' 'One minute, thirty-five seconds,' warns Number 6. 'Why did you resign?' tries Number 2. 'I didn't accept, why did *you* accept,' snaps the Prisoner. 'You resigned!' confirms Number 2. 'I *rejected*!' 'You *accepted* before you resigned.' 'I *rejected*!' 'Who?' throws back Number 2. 'You.' 'Why me?' pleads the elder. 'You're big!' 'Not tall.' 'Not tall . . . ' confirms Number 6, ' . . . big . . . Humpty Dumpty. All the king's horses. All the king's men!' snaps the Prisoner. 'That's right,' confirms the elder. 'Couldn't put *Humpty* together again,' confirms Number 6. 'Wh..what . . . ' stammers Number 2, staring at the clock. 'One minute to go.' He sighs. Clutching his heart, he elbows his way past his tormentor and races down the steps, stumbling while so doing and rolling past the mute figure of the Butler who sits unconcerned playing the organ. '59 seconds . . . 58 seconds,' counts the Prisoner. Climbing to his knees, the superior rests his hand on the organ's top. 'I'm big,' he boasts. '57,' counts Number 6. '*You're* tall,' concedes the elder to the one standing over him. '56 . . . ' grins Number 6 continuing the count. Crawling his way backwards, the superior cowers at the Prisoner's feet. (55) 'Be glad.' (54) 'God.' (53) 'Not for *me*,' pleads the elder, clutching at the playpen. '52, 51,' yells the Prisoner, snatching away the superior's hand. '50, 49, 48 . . . ' 'Why?' (47) 'WHY?' (46) 'Why RESIGN?' screams Number 2, his fingers clutching at the rocking horse. (45) 'Tell me,' pleads the elder. (44) 'WHY DID YOU . . . ?' (43)

'39' (I'll tell.) '38'

'I don't know.' (42) 'Yes?' (41) 'Any minute now,' whispers Number 2. '40!' yells Number 6. 'I'll tell . . . ' screams the superior crawling to his knees. (39) ' . . . I'll tell!' (38!) ' . . . Got no time . . . ' (37!) ' . . . No time . . . ' sobs Number 2 stumbling into the spotlight. '36!' shouts Number 6. ' . . . No time . . . ' '35,' whispers the Prisoner staring at the clock as the second hand creeps towards zero hour. 'Still time . . . ' grunts the exhausted Number 2, ' . . . not too late.' 'For *me*?' mocks Number 6. 'For *mee-ee* . . . ' screams the man on his knees patting his chest. 'You snivel and grovel!' 'I *ask*.' 'You crawl.' 'Yes . . . look,' confirms Number 2, crawling towards the other man's feet. 'To ask?' 'Yes, to ask.' 'Why?' Smiles Number 6. Head raised, the elder grunts. Then, leaping to his feet with his arms outstretched, he grabs his tormentor by the throat. 'Ask on,' grins the Prisoner. 'Ask YOURSELF!' he yells, throwing the trembling man aside. Racing back into the cage, the superior begs why. 'Why? . . . Why?' '15,' snaps the Prisoner. 'Please,' sobs Number 2. 'Don't say please,' mocks Number 6. 'I say it.' 'Don't!' 'Please . . . I plead!' exclaims the terrified man, placing his hands together in a gesture of prayer. 'Nine!' 'Too late,' concedes the other. 'Eight.' 'Seven!' barks Number 2, picking up the count. 'Six!' 'Six!' echoes Number 2. 'Die Six. Die!' yells the other. 'Five' wheezes Number 2. 'Die!' The superior gasps for breath. 'Die!' growls the Prisoner. 'Four,' gasps Number 2. 'Die!' '*Threeee*,' wheezes the other. His breathing is heavy now. 'Die!' The defeated superior raises a glass to his lips. '*Two-ooo*' he gurgles. '*DIE*!' snorts Number 6. The clock stops ticking. Number 2 collapses to the floor. Crouching, the Prisoner places his fingers to the man's neck. The superior has paid the price of defeat. His glazed eyes stare unseeing at the ceiling, no breath emits from his lips. Drawing his hand back gently across the defeated man's face, the victor climbs to his feet. With a final glance at the body lying on the floor of the cage, he retreats from the cell, slides the door to a close and locks it with the key. As the mute Butler ascends the steps to take one final look at his former master, the steel door slides open and the Supervisor marches into the room. 'Congratulations . . . we shall need the body for evidence,' he says, joining the men by the cage. In a fit of pique, Number 6 flings his glass to the floor. 'What do you desire?' asks the newcomer. 'Number 1.' 'I'll take you,' confirms the Supervisor. Crossing over to the time lock, he depresses a switch and a huge metal shield descends from the ceiling to cover Number 2's well-protected tomb. To the tune of the nursery rhyme 'Baa-Baa Black Sheep' the three men depart from the room – a room that is now as silent as a grave.

AUTHOR'S NOTE: Originally conceived as the final (13th) story of the first series, this episode was put on the shelf to be shown as the penultimate story - leading directly into *Fall Out*. (The episodes should always be viewed together!)

A time span of over 12 months separated the production of this story and the final denouement, by which time Leo McKern was beardless. As the actor had an aversion to false whiskers, the production personnel came up with an ingenious solution – the bizarre machine which brought the 'dead' Number 2 back to life and, in so doing, gave him a shave and a new haircut!

Although credited, actor John Maxim as 'Number 86' does not actually appear in the story - his scenes being trimmed prior to transmission.

Almost all of the answers Number 6 gives to Number 2 are based on McGoohan's own life.

Filmed under the working title *Degree Absolute*.

THIS IS IT . . . for better or for worse . . . who knows. One week . . . one teeny-weeny week my boyboy . . . Neither of us can leave, till death do us part . . . and I've brought it on myself . . . who knows,' says Number 2, setting the time lock of the massive steel door and drawing a heavy curtain over the exit door. 'Come ahead son . . . let's see what you're made of . . . find out what's in that noddle of yours . . . ' Turning, he writes on a blackboard. 'A . . . find missing link, and when I have found it, I will refine it, tune it and you will play our game . . . ' 'No sir,' says the Prisoner, staring into the superior's face. 'Top Secret . . . ?' 'State Secret,' snaps Number 6. 'Yes,' sighs the other. 'State Secret sir . . . ' 'Top. State. Confidential . . . !' screams Number 2, grabbing the lapels of the pupil's jacket. ' . . . Why? Why? Why did you resign?' 'No . . . No-ooo!!!' screams Number 6, throwing the interrogator round in circles. Grunting, he grits his teeth, draws back his fist and with a vicious right hand sends the other reeling to the floor.

'Don't move that right and leave the left asleep boy – Hit me!' exclaims Number 2 throwing a short right cross to the Prisoner's jaw.

'Kill! Kill! Kill!' screams Number 2. Countering his opponent's thrust, the Prisoner sends Number 2's duelling weapon soaring to the back of the room. Removing his head guard, the superior stares at his opponent, daring Number 6 to end the game. ' . . . Now kill!' Circling Number 2's head with the epee's tip, the Prisoner thrusts his arm forward. 'Ah!' yells Number 2, as the weapon flicks past his ear and rattles into the door, the force of the lunge removing its safety cap. Drawing back his arm, the one being challenged places the razor sharp point to the tip of the superior's nose. 'Kill!' grins Number 2. 'Kill boy . . . you can do it boy, you're the one-man band . . . but you can't step over the threshold because you're scared . . . go on kill,' defies Number 2. Emitting a fearful scream, Number 6 rams the epee into the superior's shoulder.

'WHY DID YOU RESIGN?' snorts Number 2 to the man in the cage. 'Know who you are?' mocks the Prisoner. (What?) 'A fool.' (What?) 'Yes . . . ' (No don't) ' . . . yes, you're an idiot.' (I'll kill you.) 'I'll die,' whispers the caged man, staring defiantly into the other man's face. 'You're dead,' mocks Number 2.

'Twelve seconds to zero,' Number 2 warns his co-pilot. 'Stand by to release. All set?' 'Set,' confirms Number 6. 'Eleven,' says Number 2. (Eleven.) 'Ten.' (Ten.) 'Nine.' (Nine.) 'Eight.' (Eight.) 'Seven.' (Seven.) 'Six.' (Five.) 'Six.' 'Stand by,' replies Number 6. 'Approaching . . . let go . . . Now!' 'Bombs gone,' confirms Number 6, pressing the make-believe bomb release button. 'Good boy . . . bull's-eye!' confirms Number 2.

'Built in bars?' whispers Number 6, sliding the cell door almost to a close. 'Also self-contained,' grins the superior, walking around the interior. 'Kitchen, bathroom, air conditioning. Food supplies for six months. You could go anywhere in it . . . It even has a waste disposal unit.' 'It moves?' quizzes Number 6. 'It's detachable,' confirms the elder. 'What's behind it?' grins Number 6, sliding the cell door closed with a clunk. 'Steel . . . steel,' nods Number 2, as he leaps at the door.

'Die Six Die!' yells the Prisoner. 'Five,' wheezes Number 2. 'Die!' 'Four,' gasps Number 2. 'Die!' 'Three-ee,' wheezes the superior. 'Die!' The defeated Number 2 raises a glass to his lips. 'Two-ooo,' he gurgles. 'DIE!' 'One,' gasps the drinker, removing the glass from his lips. 'DIE!' snorts Number 6. The clock stops ticking. Number 2 collapses to the floor. With a final glance at the body lying on the floor of the cage, Number 6 retreats from the cell, slides the door to a close and locks it with the key. The steel entrance door slides open and the Supervisor marches into the room. 'Congratulations . . . we shall need the body for evidence.' In a fit of pique, Number 6 flings his glass to the floor. 'What do you desire?' asks the newcomer. 'Number 1.' 'I'll take you,' confirms the Supervisor. Crossing over to the time lock, he depresses a switch and a huge metal shield descends from the ceiling to cover Number 2's well protected tomb. His duty done, the Supervisor follows Number 6 and the Butler out of the Embryo Room . . . .

FALL OUT

Written by Patrick McGoohan
with guest star **Leo McKern**

The President **Kenneth Griffith**

Alexis Kanner

The Butler **Angelo Muscat**
The Supervisor **Peter Swanwick**
The Delegate **Michael Miller**

Directed by Patrick McGoohan

ESCORTED BY THE Supervisor, Number 6 and the mute manservant walk down a long corridor to the blackness beyond – a darkness which contains a circular elevator platform. When mounted, this takes them deep into the bowels of the earth. But to what? What new nightmares await the Prisoner in this underground world far beneath the Village? What further torment lies ahead for the man who dared to take on the opposition – and win! After a long descent, the elevator grinds to a halt. Its steel-encased doors slide open to reveal a solitary motionless figure beckoning them onward – a figure bearing a clay mask modelled in the likeness of . . . himself! 'We . . . thought you would feel . . . happier as yourself,' greets a disembodied voice. Stepping over to his likeness, the Prisoner blinks as a fanfare of trumpets pipe out the opening bars of a pop song. (*All You Need Is Love*).

'All you need is love'

Moving forwards the trio pass through a gauntlet of colourful juke boxes and approach a huge wooden door set into the rock, its rusted hinges beckoning . . . what? The Butler inserts his key and the huge door swings open to reveal a vast subterranean cavern. 'Well Come' invites a sign on the back of the door as the Butler and Supervisor stand aside to allow Number 6 to enter. The chamber is immense. Stalactites hang from the ceiling. Banks of computers and other machinery stand on metal gantries, attended by men in white robes, their faces hidden from view beneath white hoods. A squad of troops march proudly in unison across the cavern floor, their white helmets, gloves and boots matching the white rifle harness they carry strapped to their shoulders. Along one wall of the room sits an assembly of robed figures – delegates representing the defectors, reactionists, rationalists and every shade of opinion and activity in the village. In the centre of the room is a throne standing on a majestic blue-carpeted dais, its place of honour guarded by four of the uniformed troops. Walking past Number 6, the Supervisor and Butler pace proudly across the floor, the former accepting a white robe and mask from a hooded attendant. (The black and white mask matching those of the delegates.) 'All you need is love . . . all you need is love . . . ' sing the juke boxes as, to an ovation from the assembly, the Supervisor pulls the robe over his head and dons his face mask ready to take his place with his fellow representatives. The music ceases abruptly and Number 6 is greeted by a bewigged man dressed in the scarlet robes of a judge. 'Welcome,' bids the President, as the Prisoner walks slowly towards the pulpit on which the man stands. Behind him, the Supervisor sits in the seat designated 'Identification.' As he does so, the assembly breaks into applause. 'This session is called in a matter of democratic crisis . . .' opens the President, banging down his gavel to bring the assembly to order. ' . . . and we are here gathered to resolve the question of revolt.' Applause from the delegates. 'We desire that these proceedings be conducted in a civilised manner, but remind ourselves that humanity is not humanised without force and that errant children . . . ' he points in the direction of the Prisoner ' . . . must sometimes be brought to book with a smack on their *backsides*.' Gleefully smacking his hands together, he silences further applause with a bank of his gavel. 'We draw your attention to the regrettable bullet . . . The community is at stake . . . and we have the means to protect it. The assembly is now in security . . . ' he ends, looking down at the white-robed figure of the Supervisor standing before him. 'Number 6 is presented to you,' announces the mask-covered face. 'I understand he survived the ultimate test,' says the President. 'Indeed,' confirms the Supervisor. 'Then he must no longer be referred to as Number 6 . . . or a number of any kind. He has gloriously vindicated the right of the individual to be individual . . . and this assembly rises to you . . . Sir,' grins the President. As one, the delegates rise to their feet and give the newcomer a hearty ovation. Raising his hand for silence and staring directly at the Prisoner, the President continues. 'Sir. We crave your indulgence for a short while . . . the er, transfer of ultimate power requires some tedious ceremony and perhaps you would care to observe the preliminaries from the chair of honour.' Directed to the throne, the Prisoner mounts the steps to a fanfare of trumpets, and seats himself comfortably in the chair. A wry smile crossing his lips as the President continues. 'Sir. We thank you and promise to be as brief as possible.' A machine attendant pushes a button and amid clouds of

steam, the huge self-contained metal 'tomb' containing the body of the dead Number 2 descends from the ceiling, coming to rest with a gentle thud behind four uniformed guards. The metal shield slides to one side and two green-coated medical men wheel a stretcher-trolley into position in front of the cage. Turning to look at a tubelike silver metal container – its foremost side denoted by a large red number '1' – the President barks out the command 'Resusitate.' In an instant, the huge television monitor screen in front of him flickers into life and displays the lifeless body of the deposed Number 2. A second machine operator slides a lever to the right, and the final minutes of the encounter between the man sitting in the chair of honour and the dead superior is played in reverse: the 'dead' Number 2 leaping back to his feet and placing the whisky glass to his lips! 'A revolution . . . ' grins the President ' . . . Get him out. Key!' Appearing from nowhere, the Butler unlocks the cage door. Then, crossing to mount the dais steps, he bows to the man seated in the throne and positions himself at the man's shoulder. The body of Number 2 is carried out of his tomb by the medical men, placed on the stretcher and wheeled into an area occupied by more green-coated figures. Carried to a

An individual at last

seat, a flashing white light encased in a metal hood is lowered over the reclining figure's head and its visor is lowered over the man's face. Canvas straps are snapped into place around his wrists and ankles and a resusitator device is placed against the dead man's ample belly. As the visor is lifted from the seated figure's face, a circular rubber face pad extending from an elongated metal arm slides forwards to encase the bearded face and the apparatus purrs into motion with a throbbing electrical hum.

'Revolt, can take many forms . . . ' announces the President, ' . . . and here we have three specific instances . . . ' On the far side of the chamber, a piston-like pole rises from a circular pit. ' . . . Number 48!' confirms the President. From the smoke-filled pit emerges a young man dressed in black, a top hat perched rakishly on his head. He is strapped to the pole by a wide metal belt, unable to move anything but his head. The newcomer stares at the assembly. 'Thanks for the trip dad,' sings the youngster tunefully. 'Be grateful for the opportunity of pleading your case before the assembly,' cautions the figure in the scarlet robe. 'Oh baby . . . what a crazy scene . . . ' laughs the youngster, rocking his head from side to side and breaking into the words of a well-known song: 'The collar bone's connected to the neck bone and the neck bone's connected to the head bone. Now hear the word of the Lord . . . ' 'Number 48!' exclaims the President, banging his gavel. Shaking their black and white faces in disgust, the assembly rises to its feet. 'Dem bones 'dem bones gonna walk around. Dem bones 'dem bones gonna walk around . . . ' continues the one strapped to the piston arm. 'Number 48!' screams the President, attempting to regain order. ' . . . Them bones, them bones them dry bones,

'Dem bones, dem bones, dem dry bones'

them bones them bones them dry bones . . . ' sings the grinning Number 48 as, in total confusion, the delegates dance around in their seats, keeping time with the young man's words. 'NUMBER 48!' screams the bewigged man. ' . . . Now hear dat word of the Lord,' continues the vocalist, ignoring all attempts to shut him up. Suddenly, a flashing green light attracts the President's attention. Looking over his shoulder towards the large camera eye positioned on the wall beside the tubular metal container and seeing its inner lens pulsating with an intense white light, the President calls for order. 'Order, order . . . release him, release him.' Accompanied by another uniformed guard, a sentry walks swiftly over to the young man and releases the wide metal strap that ties him to the pole. 'Youth . . . with its enthusiasm . . . ' begins the President, as the released man climbs, cat-like, out of the pit, ' . . . which rebels against any accepted norm because it must and we sympathise . . . It may wear flowers in its hair, bells on its toes, but . . . ' The young man takes several faltering steps forward – approaching the area where the Prisoner sits in his chair of honour. ' . . . when the common good is threatened, when the function of society is endangered, such revolts must cease . . . ' states the President. Passing the group of medical men working on the dead Number 2, the young man moves forward. ' . . . The are non-productive and *must* be *abolished*!' concludes the bewigged President. Standing motionless before the man seated on the throne, the young man raises the small golden cow bell that hangs around his neck and rings it defiantly. 'Number 48,' sighs the man dressed in scarlet. 'Hmm,' says the youngster, 'Hear the word . . . of the Lord.' Without warning, he begins to race around the chamber singing the words of his song. The medics leap out of his way as he jumps down from a rock and sends his pursuers flying like skittles as he leaps aboard the stretcher trolley and propels himself towards them like a torpedo. Escaping from their clutches, he races up a gantry, grabbing a microphone from a controller as the delegates race across the floor and attempt to ensnare him. The chamber is in uproar. Total confusion reigns as he races around the room, pushing a button here, pulling a lever there, running, running from the uniformed men who chase after him. Falling to the floor, he rolls over in a heap and finds himself surrounded by soldiers, their rifles directed to his head. 'Young man,' snaps the man sitting in the chair of honour. 'Give it to me again,' calls Number 48. 'Don't knock yourself out . . . ' says the Prisoner. 'Give me a rest,' pleads the youngster. ' . . . Young . . . man,' the Prisoner concludes. 'I'm born all over,' quips the top-hatted youth, springing to his feet amid the circle of gun-toting troops. 'Sir, we thank you for your intervention, but fear that such familiarity is not in keeping with procedure,' grins the President. ' . . . we must maintain the status quo . . . Now, Number . . . ' A siren screams and the man dressed in scarlet turns back to the flashing green light which emits from the tube-shaped cylinder denoted by the large letter 'I'. 'Yes, of course,' confirms the President as the pulsating green light flashes out its warning. 'Naturally, it would expedite matters. Very well . . . to your places.' As one, the troops guarding Number 48 break formation and return to their posts, leaving the youngster standing motionless in the centre of the chamber. 'Sir, it would appear that temporarily, we may use the new form of address in order to bring these proceedings to an early and satisfactory conclusion,' announces the President, turning to the assembly to invite them to cast their vote. 'Those in favour?' As one the delegates applaud. 'Carried. We are obliged . . . sir,' he concludes, staring at the Prisoner. 'Don't mention it, Dad,' returns the one seated in the chair of honour.

This appears to please the young man, who, his face breaking into a grin, turns to face the President. 'Young . . . man,' says the one in the scarlet robe. 'You got the message?' quips the youngster. 'I just got it,' confirms the President. (What gives?) 'You've never been with it . . . I mean us,' corrects the one wearing the wig. (I'm gone, gone away.) 'But you were then you went and gone.' (Got da word.) 'Oh yes, yes,' nods the President. (The bright light, Dad. Got the sign.) 'The sign?' (The light.) 'The light?' (The Message.) 'Then you went and gone,' grins the President. 'Why?' smiles Number 48. 'Give it to me, baby,' laughs the man in the scarlet robe. 'That's it,' urges the young man. 'Give me the rest!' 'Give. All you want is give. That's it,' nods Number 48. 'That's it,' mocks the President. 'And take,' confirms the other. 'That's it.' (Take is all you want.) 'That's it.' (Take.) 'That's it!' 'And take,' grins the young man. 'Take, take, take . . . ' yells the President. 'Take . . . take,' growls Number 48, spreading his arms to lead the assembly into a chant. *'Take, take, take, take, take . . . '* shout the delegates, thumping their fists to their desks as the young man sinks to his knees arms outstretched. 'Take, take, take,' mouths the President, turning to the large television lens, his words lost in the babble of voices. The man sitting in the chair of honour and the Butler remain silent, watching stoically from the dais. 'TAKE!' yells the President, crashing down his gavel to bring the assembly to order. Still kneeling, the young man rings his bell. 'Now you're high,' barks the man wearing the wig. 'I'm *low*,' smirks the other. 'Give it to me baby! Confess!' exclaims the President. 'Oh Dad, I'm your baby, Dad. You owe your baby something, Daddy.' 'Confess now you're hep,' hisses the man in the red robe. 'Hip dad,' mocks Number 48. *'Hip!'* 'Confess!' 'Ah hip bone . . . ' grins the one on the floor. 'Confess!' ' . . . and de thigh bone . . . ' 'Confess!' ' . . . Shin bone, knee bone . . . ' 'Confess!' ' . . . Back bone, all yours, Dad . . . ' 'Confess!' 'Knee bone . . . ' yells the young man, stretching out his arms as a record of 'Dem Bones' blasts out from a juke box. Within seconds, the entire assembly including the President picks up the words of the song and begins to sing and sway in time with the music – the instigator, Number 48, turning his head to give a mock salute to the silent figure seated behind him on the dais. Dancing to his feet, the young man begins to snap his fingers and join in with the chant. The delegates sway more and more wildly, their white-gloved hands clapping in silent beat with the music. Grinning, Number 48 slides to a kneeling position, then, crossing his legs beneath him into a yoga position, he sits back, content to let the court make a mockery of itself. 'Hip Hip,' yells the President, as the music ceases abruptly. 'Hurrah,' yell the delegates throwing their hands in the air as they thump back into their seats in unison. ' . . . And hear de word of the Lord,' sighs the man on the floor. 'Guilty!' roars the President, bringing his gavel crashing down before him. 'Read the charge.' Climbing to his feet, the delegate representing the anarchist division of the assembly addresses the court. 'The prisoner has been charged with the most serious breach of social etiquette . . . ' The young man rings his bell. ' . . . total defiance of the elementary laws which sustain our community . . . questioning the decisions of those voted to govern us . . . unhealthy aspects of speech and dress not in accordance with general practice, and the refusal to observe, wear or respond, to his NUMBER . . .!' Grinning, Number 48 turns to the delegate and rings his bell mockingly. 'Sir, you approve the proceedings?' the President asks the man sitting on the throne. 'I *note* them,' comes the wry reply. 'Sir, I take it you have no comment at this stage.' 'Not at this stage,' replies the Prisoner after a pause. 'Then the accused will be held in a place of sentence until after your inauguration. Remove him,' orders the President. Carried away by two guards, the young man is strapped back onto the pole from whence he came. 'Hear the word of the Lord, Dem bones dem bones, dem dry bones . . . ' sings Number 48 as a button is pressed and the condemned man sinks back into the smoke-filled pit. 'A most regrettable demonstration,' the President comments, turning to look at the Prisoner. 'My apologies, sir.' 'Oh don't mention it,' grins the man in the chair. 'I think you'll find our next revolutionary a different kettle of fish altogether,' grins the bewigged man as, looking at the television monitor screen, he begins to laugh.

'Next,' grins the President as the circular rubber pad extending from the elongated arm is removed from Number 2's face, which has now been shorn of its beard, although he still retains his neatly-trimmed moustache. Seeing this, the President and the delegates break into laughter. Miraculously the 'dead' man stirs. His eyes flicker open and stare blankly at the ceiling. The medical team remove the straps from the patient's wrists and feet and, rising to his feet, the 'reborn' Number 2 takes a few faltering steps forward, his fingers stroking his now naked chin. Pausing before the assembly he raises his hand. The laughter ceases abruptly. 'I FEEL A NEW MAN . . . !' he exclaims. With a hearty chuckle, he turns to look at the man sitting in the chair of honour. 'My dear chap!' he exclaims, mounting the dais steps to shake the Prisoner's hand. 'How've you been keeping? The throne at last eh . . . I knew it. It had to be . . . And you my little friend . . . ' he greets the silent Butler ' . . . Ever faithful.' Descending the steps, he beckons for the manservant to follow him. 'Come on . . . come on come on . . . ' Staring at the Prisoner, the Butler does not budge. ' . . . New allegiances,' says Number 2, shrugging his shoulders. 'Such is the price of fame . . . and failure. Dear me, how sad.' Spreading his arms, he begins to address the large assembly. 'My Lords, Ladies and Gentlemen . . . a most extraordinary thing happened to me on my way . . . here.' Breaking into laughter, the delegates give him a rousing ovation. Mounting the President's pulpit, the superior calls for silence by raising his hand. 'It has been my lot, in the past, to wield a not inconsiderable power. Nay, I have had the ear of statesmen, kings and princes of many lands. Governments have been swayed, policies defined and revolutions nipped in the bud at a word from me in the right place and at the propitious time . . . ' A pause, a wry grin and he turns to address himself directly to the President. ' . . . not surprising therefore, that this *community* should find a use for me. Not altogether by accident, that one day I should be *abducted* and wake up here amongst you . . . ' He returns his attention to the assembly. ' . . . What is deplorable, is that *I* resisted for so *short a* time . . . a fine tribute to your methods.' To a man, the delegates applaud his words. Again he motions for silence. 'I wish to thank you for recognition of my talents, which placed me in a position of power second only – to ONE . . . ' Descending from the pulpit, he continues his address from the floor. 'This authority, gave me the right to make decisions. My last decision concerned this gentleman here . . . ' Holding out his arm, he points to the man sitting in the chair of honour. ' . . . which could be resolved only in the death of either one or the other of us. He emerged victorious . . . I . . . apparently . . . ' Pausing, he turns to state at the man who 'killed' him. Confused, his attention is drawn to the monitor screen on which is being played out the final excruciating seconds of his final defeat. '*Die Six Die*!' says the figure on the screen. '*Four* . . . ' he hears himself mutter. '*Die*! screams the figure of the screen. '*Two-ooo*' his image gurgles. Bemused, the superior stares at the assembly. ' . . . *Died*?' says the revived Number 2. '*Die*!' echoes the voice from the screen. In graphic detail, his 'death' continues to unfold before him. '*Die*!' screams the image of Number 6. '*One-oone*,' wheezes his voice. '*DIE*!' 'Was it the drink?' yells Number 2, turning to the President, who stares back in silence. 'You couldn't even let me rest in peace,' sneers the superior, having watched the man on the screen sink into oblivion. 'How was it DONE?' 'There have to be some security secrets that are kept from a . . . late Number 2,' confirms the man on the pulpit. 'Did you ever meet him,' asks the Prisoner. 'What's that?' asks the dejected Number 2. 'Did you ever *meet* Number 1?' 'Face to face?' 'Yes,' urges the one once denoted as '6'. 'Meet *HIM* . . . ' laughs the other, walking across the chamber to stand mockingly in front of the tubular metal container denoted '1'. ' . . . Meet him.' The metal eye set into the column emits a green light into the superior's face, daring the deposed man to continue. 'Shall I . . . give him a stare?' whispers Number 2 in a show of boldness. 'You transgress!' yells the President. 'I *shall* give him a stare . . . ' mocks the man standing in the pulsating green light. Defiantly, he turns to stare at the metal-lidded lens. 'Look me in the eye . . . ' he sneers. The eye flickers open, its intense white cornea defying the deposed leader's challenge. His face a mask of determination, Number 2 walks purposefully towards the mechanical eye. ' . . . Whoever you are . . . *what*ever you are . . . ' 'You'll die!' screams the man in the scarlet robe. 'Then . . . I'll die . . . with my own mind . . . ' returns Number 2, tearing the '2' badge off his blazer lapel. ' . . . You'll hypnotise me no longer,' he challenges. In reply, a dense cloud of gas emits from the hooded-eye and envelopes the superior's head. Gritting his teeth, in a mock gesture of submission, Number 2 lunges forwards – and spits directly into the cortex of the mechanical eye. In an instant clouds of acrid dense smoke pour out of the container. Triumphant, Number 2 holds his arms aloft in victory – arms that are grabbed by two uniformed guards who drag the deposed leader before the President's pulpit. 'Sir?' calls the bewigged man. 'Hold him,' snaps the Prisoner. 'In the place of sentence?' 'Until my inauguration,' commands the seated man. 'Secure him!' orders the President and Number 2 is dragged away to be strapped to a second piston-pole and suffers the same fate as Number 48 – but not before he holds up a challenging finger in a gesture of warning and guffaws an ominous 'Be seeing you' as he descends into the darkness of the pit. 'We have just witnessed two forms of revolt . . . ' sighs the President. ' . . . The first, uncoordinated *youth*, rebelling against nothing it can define. The second, an established, successful, secure member of the establishment, turning upon, and biting the hand that feeds him. Well these attitudes are dangerous, they contribute nothing to our culture and are to be stamped *out* . . . !' Applause from the assembly, which stops abruptly as the flasing green light emits from the container, denoted with a large red letter '1'. As if by magic, two civilians appear on the monitor screen and are seen removing a 'For Sale' sign from the railings outside the Prisoner's London home. ' . . . At the other end of the scale . . . ' continues the President. ' . . .

'Be seeing you'

we are honoured to have with us, a revolutionary of different calibre . . . ' On screen, the one once known as Number 6 is pictured driving up to his front door in KAR 120C. ' . . . He has revolted. Resisted. Fought. Held fast. Maintained. Destroyed resistance. Overcome coercion. The right to be Person, Someone or Individual . . . ' A man dressed in maintenance overalls is seen cleaning the yellow and green Lotus. ' . . . We applaud his private war, and we concede that despite materialistic efforts he has survived intact and secure . . . All that remains is, recognition of a *man* – a man of steel . . . A man magnificently equipped to lead us . . . That is . . . lead us or *go*. In this connection, we have a prize . . . ' Below him, one of the robed figures wheels an ornate coffee table on castors into the chamber. On its top sits a golden chest. ' . . . You will see that your home is being made ready. Above and beyond this, we have the means for you to desert us and go *anywhere* . . . ' informs the President. Having parked the table before the dais, the hooded delegate delves into the chest and holds up an object. ' . . . The key to your house,' states the man dressed in the scarlet robe, as the robed figure holds up several other items in turn. 'Travellers' cheques . . . a million. Passport . . . valid for anywhere. And er, petty cash . . . You are free to go!' confirms the man in the pulpit. 'Free to go?' echoes the Prisoner. 'Anywhere,' grins the President. 'Why?' 'You have been such an example to us . . . ' 'Why?' asks the man sitting in the chair of honour. ' . . . You have convinced us of our mistakes . . . ' '*Why*?' ' . . . You are pure. *You* know the way. Show *us* . . . ' 'Why?' enquires the seated man. ' . . . Your revolt is good and honest. You are the only individual. We *need* you.' 'I see,' quips the man on the dais. ' . . . You do,' confirms the President. '*You see all*.' '*I'm* an individual?' urges the one being addressed. 'You are on your own.' 'I fail to see,' mocks the other. Leaning forwards, the bewigged President spreads his arms. 'All about you is . . . *yours*. We *concede*. We offer. We *plead* . . . ' states the speaker, leaving his pulpit and pacing the floor ' . . . for *you* to lead *us*.' 'Or go.' 'Go if you wish.' 'Well, I . . . I . . . don't know,' says the seated man, inclining his head in a gesture of thought. 'Take the stand. Address us,' pleads the President. 'Should I?' enquires the Prisoner. 'You *must*. You *are* the greatest. Make a statement . . . a *true* statement which could only be yours . . . but for us. Remember us, don't forget us . . . ' says the other. ' . . . Keep *us* in mind. Sir, we are all yours.' Having given some thought to the President's words, the man sat on the throne rises to his feet. To a flourish of music, he purposefully descends the dais steps and picks up his passport from the table. The delegates applaud. Acknowledging their ovation, he slips his possessions into the pockets of his jacket and, picking up the stringed purse containing the petty cash, walks proudly to the pulpit vacated by the President. Placing the coins into his trouser pocket and silencing the assembly with a bang of his gavel, he begins his address. 'I . . . ' 'Aye, aye, aye, aye, aye . . . ' echo the delegates. He brings down his gavel a second time. 'I feel . . . ' His words are lost in shouts from the delegates. He tries again. 'I . . . ' 'Aye, aye, aye, aye . . . ' '*I* feel . . . ' 'Aye, aye, aye, aye, aye, aye.' stamp the delegates, drowning out his words. His attempts to get across his message continues for several minutes until, losing his temper, he is about to scream for silence, when, with a solitary raised finger, the President motions the assembly to silence. 'Sir, on behalf of us all,' states the man dressed in scarlet, 'We thank you. And now I take it that you are prepared to meet . . . er, Number 1. Follow me if you would be so kind, sir.'

Following the bewigged figure across the floor of the chamber, the Prisoner walks over to stand beside one of the pits. Bowing as the President leaves, he steps onto a platform and descends into the darkness below. The doors before him slide open and, passing the rows of uniformed guards who stand at attention on either side of a long passage, he walks down the brightly-lit corridor to find the youth and the deposed Number 2 encased in two plastic tubes denoted Orbit 48 and Orbit 2 respectively. The young man is still humming the garbled words of his song, the other continuing his raucous laughter. To the right of the figures stands a third tube labelled 'Orbit'. Empty, it opens at the push of a button from a robed controller. A claxon sounds and turning, the intruder sees the Butler striding down the corridor towards him. Passing silently before the uniformed guards, bowing to his new master, the manservant invites the Prisoner to ascend a spiral staircase. Having climbed cautiously upwards, he finds his way blocked by a huge metal door. At the push of a button, it slides back to reveal a circular antechamber protected by glass. Globes of varying sizes sit on top of a circular glass table. Rotating slowly, each represents the planet earth. Before him stands a robed figure, watching the ubiquitous television monitor screen on which events from the onlooker's past life are being projected. '*I will not be pushed, filed, stamped, indexed, briefed, debriefed or numbered. . . . I will not be push* . . . ' drones the image behind him, as, accepting the clear glass orb, the white-robed figure hands to him, the hooded figure suddenly lifts up its arms and rears like a spectre before him. For the first time, the intruder notices the circled numeral painted over the robed man's heart – an ominous black number '1'! Dropping the glass orb to the floor, he reaches out his hand to tear away the black and white mask that covers the spectre's face. (At last, Number 1!) Snatched away, the mask reveals the grinning countenance of a grinning ape. This, too, is torn aside to reveal . . . the hideous distorted face of himself!! To the accompaniment of the spectre's hysterical laughter, the intruder chases his duplicate around the room. Round and round they race until, emitting a terrifying scream, the duplicate races up a ladder and escapes through a safety hatch into the chamber above. Its grotesque face is shut off from sight when its pursuer pulls down the safety hatch cover and swings the locking device shut. Above them, sitting on the Prisoner's vacated throne, the President twitches his fingers nervously across his lips as, staring at the metallic container marked '1', he sees the mechanical eye snap shut with a clunk. Grabbing up a fire-extinguisher from the wall, the Prisoner quietly descends the spiral staircase, to find the mute manservant standing silently on its lower rung. Although unable to speak, the servant motions with his eyes that danger lies ahead. Leaping down from the staircase, his master springs into action, blasting the hooded figures in the room with the fire-extinguisher. Having cut down several of the opposition, he flings the fire-extinguisher to the Butler and turns on the guards with his fists. To the accompaniment of Number 2's raucous laughter, the man and the Butler cut down the opposition like nine-pins. Several minutes later, the door to the ante-room slides back to expose a hooded figure inviting the uniformed guards into the room. They enter and find themselves mowed down by the Butler who, wielding the fire-extinguisher like a tommy-gun, soon puts a stop to their antics. Stripping off his robe as he races back up the spiral staircase, the Prisoner flicks on the controls of the television monitor. Seeing the President and the assembly patrolling the floor of the cavern, he depresses a red button on the panel in front of him – a red fuel injection button. The room is not a room at all, but a rocket! For a second, nothing happens, until, noting that the man dressed in scarlet is staring directly at the rocket labelled '1', the Prisoner jams his finger onto the button a second time. He then rotates a disc marked 'Maximum Hold'. 'Contact . . . Control . . . ' screams the President's voice over the public address system above the Prisoner's head. ' . . . Confirm contact. Priority . . . ' Spotting the rocket's countdown button, the man at the control console flicks it downwards. ' . . . Contact Priority . . . contact,' screams the President, as he races to the gantry and attempts to reach the control room by radio. ' . . . Emergency, contact . . . Contact . . . Control, emergency,' he screams into a microphone as he races before the rows of computers and machinery. 'All personnel take cover . . . ' Disguised under a mask and robe, the Prisoner rises from a pit. He tears off his hood and opens fire on the troops with a machine gun. An all-out battle ensues on the floor of the chamber during which, released by the Prisoner earlier, Numbers 2 and 48 join in, mowing down the uniformed guards with glee. '*All You Need Is Love*' throbs the juke box as the Prisoner and his comrades embark on their orgy of destruction. Within minutes the President, delegates and the uniformed guards are forced to race from the cavern. Above them in the Village, the sirens scream and the President's voice calls out 'Evacuate, evacuate, evacuate . . . ' Pouring out of their cottages in droves, the inhabitants race wildly through the streets of the Village. Helicopters take off and soar high over the community. Below ground, the Prisoner and his companions leap into the self-contained cage that had until recently served as Number 2's tomb. With the Butler at its controls, the unit slowly departs from the cavern, the wheels of its trailer picking up speed as the 'home from home' enters a long, dark corridor.

Zero minus two minutes registers the dial of the countdown clock as the Butler eases the trailer down towards the daylight ahead. 'Evacuate, evacuate . . . ' screams the voice of the Village public address system as the Villagers race for their lives across the golden sands of the beach. The noise of sirens from buggies driven at speed combine with the drone of the helicopter engines as, within minutes of the alarm being raised, the Village is evacuated. 'Five, four, three, two, one' ticks the countdown clock as the Butler rams his foot on the accelerator and smashes down the iron gates that protect the tunnel's mouth. In the intense white heat of its exhaust flame, the rocket rises high over the Village, its seering white tail-flames lighting up the dome of the residence once occupied by Number 2. A Rover rises from the bubbling ocean, gurgling its way to the surface. Dying, it sinks back into the bubbling mud that was once the cavern floor. High above the once-thriving community, a helicopter soars across the sky, leaving the panoramic view of the Village far behind.

Out on the road, the free men throw sections of the kitchen out onto the highway. Some distance behind them, a bowler-hatted civil servant switches on his car radio, the words of 'Dem Bones' blaring out from its speaker. Drawing alongside the unusual trailer the escapee and his companions pick up the rhythm through the car's open window and dance a jig in the cage. Seeing their frivolous antics, the man at the wheel of the car rams his foot hard on the accelerator and speeds away from the madmen. A roadside sign informs him that London is but 27 miles away.

Braking to a stop at the roadside, the trailer deposits the man once known as Number 48 onto a grass verge. Waving goodbye to his friends, the top-hatted figure sets out on foot to hitch-hike his way home. Entering the busy London streets, the somewhat odd-looking transport pulls over to the curb, waved down by a policeman on a motorcycle. Barely a hundred yards down the street, loom the Houses of Parliament, the tower of Big Ben beckoning

Home at last. The man and his Butler allow a hearse to pass before he climbs into the seat of his beloved Lotus and drives off to face – what?

the citizens home. Its passengers alight and the former Number 2 walks proudly in the direction of the seat of power. Hopping down from the vehicle the Butler joins his new master at the roadside in front of the bemused constable. Alone with his thoughts, the ex-Number 2 stares up at Big Ben, then trots across the road and turns to give his companions a wave. Turning to see the Butler standing some distance away, the man once known as Number 6 smiles wryly. Turning to look over his shoulder at the strangely-garbed manservant, the policeman approaches him. The scene which ensues (seen through the Butler's eyes) is nothing if not ludicrous. Engaging the policeman in conversation, the ex-Number 6 breaks into a pantomimic description of how he and his oddly-dressed little friend came to be walking the streets of London in such unusual circumstances. Before the bemused law officer can catch his breath, the ex-Prisoner walks calmly to the small man, clasps him by the hand and together they race away from the scene to hop on board a number 59 double-decker bus.

In the closing minutes of the story, the young man in the top-hat is seen hitch-hiking his way down a dual carriageway. (The actor's name, Alexis Kanner, is flashed onto the screen.) Placing his thumbs into his belt, he races across the highway and lifts his thumb high to hitch-hike in the opposite direction.

In a London street, the man and his Butler reach the man's former home. Pausing for a moment to allow a long black hearse to drive past, the man climbs into the seat of his beloved yellow and green Lotus which sits parked at the curb. He guns its engine. It throbs into life. Turning, the Butler mounts the steps of the house (the name Angelo Muscat appears on the screen) and passes through the door which has opened of its own volition. Behind him, the man at the wheel of the Lotus guns its engine and joins the busy London traffic. (A single word appears on the screen 'Prisoner'.)

Dressed now in a smart pin-stripe business suit, a black bowler perched on his head, a white carnation in the lapel of his jacket, the one once known as Number 2 stares up at the Houses of Parliament. (The name Leo McKern appears on the screen.) Smiling as thunderclaps heave across the sky, swinging his umbrella and briefcase, he marches purposefully past a policeman who stands beneath an archway, and enters the building's forecourt.

Having left the London streets far behind, the custom built Lotus races at speed down a deserted highway. Its driver, clad entirely in black, his face set in determination, places his foot on the accelerator and motors on at speed.

AUTHOR'S NOTE: After a reprise of scenes from *Once Upon A Time,* a special credit sequence with a different version of the theme music, revealed (for the very first time) that the Village location was set 'In the grounds of Portmeirion, Penrhyndeudraeth, North Wales, by courtesy of Mr Clough William Ellis.'

KAR 120C, seen in this story, was a 'lookalike' – the one used in the standard opening sequence having been sold and exported overseas.

PRODUCTION CREDITS

(*Episodes 1 to 12 inclusive, and Episode 16*)

Produced by:
David Tomblin

Executive Producer:
Patrick McGoohan

Script Editor:
George Markstein

Production Manager:
Bernard Williams

Director of Photography:
Brendan J. Stafford B.S.C.

Art Director:
Jack Shampan

Editors:
Lee Doig, Geoffrey Foot, John S. Smith, Spencer Reeve

Theme by:
Ron Grainer

Incidental Music By:
Albert Elms
(Episodes 2, 4, 6, 7, 9 to 17)

Music Editors:
Bob Dearberg (Episodes 1, 3, 5)
John S. Smith (Episode 7)
Eric Mival (All others)

Assistant Directors:
Gino Marotta (Episodes 1 to 11 and 16)
Ernie Morris (Episode 12)

Casting Director:
Rose Tobias Shaw

(*Episodes 13, 14, 15 and 17*)
Production personnel as above with the following changes

Production Manager:
Ronald Liles

Editors:
Eric Boyd-Perkins, Maureen Ackland

Assistant Directors:
Gino Marotta (All episodes)
Ernie Lewis (Episode 13)

An ITC Production by Everyman Films Ltd.
Made on location and at Metro Goldwyn Mayer Studios, Borehamwood, England